6-50

APP
LINEAR ALGEBRA

MATHEMATICS & ITS APPLICATIONS

Series Editor: Professor G. M. Bell
Chelsea College, University of London

Mathematics and its applications are now awe-inspiring in their scope, variety and depth. Not only is there rapid growth in pure mathematics and its applications to the traditional fields of the physical sciences, engineering and statistics, but new fields of application are emerging in biology, ecology and social organisation. The user of mathematics must assimilate subtle new techniques and also learn to handle the great power of the computer efficiently and economically.

The need of clear, concise and authoritative texts is thus greater than ever and our series will endeavour to supply this need. It aims to be comprehensive and yet flexible. Works surveying recent research will introduce new areas and up-to-date mathematical methods. Undergraduate texts on established topics will stimulate student interest by including applications relevant at the present day. The series will also include selected volumes of lecture notes which will enable certain important topics to be presented earlier than would otherwise be possible.

In all these ways it is hoped to render a valuable service to those who learn, teach, develop and use mathematics.

MODERN INTRODUCTION TO CLASSICAL MECHANICS AND CONTROL
David Burghes, Cranfield Institute of Technology and Angela Downs, University of Sheffield.

TEXTBOOK OF DYNAMICS
Frank Chorlton, University of Aston, Birmingham

VECTOR & TENSOR METHODS
Frank Chorlton, University of Aston, Birmingham

ADVANCED TOPICS IN OPERATIONAL RESEARCH
Brian Conolly, Chelsea College, University of London

LECTURE NOTES ON QUEUEING SYSTEMS
Brian Conolly, Chelsea College, University of London

MATHEMATICS FOR THE BIOSCIENCES
G. Eason, C. W. Coles, G. Gettinby, University of Strathclyde

HANDBOOK OF HYPERGEOMETRIC INTEGRALS: Theory, Applications, Tables, Computer Programs
Harold Exton, The Polytechnic, Preston

MULTIPLE HYPERGEOMETRIC FUNCTIONS
Harold Exton, The Polytechnic, Preston

COMPUTATIONAL GEOMETRY FOR DESIGN & MANUFACTURE
I. D. Faux and M. J. Pratt, Cranfield Institute of Technology

APPLIED LINEAR ALGEBRA
Ray J. Goult, Cranfield Institute of Technology

MATRIX THEORY & APPLICATIONS FOR ENGINEERING & CONTROL
Alex Graham, The Open University, Milton Keynes

GENERALISED FUNCTIONS: Theory and Applications
Roy F. Hoskins, Cranfield Institute of Technology

MECHANICS OF CONTINUOUS MEDIA
S. C. Hunter, University of Sheffield

USING COMPUTERS
Brian Meek and Simon Fairthorne, Queen Elizabeth College, University of London

ENVIRONMENTAL AERODYNAMICS
R. S. Scorer, Imperial College of Science and Technology, University of London

LIQUIDS & THEIR PROPERTIES: A Molecular and Macroscopic Treatise with Applications
H. N. V. Temperley, University College of Swansea, University of Wales and
H. D. Trevena, University of Wales, Aberystwyth

MATHEMATICAL MODELS OF MORPHOGENESIS: Catastrophe Theory and its Applications
René Thom, Institut des Hautes Etudes Scientifiques, Bures-sur-Yvette, France

APPLIED LINEAR ALGEBRA

by
R. J. GOULT, B.Sc., MSc.,
Department of Mathematics,
Cranfield Institute of Technology

ELLIS HORWOOD, LIMITED
Publishers Chichester

Halsted Press, a division of
JOHN WILEY & SONS
New York · Chichester · Brisbane · Toronto

The publisher's colophon is reproduced from James Gillison's drawing of the ancient Market Cross, Chichester

First published in 1978 by
ELLIS HORWOOD LIMITED
Market Cross House, Cooper Street, Chichester, West Sussex, England

Distributors:

Australia, New Zealand, South-east Asia:
Jacaranda-Wiley Ltd., Jacaranda Press,
JOHN WILEY & SONS INC.,
G.P.O. Box 859, Brisbane, Queensland 40001, Australia.
Canada:
JOHN WILEY & SONS CANADA LIMITED
22 Worcester Road, Rexdale, Ontario, Canada.
Europe, Africa:
JOHN WILEY & SONS LIMITED
Baffins Lane, Chichester, West Sussex, England.
North and South America and the rest of the world:
HALSTED PRESS, a division of
JOHN WILEY & SONS
605 Third Avenue, New York, N.Y. 10016, U.S.A.

British Library Cataloguing in Publication Data

Goult, Raymond John
Applied linear algebra. –
(Ellis Horwood series in mathematics and its applications).
1. Algebra, Linear
I. Title
512'.5 QA184 78-40608

ISBN 0-85312-076-5 (Ellis Horwood Ltd., Publishers)
ISBN 0-470-26402-0 (Halsted Press)

Typeset in Press Roman by Ellis Horwood Ltd.
Printed in England by Cox & Wyman Ltd., Fakenham.

Table of Contents

Preface

Linear algebra is a branch of pure mathematics but it has applications in subjects as diverse as mechanical engineering and operational research. The efficiency with which modern digital computers can perform matrix computations has done much to bring the subject to the forefront of applied mathematics It is the author's belief that those wishing to apply the subject need an introduction to the fundamental concepts without the complication of too many abstractions. The aim of this book is thus to provide a gentle introduction to the theory and, at the same time, to give examples of some of the many applications. The applications are chosen to provide motivation for, and clarification of, the abstract ideas being introduced.

The book is arranged in alternate chapters of algebraic concepts and applications. The intention is that the reader with practical interests should see physical realisations of the mathematical structures before the theory advances too far. For the more mathematical reader the book should provide a useful introduction to some of the fields to which his mathematics can be applied.

It is assumed that the reader is already familiar with elementary calculus and simple matrix algebra but no prior knowledge of abstract algebra is assumed. A summary of elementary matrix algebra and the properties of determinants is given in the Appendix.

Chapters 1 and 2 are concerned with the fundamental concepts of vector spaces and the application of these to linear equations and linear programming problems. Chapters 3 and 4 give the theory of scalar products and quadratic forms and apply this theory to a variety of problems in numerical analysis and optimization. The final Chapters are concerned with linear transformations and eigenvalues, the applications including statistics, solid mechanics, mechanical engineering and control theory. The applications chosen for this book are not intended to form an exhaustive list but should give some idea of the many fields in which linear algebra can be used with advantage.

Finally I would like to thank Mrs. I. Harrison for her careful work in typing the manuscript.

Notation used in this book

Vector quantities are distinguished in bold type, e.g. vector **v**.

Scalar quantities are denoted by lower case italic or Greek letters, e.g. c, k or α.

Matrices are denoted by capital letters, e.g. 3×3 matrix A.

In proofs and logical arguments, the symbol $\Rightarrow$ is used to denote logical implication or 'it follows that'; for example $x + 2 = 5 \Rightarrow x = 3$. The symbol ϵ should be interpreted as 'is contained in' or 'is a member of'; for example "**v** is in vector space V" is abbreviated to "$\mathbf{v} \in V$."

Chapter 1

Vector Spaces

INTRODUCTION

In this chapter we introduce the property of linearity which is basic to many mathematical and physical systems. The real vector space R^n is introduced as a simple generalisation of the 'ordinary' 3-dimensional vector space of geometry or mechanics. The study of R^n leads to the axioms of a real vector space and from these the important concepts of linear dependence, subspaces and dimension are developed.

1.1 LINEARITY

Many mathematical and physical systems exhibit the properties which are generally referred to as **linear**. Essentially these properties are the ability to add together any two objects in the system to obtain a new object of the system and the ability to multiply any object of the system by a real number. The results obtained should be consistent with the ordinary arithmetic laws. Expressed in symbols the requirements are that if x and y are in our system, then so is $x + y$ and that for all real constants k, kx should be in our system. Simple examples of linear systems are complex numbers, 3×3 matrices, or real differentiable functions (the sum of any two differentiable functions being differentiable as is any real multiple of a differentiable function).

An alternative means of expressing the linear properties is to say that if x and y are in the system so is any 'linear combination' $ax + by$, where a and b are real constants. As will be shown in the following pages, **a real vector space is a system with the linear properties in which the objects in the system, called vectors, obey a few basic algebraic rules or axioms.**

1.2 THE REAL VECTOR SPACE R^n

1.2.1 Definitions and simple properties

Most readers will be familiar with the vectors or directed line segments of real 3-dimensional space which are frequently applied to solve problems in mechanics or solid geometry. Once a system of axes has been chosen, these vectors can be described in terms of their components parallel to the coordinate axes. Hence $\mathbf{x} = (x_1,x_2,x_3)$ describes a vector with components x_1, x_2 and x_3 parallel to the axes OX, OY and OZ respectively. It can be shown [see Goult, Hoskins, Milner, Pratt, 1973, Chapter 10], that the triangle or parallelogram law of vector addition corresponds to the addition of vectors in component form according to the rule:

$$\begin{aligned}(\mathbf{x}+\mathbf{y}) &= (x_1,x_2,x_3) + (y_1,y_2,y_3)\\ &= (x_1 + y_1,x_2 + y_2,x_3 + y_3)\end{aligned}$$

Similarly the multiplication of the vector $\mathbf{x}$ by the real number α is given in component form by the rule:

$$\alpha(x_1,x_2,x_3) = (\alpha x_1,\alpha x_2,\alpha x_3)^\dagger$$

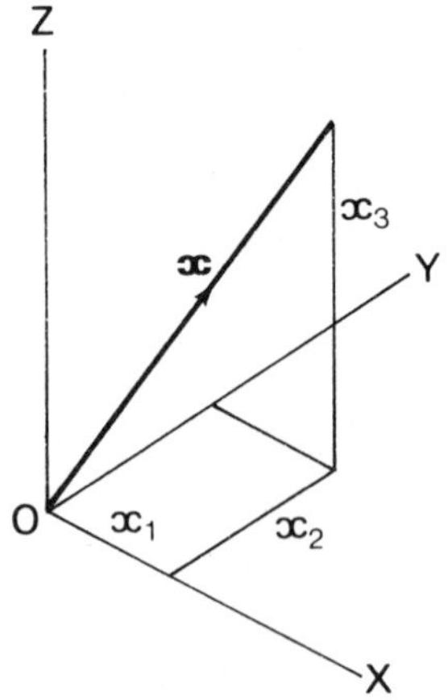

Figure 1.1

An obvious generalisation of these ideas occurs if we define the real vector space R^n as the set of all vectors of the form $\mathbf{x} = (x_1,x_2,\ldots,x_n)$ where the components x_i are real numbers. In R^n two vectors $\mathbf{x}$ and $\mathbf{y}$ are defined to be equal if all their corresponding pairs of components are equal.

$\mathbf{x}+\mathbf{y}$ is defined as:

$$(x_1,x_2,\ldots,x_n) + (y_1,y_2,\ldots,y_n) = (x_1 + y_1,x_2 + y_2,\ldots,x_n + y_n),$$

†Throughout this book any bold characters $\mathbf{x}$, $\mathbf{y}$, etc. denote a vector quantity and Greek letters α, β, γ, alpha, beta, gamma and so on denote real numbers or scalar quantities.

and for any real number α, αx is defined as:

$$\alpha(x_1,x_2,\ldots,x_n) = (\alpha x_1,\alpha x_2,\ldots,\alpha x_n).$$

In this way we obtain, for different values of the positive integer n, a family of vector spaces, the ordinary 3-dimensional vector space being a special case for $n = 3$. The decision to write the vectors in R^n horizontally as row vectors is merely one of notation; they could equally well be expressed in vertical arrays as column vectors and this would have no effect on the algebraic properties of the vector space being defined. In some of the later sections of this book, it will in fact be more convenient to consider R^n as a space of column vectors.

Once the fundamental operations of addition and multiplication have been defined in R^n, it is a simple matter to verify that R^n has the basic algebraic properties listed below. These properties ($V1$ to $V10$) will later be taken as the axiomatic properties which define a more general vector space. If $V = R^n$, the properties are:

$V1$; for all vectors $\mathbf{x}$ and $\mathbf{y}$ in V, $\mathbf{x} + \mathbf{y}$ is in V, (the closure property for addition).

$V2$; $\mathbf{x} + \mathbf{y} = \mathbf{y} + \mathbf{x}$ for all vectors $\mathbf{x}$ and $\mathbf{y}$ in V,

$V3$; $\mathbf{x} + (\mathbf{y} + \mathbf{z}) = (\mathbf{x} + \mathbf{y}) + \mathbf{z}$ for all vectors $\mathbf{x}, \mathbf{y}$ and $\mathbf{z}$,

$V4$; there is a vector $\mathbf{0}$ with the property that $\mathbf{x} + \mathbf{0} = \mathbf{x}$ for all $\mathbf{x}$ in V,

$V5$; for each $\mathbf{x}$ in V there is a vector $-\mathbf{x}$ in V such that $\mathbf{x} + (-\mathbf{x}) = \mathbf{0}$.

$V6$; for all $\mathbf{x}$ in V and all real numbers α, $\alpha\mathbf{x}$ is an unambiguously defined vector in V, (the closure property for multiplication by a scalar),

$V7$; for all real numbers α and β and all vectors $\mathbf{x}$, $(\alpha\beta)\mathbf{x} = \alpha(\beta\mathbf{x})$,

$V8$; for all real α and all vectors $\mathbf{x}$ and $\mathbf{y}$, $\alpha(\mathbf{x} + \mathbf{y}) = \alpha\mathbf{x} + \alpha\mathbf{y}$,

$V9$; for all real α, β and all vectors $\mathbf{x}$, $(\alpha + \beta)\mathbf{x} = \alpha\mathbf{x} + \beta\mathbf{x}$.

$V10$; $1\mathbf{x} = \mathbf{x}$ (1 denotes the real number one).

props. for Abelian group

props. when mult. by α

For the real vector space R^n most of the above axiomatic properties are direct consequences of the simple algebraic properties of the real numbers. In R^n the zero vector is of course the vector with each component zero, $\mathbf{0} = (0,0,\ldots,0)$ and for $\mathbf{x} = (x_1,x_2,\ldots,x_n)$, $-\mathbf{x} = (-x_1,-x_2,\ldots,-x_n)$. The reader familiar with some of the ideas of abstract algebra will recognise properties $V1$ to $V5$ as the axioms of an additive Abelian group. $V8$ and $V9$ are the distributive laws which define the rules for the interactions between the two operations of addition and multiplication by scalars. $V10$ ensures such arithmetically consistent results as $\mathbf{x} + \mathbf{x} = 2\mathbf{x}$.

1.2.2 Further properties of R^n

A number of properties of R^n can be deduced from the axiomatic properties $V1$-$V10$. Because these properties depend for their validity upon the axioms and not on the particular definitions of addition and multiplication by a scalar in

R^n, they will also be valid for any real vector space.

A useful consequence of $V3$, $V4$ and $V5$ is the cancellation law which facilitates the solution of simple equations. This law can be stated symbolically as:

$$\text{if } \mathbf{a} + \mathbf{x} = \mathbf{a} + \mathbf{y}, \text{ then } \mathbf{x} = \mathbf{y}.$$

The proof follows from the existence of $-\mathbf{a}$, the additive inverse of the vector $\mathbf{a}$. Adding $-\mathbf{a}$ to each side of the above equation gives,

$$-\mathbf{a} + (\mathbf{a} + \mathbf{x}) = -\mathbf{a} + (\mathbf{a} + \mathbf{y}).$$

$$\text{Thus, using } V3,\ (-\mathbf{a} + \mathbf{a}) + \mathbf{x} = (-\mathbf{a} + \mathbf{a}) + \mathbf{y},$$

$$\text{or, by } V2 \text{ and } V5,\ \mathbf{0} + \mathbf{x} = \mathbf{0} + \mathbf{y}.$$

Finally the application of $V4$ gives the result $\mathbf{x} = \mathbf{y}$. The above proof illustrates in detail the way in which the axiomatic properties are assumed in normal processes of simple algebraic manipulation. Some other generally assumed properties which are direct consequences of the axioms are:

$$O\mathbf{x} = \mathbf{0} \text{ for any vector } \mathbf{x}.$$

$$-(-\mathbf{x}) = \mathbf{x},$$

$$-1(\mathbf{x}) = -\mathbf{x},$$

$$\alpha\mathbf{0} = \mathbf{0} \text{ for any real } \alpha.$$

The proofs of these properties are left as simple exercises for the reader.

1.3 REAL VECTOR SPACES AND SUBSPACES

1.3.1 Real Vector spaces

Having defined R^n as a generalisation of the 'ordinary' 3-dimensional vector space, it is possible to make a further generalisation and define a vector space as anything which has properties similar to those of R^n. To be more precise, **a vector space V is defined to be any set of objects which can be added together and multiplied by real scalars in accordance with the axioms** $V1$ to $V10$. This generalisation enables us to obtain some very useful results by applying the properties of vector spaces to objects such as real functions or polynomials which are not normally regarded as 'vectors'. Some examples of vector spaces are to be found in the following paragraphs and in the problems at the end of the Chapter.

Examples of Real Vector Spaces

1. **The set of all complex numbers.**

Clearly the addition of complex numbers is compatible with the axioms $V1$

to $V5$. Also the multiplication of a complex number by a real number is always possible and the results are consistent with the requirements of axioms $V6$ to $V10$. These properties of complex numbers as a vector space are clearly illustrated by the geometric interpretation of complex numbers on the Argand diagram.

2. **The set of all real polynomials of degree $\leqslant 2$.**
In this space the 'vectors' are expressions of the form $ax^2 + bx + c$, where a, b, and c are real numbers. Two such polynomials can be added together to produce a polynomial of the same type. In addition multiplication by a real number produces a well defined polynomial in the set. It is a simple matter to verify that the polynomials possess those algebraic properties required by the vector space axioms and so constitute a real vector space.

3. **The set of all real functions of x continuous in the interval $0 < x < 1$.**
If $f(x)$ and $g(x)$ are two such functions, then the function $f(x) + g(x)$ will be a continuous function, as is $\alpha f(x)$ for any real number α. Because the algebraic properties are valid for the manipulation of functions, we have a real vector space once more. However, as we shall see later this particular space differs in one significant respect from each of the previous examples.

4. **The set of all arithmetic progressions**
An arithemetic progression is an infinite sequence of real numbers of the form 1, 3, 5, 7, 9, . . . in which the difference between each number and the preceding one is constant. If we define the sum of two arithmetic progressions as the result obtained by adding corresponding terms together and define multiplication by a real number in the obvious way, it is a simple matter to verify that all the axioms of a vector space are valid.

1.3.2 Subspaces

A subspace of a real vector space can be defined as **any subset of a vector space which forms a vector space in its own right.** For example, in the space of all complex numbers $z = x + iy$, the subset consisting of all 'purely imaginary' numbers iy is a subspace because it can be verified that these numbers have all the axiomatic properties.

In practice, when considering whether or not a particular subset of a space is a subspace, it is not necessary to verify all the axioms. The axioms which describe purely algebraic properties, such as $V2$ $\mathbf{x} + \mathbf{y} = \mathbf{y} + \mathbf{x}$, will be satisfied automatically because all elements in the subset are contained in the original vector space. The only axioms which need independent verification are those which require that particular vectors should be in the subset; these are $V1$, $V4$, $V5$ and $V6$. Even this check-list of four axioms can be further reduced by using the algebraic properties already established for a vector space. Sufficient conditions for a subset S of V to be a subspace are:

$S1$; for all $\mathbf{x}, \mathbf{y}$ in S, $\mathbf{x} + \mathbf{y}$ is in S,
$S2$; for all $\mathbf{x}$ in S and all real α, $\alpha\mathbf{x}$ is in S.

By letting α take the values 0 and -1 respectively, condition $S2$ ensures that $\mathbf{0}$ and $-\mathbf{x}$ are in the subspace.

Examples of subspaces

1. Let V be the vector space R^4, define S as the set of all vectors $\mathbf{x}$ in V with $x_1 = x_2 = 0$. The vectors of S are thus of the form $\mathbf{x} = (0,0,x_3,x_4)$ or $y = (0,0,y_3,y_4)$.

Clearly $\mathbf{x} + \mathbf{y} = (0,0,x_3+y_3,x_4+y_4)$ is also in S as is $\alpha\mathbf{x} = (0,0\alpha x_3,\alpha x_4)$.
Hence S is a subspace of R^4.

2. Let V be any vector space, two simple subspaces of V are $S = [V]$ and $S = [\mathbf{O}]$, that is V itself and the set consisting only of the zero vector. These subspaces are generally referred to as the **trivial subspaces.** Any other subspace which contains some non-zero vectors but does not contain every vector in V is called a **proper subspace.**

3. Let V be the set of all real polynomials of degree $\leqslant 3$, let S be the subset of V consisting of all polynomials divisible by $x - 1$.

If $f(x)$ and $g(x)$ are in S, then we must have $f(x) = (x - 1)f_1(x)$ and $g(x) = (x - 1)g_1(x)$ for some polynomials $f_1(x)$ and $g_1(x)$.
Then $f(x) + g(x) = (x - 1)f_1(x) + (x - 1)g_1(x) = (x - 1)(f_1(x) + g_1(x))$, and $\alpha f(x) = \alpha(x - 1)f_1(x) = (x - 1)\alpha f_1(x)$.

These properties confirm that S is a subspace of V, and since not every polynomial is divisible by $(x - 1)$, S is a proper subspace of V.

4. Let V be any real vector space and let $\mathbf{a}$, $\mathbf{b}$ and $\mathbf{c}$ be three vectors in V. Define S as the subset of V which consists of all vectors of the form $\mathbf{v} = \alpha\mathbf{a} + \beta\mathbf{b} + \gamma\mathbf{c}$ where α, β, γ are real scalars.

If $\mathbf{v}_1$ and $\mathbf{v}_2$ are in S, we obtain immediately the result,

$$\begin{aligned}\mathbf{v}_1 + \mathbf{v}_2 &= (\alpha_1\mathbf{a} + \beta_1\mathbf{b} + \gamma_1\mathbf{c}) + (\alpha_2\mathbf{a} + \beta_2\mathbf{b} + \gamma_2\mathbf{c})\\ &= (\alpha_1 + \alpha_2)\mathbf{a} + (\beta_1 + \beta_2)\mathbf{b} + (\gamma_1 + \gamma_2)\mathbf{c},\end{aligned}$$

showing that the sum of these vectors is in S.

Also, for any real constant λ, $\lambda\mathbf{v}$, is in S.

The above argument shows that S is a subspace of V. It is in fact an example of an important type of subspace, that is one which generated by a particular set of vectors. In our case S is the subspace generated by $[\mathbf{a},\mathbf{b},\mathbf{c}]$. S can be considered as the smallest subspace of V which contains all the vectors in the generating set. It will be shown in the later sections of this Chapter that for any subspace of a finite dimensional vector space we can find an appropriate set of generators. (In example 3 above a generating set for S is $[x-1, x^2-x, x^3-x^2]$).

1.4 LINEAR DEPENDENCE

One of the most important concepts in linear algebra is that of **linear dependence.** The idea is one of geometric origin. In two dimensions the condition for two points A and B to lie in the same line through the origin is that their position vectors $\mathbf{a} = OA$ and $\mathbf{b} = OB$ should be proportional to each other (see figure 1.2). Algebraically this condition is equivalent to the statement that for some non-zero values of α and β we have $\alpha\mathbf{a} + \beta\mathbf{b} = 0$.

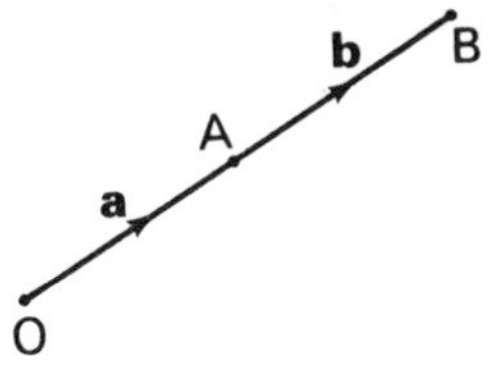

Fig. 1.2

More generally we define a set of vectors $\mathbf{v}_1, \mathbf{v}_2, \ldots, \mathbf{v}_n$ to be linearly dependent if we can find some scalars $\alpha_1, \alpha_2, \ldots, \alpha_n$ not all zero such that $\alpha_1\mathbf{v}_1 + \alpha_2\mathbf{v}_2 + \ldots + \alpha_n\mathbf{v}_n = \mathbf{0}$.

Note that it is of course necessary in this definition to exclude the possibility of having all the scalar multipliers α_1, α_2, etc., equal to zero (otherwise every set of vectors would be linearly dependent), but some of these scalars may take the value 0.

In 3-dimensional geometry the interpretation of linear dependence is that if three points have linearly dependent position vectors, then the points all lie in a plane through the origin.

Example

In R^3 the vectors $\mathbf{x} = (1,2,1)$, $\mathbf{y} = (2,3,1)$, $\mathbf{z} = (2,2,0)$ are linearly dependent because $2\mathbf{x} - 2\mathbf{y} + \mathbf{z} = \mathbf{0}$. If we interpret these as positions of 3 points X, Y, Z referred to rectangular Cartesian coordinates, the points all lie on the plane $x_1 - x_2 + x_3 = 0$ which passes through the origin (0,0,0).

The definition of linear dependence implies one of **linear independence.** Specifically, the vectors $\mathbf{v}_1, \mathbf{v}_2, \ldots, \mathbf{v}_n$ are linearly independent if the only solution of the equation $\alpha_1\mathbf{v}_1 + \alpha_2\mathbf{v}_2 + \ldots + \alpha_n\mathbf{v}_n = \mathbf{0}$ is $\alpha_1 = \alpha_2 = \ldots = \alpha_n = 0$.

Example

In R^3 the vectors $\mathbf{e}_1 = (1,0,0)$, $\mathbf{e}_2 = (0,1,0)$, $\mathbf{e}_3 = (0,0,1)$ are clearly linearly independent since a linear relation of the form $\alpha_1\mathbf{e}_1 + \alpha_2\mathbf{e}_2 + \alpha_3\mathbf{e}_3 = \mathbf{0}$ gives immediately $(\alpha_1,\alpha_2,\alpha_3) = (0,0,0)$ or $\alpha_1 = \alpha_2 = \alpha_3 = 0$.

However, in this case, if we add any other vector to the set we are bound to obtain a linearly dependent set. For example, if $\mathbf{x} = (x_1,x_2,x_3)$, we have the linear relation $x_1\mathbf{e}_1 + x_2\mathbf{e}_2 + x_3\mathbf{e}_3 - \mathbf{x} = \mathbf{0}$. This example illustrates the fact that in many real vector spaces there is a strict limit to the number of vectors in a linearly independent set.

From the definitions of linear dependence and independence we can deduce a number of rather obvious properties which are sufficiently useful to be worthy of consideration.

Any set containing the zero vector is linearly dependent. A suitable linear relation is given immediately by taking 1 as the scalar multiplier of **0** and 0 as the multiplier of every other vector in the set.

Any subset of a linearly independent set is linearly independent. If this were not true we could easily obtain, from a linear relation for the subset, a linear relation for the whole set obtained by adding 0 times the remaining vectors.

Theorem 1.1

If the vectors $\mathbf{v}_1, \mathbf{v}_2, \ldots, \mathbf{v}_n$, are linearly dependent, then at least one of these vectors is linearly dependent upon the remainder.

Proof

Since the vectors are linearly dependent, we have a linear relation of the form:

$$\alpha_1\mathbf{v}_1 + \alpha_2\mathbf{v}_2 + \ldots + \alpha_n\mathbf{v}_n = \mathbf{0}, \tag{1.1}$$

and at least one of the coefficients $\alpha_1,\alpha_2,\ldots,\alpha_n$ is non-zero.

If, in particular, $\alpha_i \neq 0$, (1.1) can be re-written:

$$\alpha_i\mathbf{v}_i = -\alpha_1\mathbf{v}_1 - \alpha_2\mathbf{v}_2 \ldots - \alpha_{i-1}\mathbf{v}_{i-1} - \alpha_{i+1}\mathbf{v}_{i+1} \ldots - \alpha_n\mathbf{v}_n. \tag{1.2}$$

Dividing (1.2) by α_i gives an expression for $\mathbf{v}_i$ as a linear combination of the remaining vectors in the set.

Note that although we have been able to obtain this expression for $\mathbf{v}_i$, it may not be possible to obtain a similar expression for every vector in the set because some of the coefficients in (1.1) may be zero.

1.5 GENERATING SETS, BASIS AND DIMENSION

In this Section we apply the ideas of linear dependence in an attempt to find finite sets of vectors on which all vectors in the space are linearly dependent. If this is possible, the space is said to be **finite dimensional** and we can give a precise meaning to the term **dimension**.

1.5.1 Generating set and basis

If, in a particular vector space or subspace S, we can find a set of vectors $\mathbf{v}_1, \ldots, \mathbf{v}_m$ such that every vector in S is linearly dependent upon these vectors, we say that the vectors form a **generating set** for S. More specifically, every vector $\mathbf{v}$ in S must have an expression of the form $\mathbf{v} = \sum_{i=1}^{m} \alpha_i \mathbf{v}_i$.

A basis of S is a generating set consisting of linearly independent vectors.

Because there is always at least one vector which is linearly dependent upon the remainder in any linearly dependent set, it is always possible to obtain a basis from a finite generating set by eliminating vectors dependent upon the remainder.

Examples

1. The vectors $\mathbf{e}_1 = (1,0,0)$, $\mathbf{e}_2 = (0,1,0)$, $\mathbf{e}_3 = (0,0,1)$ form a basis for R^3.

Any vector in R^3 is of the form $\mathbf{x} = (x_1, x_2, x_3)$. $\mathbf{x}$ can be expressed as $\mathbf{x} = x_1\mathbf{e}_1 + x_2\mathbf{e}_2 + x_3\mathbf{e}_3$, showing that these vectors generate R^3. Also $\mathbf{e}_1$, $\mathbf{e}_2$, $\mathbf{e}_3$ are linearly independent vectors, a result established in Section 1.4.

This basis of R^3 is a particularly simple one which is sometimes referred to as the **elementary** or **natural basis.** It is a very simple generalisation to obtain a corresponding simple basis for R^n. Later it will be proved that although this is in many ways the simplest basis of R^3, it is by no means the only basis and for some applications a different basis can offer computational advantages.

2. The vectors $\mathbf{a}_1 = (1,1,0)$, $\mathbf{a}_2 = (1,-1,0)$, $\mathbf{a}_3 = (0,1,1)$, $\mathbf{a}_4 = (0,1,-1)$ form a generating set for R^3.

Any vector in R^3 is expressible in terms of $[\mathbf{e}_1, \mathbf{e}_2, \mathbf{e}_3]$; to show that $[\mathbf{a}_1, \mathbf{a}_2, \mathbf{a}_3, \mathbf{a}_4]$ form a generating set it is sufficient to show that each of $\mathbf{e}_1$, $\mathbf{e}_2$, $\mathbf{e}_3$ is linearly dependent on $[\mathbf{a}_1, \mathbf{a}_2, \mathbf{a}_3, \mathbf{a}_4]$. The relations are:

$$\mathbf{e}_1 = (1,0,0) = \tfrac{1}{2}\mathbf{a}_1 + \tfrac{1}{2}\mathbf{a}_2.$$
$$\mathbf{e}_2 = (0,1,0) = \tfrac{1}{2}\mathbf{a}_1 - \tfrac{1}{2}\mathbf{a}_2.$$
$$\mathbf{e}_3 = (0,0,1) = \tfrac{1}{2}\mathbf{a}_3 - \tfrac{1}{2}\mathbf{a}_4.$$

These vectors do not however form a basis since $\mathbf{a}_1 - \mathbf{a}_2 - \mathbf{a}_3 - \mathbf{a}_4 = 0$, showing their linear dependence. This Equation in fact shows that any one of these 4 vectors can be omitted and the result is still a generating set.

3. The space of complex numbers $z = x + iy$ has, as simple basis, the numbers 1 and i.

Theorem 1.2

If $[\mathbf{b}_1, \mathbf{b}_2, \ldots, \mathbf{b}_n]$ is a basis of a real vector space V and if $\mathbf{v}$ is any vector in V, then the expression $\mathbf{v} = \sum_{1=1}^{n} \alpha_i \mathbf{b}_i$, determines the coefficients uniquely.

Proof

Suppose, if possible, we have two expressions:

$$\mathbf{v} = \sum_{i=1}^{n} \alpha_i \mathbf{b}_i \text{ and } \mathbf{v} = \sum_{i=1}^{n} \beta_i \mathbf{b}_i.$$

Subtracting these gives:

$$\mathbf{0} = \sum_{i=1}^{n} (\alpha_i - \beta_i)\mathbf{b}_i.$$

The linear independence of the basis vectors shows that for each value of i, $\alpha_i - \beta_i = 0$, or $\alpha_i = \beta_i$. This establishes the uniqueness of the coefficients in the expression.

Theorem 1.3 (Steinitz Replacement Theorem)

If $\mathbf{v}_1, \mathbf{v}_2, \ldots, \mathbf{v}_m$ is a generating set for a real vector space V, then any set of linearly independent vectors in V contains at most m vectors.

Proof

The method of proof, which explains the name of the theorem, is to show that the vectors in the generating set can be systematically replaced by vectors from the linearly independent set.

Suppose $[\mathbf{u}_1, \mathbf{u}_2, \ldots, \mathbf{u}_n]$ is a set of linearly independent vectors. We shall prove by induction on r that the vectors $\mathbf{u}_1, \mathbf{u}_2, \ldots, \mathbf{u}_r$ can replace r of the vectors in the generating set. When $r = 1$ we have, since $[\mathbf{v}_1, \mathbf{v}_2, \ldots, \mathbf{v}_m]$ are generators,

$$\mathbf{u}_1 = \alpha_1 \mathbf{v}_1 + \alpha_2 \mathbf{v}_2 + \ldots + \alpha_m \mathbf{v}_m \tag{1.3}$$

Since $\mathbf{u}_1$ is a member of a linearly independent set, at least one of the coefficients in (1.3) is non-zero. Rearranging the set of generators if necessary, we can assume $\alpha_1 \neq 0$.

Dividing by α_1 we obtain:

$$\mathbf{v}_1 = \frac{1}{\alpha_1}\mathbf{u}_1 - \sum_{i=2}^{m} \frac{\alpha_i}{\alpha_1}\mathbf{v}_i. \tag{1.4}$$

Equation (1.4) shows that any vector linearly dependent upon $[\mathbf{v}_1, \mathbf{v}_2, \ldots, \mathbf{v}_m]$ is also linearly dependent upon the modified generating set $[\mathbf{u}_1, \mathbf{v}_2, \ldots, \mathbf{v}_m]$.

We now assume that $r-1$ of the generators have been replaced in this way. $\mathbf{u}_r$ is dependent upon $[\mathbf{u}_1, \mathbf{u}_2, \ldots, \mathbf{u}_{r-1}, \mathbf{v}_r, \ldots, \mathbf{v}_m]$. Thus we have a linear expression:

$$\mathbf{u}_r = \sum_{i=1}^{r-1} \alpha_i \mathbf{u}_i + \sum_{j=r}^{m} \beta_j \mathbf{v}_j \tag{1.5}$$

In Equation (1.5) at least one of the coefficients β_j must be non-zero, otherwise the linear independence of $[\mathbf{u}_2, \mathbf{u}_2, \ldots, \mathbf{u}_r]$ is contradicted. With a suitable numbering of the generators we can assume $\beta_r \neq 0$, hence:

$$\mathbf{v}_r = \frac{1}{\beta_r}\mathbf{u}_r - \sum_{i=1}^{r-1} \frac{\alpha_i}{\beta_r}\mathbf{u}_i - \sum_{j=r+1}^{m} \frac{\beta_i}{\beta_r}\mathbf{v}_j \tag{1.6}$$

Eqn. (1.6) shows that an alternative generating set is $[\mathbf{u}_1, \mathbf{u}_2, \ldots, \mathbf{u}_r, \mathbf{v}_{r+1}, \ldots, \mathbf{v}_m]$. The induction proof is now complete and shows that for all integer r, $1 \leqslant r \leqslant n$ we can replace r generators by r vectors from the linearly independent set.

If $n > m$ this leads to the contradictory situation of having $\mathbf{u}_n$ linearly dependent upon the preceding vectors $\mathbf{u}_1, \mathbf{u}_2, \ldots, \mathbf{u}_m$. Thus we must have the inequality $n \leqslant m$.

Theorem 1.3 has many important consequences which will be explained in the following Section.

1.5.2 Dimension of a vector space

An immediate consequence of the replacement theorem enables us to classify vector spaces by their dimension. **The dimension of a space is defined to be the number of vectors in a basis** (thus, for example, dimension $R^n = n$.) The validity of this definition is established by Theorem 1.4.

Theorem 1.4

If $[\mathbf{b}_1, \mathbf{b}_2, \ldots, \mathbf{b}_n]$ is a basis of real vector space V then every basis of V will contain precisely n vectors. Any set of n linearly independent vectors will form a basis.

Proof

Suppose $[\mathbf{a}_1, \mathbf{a}_2, \ldots, \mathbf{a}_m]$ is an alternative basis of V. Applying Theorem 1.3 to the linearly independent set $[\mathbf{a}_1, \ldots, \mathbf{a}_m]$ and the generating set $[\mathbf{b}_1, \ldots, \mathbf{b}_n]$ gives $m \leqslant n$.

A similar argument considering the set $[\mathbf{a}_1, \ldots, \mathbf{a}_m]$ as generators gives $n \leqslant m$. Thus $m = n$ and all bases contain the same number of vectors.

Now let $[\mathbf{x}_1, \ldots, x_n]$ be any set of linearly independent vectors in V; let $\mathbf{v}$ be any vector in V. By Theorem 1.3 the set $[\mathbf{v}, \mathbf{x}_1, \ldots, \mathbf{x}_n]$ must be linearly dependent. Hence for some α, β_i, not all zero,

$$\alpha\mathbf{v} + \sum_{i=1}^{n} \beta_i \mathbf{x}_i = \mathbf{0}\cdot \tag{1.7}$$

α, in particular, must be non-zero otherwise the linear independence of $[\mathbf{x}_1, \ldots, \mathbf{x}_n]$ is contradicted. Equation (1.7) can now be divided by α to show that $\mathbf{v}$ is linearly dependent upon $[\mathbf{x}_1, \ldots, \mathbf{x}_n]$, which must be a basis of V.

Corollary

If V is a real n-dimensional vector space, then any proper subspace S of V has dimension less than n (a proper subspace is any subspace other than V itself or $\mathbf{0}$ only.)

Proof

S must be finite dimensional since any infinite set of linearly independent vectors in S would be linearly independent in V also.

Suppose S has a basis $[\mathbf{b}_1, \mathbf{b}_2, \ldots, \mathbf{b}_m]$. If $m \geqslant n$ these vectors will contain a set of n linearly independent vectors in V and so contain a basis of V. In this case every vector in V will be in S. Thus $S = V$ and we do not have a proper subspace. Hence if S is a proper subspace, $m < n$.

The preceding theorem has many important consequences. First of all it justifies the classification of vector spaces by their dimension because the number of vectors in a basis is an invariant property of a vector space. It also shows that a basis need not be a particularly simple or special set of vectors, indeed any set of n linearly independent vectors will form a basis of an n-dimensional space and, following the procedure of Theorem 1.3, we can always find a basis including any given set of linearly independent vectors.

In geometric terms the choice of basis vectors corresponds to choosing a particular set of coordinate axes. The implications of the Theorem are that in 3-dimensions we need not choose a system of rectangular Cartesian coordinates but can use as reference axes any three non-coplanar directions.

1.6 INFINITE DIMENSIONAL VECTOR SPACES

Most of the examples of vector spaces introduced so far have been those for which it is possible to find a basis consisting of a finite number of vectors. For these spaces the dimension of the space is determined by simply counting the number of vectors in a basis. Not all vector spaces are of this nature and it is quite possible to find real vector spaces in which there are infinite sets of linearly independent vectors. For these spaces the dimension is said to be infinite.

Simple examples of infinite dimensional spaces are the set of all real polynomials, the set of all real continuous functions and the set of all real differentiable functions. In some cases it may be possible to find a basis in the sense of finding a countable infinite set of linearly independent vectors which generate the space, but this is not always possible. For example, a basis for the space of polynomials is the set $[1, x, x^2, x^3, \ldots, x^n, \ldots]$.

Subspaces of an infinite dimensional space may, or may not, have finite dimension. For example, the space of all real polynomials has a 3-dimensional subspace consisting of all polynomials of degree $\leqslant 2$, and has an infinite dimensional subspace of all real polynomials in x^2.

1.7 FURTHER PROPERTIES OF FINITE DIMENSIONAL VECTOR SPACES

In this Section we concentrate exclusively on **finite dimensional vector spaces.** Some of the results obtained are most readily expressed in terms of matrices and it is assumed that the reader is familiar with elementary matrix algebra. For those unfamiliar with this subject a summary of the essential results is given in the Appendix.

1.7.1 Representation of vectors in an n-dimensional space

If V is a real n-dimensional space, each vector in V can be uniquely identified by a set of n real numbers, or coordinates, once we have chosen a basis for V.

Let $\mathbf{b}_1,\mathbf{b}_2,\ldots,\mathbf{b}_n$ be the chosen basis of V. Then, since every vector $\mathbf{v}$ in V is linearly dependent upon these basis vectors, we can find real numbers $x_1,x_2,\ldots,$ x_n such that:

$$\mathbf{v} = x_1\mathbf{b}_1 + x_2\mathbf{b}_2 + \ldots + x_n\mathbf{b}_n. \tag{1.8}$$

Theorem 1.2 shows that the coefficients in (1.8) are uniquely determined by the particular vector $\mathbf{v}$. In this way $\mathbf{v}$ is associated with a unique vector $\mathbf{x} = (x_1,x_2,\ldots,x_n)$ in R^n. Moreover to each vector $\mathbf{x}$ in R^n there corresponds precisely one vector in V. This situation is usually described by saying that, '$\mathbf{v}$ is represented by $\mathbf{x}$ relative to the chosen basis $\mathbf{b}_1,\mathbf{b}_2,\ldots,\mathbf{b}_n$ of V'.

The representation described above of vectors in the n-dimensional vector space V by vectors in R^n has the added virtue of preserving the algebraic properties of the space. Hence if $\mathbf{v}$ is represented by $\mathbf{x}$ and $\mathbf{w}$ is represented by $\mathbf{y}$ it is a simple matter to show that $\mathbf{v} + \mathbf{w}$ is represented by $\mathbf{x} + \mathbf{y}$ and that, for any real α, $\alpha\mathbf{v}$ is represented by $\alpha\mathbf{x}$. R^n was initially introduced as a rather special type of real vector space but the above argument shows that every real n-dimensional space is precisely modelled by R^n.

1.7.2 Change of basis in an n-dimensional space

It was shown in the previous paragraphs that if V is a real n-dimensional vector space with a fixed basis $[\mathbf{b}_1,\mathbf{b}_2,\ldots,\mathbf{b}_n]$, each vector in $\mathbf{v}$ is associated with a unique vector in $\mathbf{x}$ in R^n. The components of $\mathbf{x}$ are defined by the equation:

$$\mathbf{v} = \sum_{i=1}^{n} x_i\mathbf{b}_i. \tag{1.8}$$

If, instead of choosing $[\mathbf{b}_1, \mathbf{b}_2, \ldots, \mathbf{b}_n]$ as basis, we refer $\mathbf{v}$ to an alternative basis $[\mathbf{c}_1, \mathbf{c}_2, \ldots, \mathbf{c}_n]$ we will obtain instead the expression:

$$\mathbf{v} = \sum_{i=1}^{n} y_i \mathbf{c}_i. \tag{1.9}$$

With our new choice of basis, $\mathbf{v}$ is represented by the vector $\mathbf{y} = (y_1, y_2, \ldots, y_n)$ of R^n.

In geometric terms the choice of basis defines the reference axes and if we change the axes we will obtain new coordinates for each point in the space. Our problem is how to compute directly the new representation $\mathbf{y}$ from the original representation $\mathbf{x}$. We shall show that the two representations are connected by a matrix which defines the representation of the basis vectors.

Each of the original basis vectors has a unique expression in terms of the new basis $[\mathbf{c}_1, \mathbf{c}_2, \ldots, \mathbf{c}_n]$. For the jth basis vector $\mathbf{b}_j$ we have:

$$\mathbf{b}_j = \sum_{i=1}^{n} p_{ij} \mathbf{c}_i. \tag{1.10}$$

There are n real coefficients p_{ij} in Equation (1.10) for each of the n basis vectors $\mathbf{b}_j$. These coefficients define a real $n \times n$ matrix P, the jth column of P giving the coefficients of the expression for $\mathbf{b}_j$ in terms of the new basis.

If $\mathbf{v}$ is any vector in V, we now have two equivalent expressions for $\mathbf{v}$ in terms of the chosen basis vectors.

$$\mathbf{v} = \sum_{j=1}^{n} x_j \mathbf{b}_j, \tag{1.8a}$$

and

$$\mathbf{v} = \sum_{i=1}^{n} y_i \mathbf{c}_i. \tag{1.9}$$

Using Equation (1.10) to substitute for $\mathbf{b}_j$ in Equation (1.8a) we obtain:

$$\mathbf{v} = \sum_{j=1}^{n} x_j \sum_{i=1}^{n} p_{ij} \mathbf{c}_i.$$

Interchanging the order of summation gives:

$$\mathbf{v} = \sum_{i=1}^{n} \left(\sum_{j=1}^{n} p_{ij} \mathbf{x}_j \right) \mathbf{c}_i. \tag{1.11}$$

Equations (1.9) and (1.11) are both expressions for $\mathbf{v}$ in terms of the new basis $[\mathbf{c}_1,\mathbf{c}_2,\ldots,\mathbf{c}_n]$. Because such an expression is unique (Theorem 1.2), we can equate the coefficients directly. This gives, for $i=1,\ldots,n$,

$$y_i = \sum_{j=1}^{n} p_{ij}x_j. \tag{1.12}$$

If we interpret the representation vectors $\mathbf{x} = (x_1,x_2,\ldots,x_n)'$ and $\mathbf{y} = (y_1,y_2,\ldots,y_n)'$ as column vectors, or $n\times 1$ matrices, then Equations (1.12) have a concise expression as a matrix product:

$$\mathbf{y} = P\mathbf{x}. \tag{1.12a}$$

Equation (1.12a) shows that the two representations $\mathbf{x}$ and $\mathbf{y}$ of the vector $\mathbf{v}$ are linked by the real matrix P. Since it must also be possible to express $\mathbf{x}$ in terms of $\mathbf{y}$, P must be a non-singular matrix with inverse P^{-1} such that $\mathbf{x} = P^{-1}\mathbf{y}$.

From the above derivation it is clear that the columns of P^{-1} describe the basis vectors $[\mathbf{c}_1,\ldots,\mathbf{c}_n]$ in terms of $[\mathbf{b}_1,\ldots,\mathbf{b}_n]$, whereas the jth column of P describes $\mathbf{b}_j$ in terms of $[\mathbf{c}_1,\ldots,\mathbf{c}_n]$.

Because any set of n linearly independent vectors can be taken as a basis of V, we can obtain a new basis of V by taking the column vectors of any $n\times n$ matrix with linearly independent columns as representations of a new set of basis vectors in terms of the original ones. This establishes a one to one correspondence between bases of V and $n\times n$ matrices with linearly independent column vectors. We shall prove later that such matrices are in fact non-singular.

1.7.3 Change of basis examples

Example 1.1 Find the matrix P which is associated with the change from basis $[\mathbf{e}_1,\mathbf{e}_2,\mathbf{e}_3]$ of R^3 to basis $[\mathbf{u}_1 = (1,1,0), \mathbf{u}_2 = (0,1,1), \mathbf{u}_3 = (1,0,1)]$.

Solution. The matrix P which represents this basis change is obtained by expressing $\mathbf{e}_1$, $\mathbf{e}_2$ and $\mathbf{e}_3$ in terms of the new basis.

$$\mathbf{e}_1 = (1,0,0) = \tfrac{1}{2}[(1,1,0) + (1,0,1) - (0,1,1)] = \tfrac{1}{2}\mathbf{u}_1 - \tfrac{1}{2}\mathbf{u}_2 + \tfrac{1}{2}\mathbf{u}_3.$$

The corresponding expressions for $\mathbf{e}_2$ and $\mathbf{e}_3$ are,

$$\mathbf{e}_2 = \tfrac{1}{2}\mathbf{u}_1 + \tfrac{1}{2}\mathbf{u}_2 - \tfrac{1}{2}\mathbf{u}_3,$$

$$\mathbf{e}_3 = -\tfrac{1}{2}\mathbf{u}_1 + \tfrac{1}{2}\mathbf{u}_2 + \tfrac{1}{2}\mathbf{u}_3.$$

Each of the above expressions defines a column of P; thus,

$$P = \begin{pmatrix} \frac{1}{2} & \frac{1}{2} & -\frac{1}{2} \\ -\frac{1}{2} & \frac{1}{2} & \frac{1}{2} \\ \frac{1}{2} & -\frac{1}{2} & \frac{1}{2} \end{pmatrix},$$ and from the preceding theory,

$$P^{-1} = \begin{pmatrix} 1 & 0 & 1 \\ 1 & 1 & 0 \\ 0 & 1 & 1 \end{pmatrix},$$ a result which is quickly

verified by matrix multiplication. (The columns of P^{-1} correspond to expressions for $\mathbf{u}_1, \mathbf{u}_2, \mathbf{u}_3$ in terms of $\mathbf{e}_1, \mathbf{e}_2$ and $\mathbf{e}_3$.)

Example 1.2 Find the matrix which represents the change from basis $[x^2,x,1]$ to basis $[f_1(x) = x^2+1, f_2(x) = x^2-1, f_3(x) = 2x+1]$ of the space of real polynomials of degree 2 or less. Use the matrix to express x^2+2x+1 in terms of the new basis.

Solution: The relations between the basis elements are:

$$x^2 = \tfrac{1}{2}[(x^2+1) + (x^2-1)] = \tfrac{1}{2}f_1(x) + \tfrac{1}{2}f_2(x),$$
$$1 = \tfrac{1}{2}[(x^2+1) - (x^2-1)] = \tfrac{1}{2}f_1(x) - \tfrac{1}{2}f_2(x)$$
and $$x = \tfrac{1}{2}[(2x+1) - 1] = \tfrac{1}{2}f_3(x) - \tfrac{1}{4}f_1(x) + \tfrac{1}{4}f_2(x).$$

Taking the coefficients in these expressions in their correct order gives,

$$P = \begin{pmatrix} \frac{1}{2} & -\frac{1}{4} & \frac{1}{2} \\ \frac{1}{2} & \frac{1}{4} & -\frac{1}{2} \\ 0 & \frac{1}{2} & 0 \end{pmatrix}.$$

In terms of the original basis x^2+2x+1 is represented by vector $\begin{pmatrix} 1 \\ 2 \\ 1 \end{pmatrix}$, multiplication by P gives $\begin{pmatrix} \frac{1}{2} \\ \frac{1}{2} \\ 1 \end{pmatrix}$. Thus, as can be verified,

$$x^2 + 2x + 1 = \tfrac{1}{2}(x^2 + 1) + \tfrac{1}{2}(x^2 - 1) + (2x + 1).$$

As an alternative method, P could have been calculated by computing the inverse of,

$$Q = \begin{pmatrix} 1 & 1 & 0 \\ 0 & 0 & 2 \\ 1 & -1 & 1 \end{pmatrix}.$$

1.8 DIMENSION OF A SUBSPACE – A COMPUTATIONAL ALGORITHM

In Section 1.5 the concept of a subspace generated by a finite set of vectors was introduced. For many practical applications of linear algebra it is necessary to calculate the dimension of such a subspace. Clearly this dimension is the maximum number of linearly independent vectors in the generating set, but this number is in many cases far from obvious. The algorithm described below determines the dimension by replacing the generating set with one in which the linearly independent vectors are clearly distinguished. The algorithm can be applied to any subspace of R^n and hence, after defining a basis of the original space, to any subspace of a real finite dimensional vector space. The method of operation is to apply elementary vector operations to the generating set in order to obtain a particularly simple alternative generating set.

1.8.1 Elementary vector operations

Let $S = [\mathbf{v}_1, \mathbf{v}_2, \ldots, \mathbf{v}_m]$ be any finite set of vectors in a real vector space V. Three types of elementary vector operations on S are defined:

(i) interchange the order of any two vectors in S,

(ii) multiply any vector in S by a non-zero scalar α,

(iii) add to any vector in S a scalar multiple of another vector in S. (Note that adding a negative multiple allows subtraction.)

The significance of the elementary vector operations is established in the following theorem.

Theorem 1.5

If $S = [\mathbf{v}_1, \mathbf{v}_2, \ldots, \mathbf{v}_m]$ is any finite set of vectors in a real vector space V and if $T = [\mathbf{w}_1, \ldots, \mathbf{w}_m]$ is obtained from S by a series of elementary vector operations, then S and T generate the same subspace of V.

Proof

It is sufficient to establish the theorem for each of the operations individually.

(i) Suppose $\mathbf{v}_r$ and $\mathbf{v}_s$ are interchanged to give the set $T = [\mathbf{w}_1, \mathbf{w}_2, \ldots, \mathbf{w}_m]$ with $\mathbf{w}_i = \mathbf{v}_i$ for $i \neq r$ or s, $\mathbf{w}_r = \mathbf{v}_s$, $\mathbf{w}_s = \mathbf{v}_r$. Then each vector $\mathbf{v} = \sum_{i=1}^{n} \alpha_i \mathbf{v}_i$ in the subspace generated by S is equal to a vector $\mathbf{w} = \sum_{i=1}^{m} \beta_i \mathbf{w}_i$, with $\beta_i = \alpha_i$ for $i \neq r$, or s, $\beta_r = \alpha_s$, $\beta_s = \alpha_r$.
Conversely each vector in the subspace generated by T is equal to a vector in the subspace generated by S.

(ii) Suppose now that T is obtained from S by multiplying $\mathbf{v}_r$ by α to give $\mathbf{w}_i = \mathbf{v}_i$ for $i \neq r$ and $\mathbf{w}_r = \alpha \mathbf{v}_r$. This argument can be repeated if $\beta_i = \alpha_i$ for $i \neq r$ and if $\beta_r = \frac{1}{\alpha} . \alpha_r$.

(iii) Suppose T is obtained from S by adding k times $\mathbf{v}_r$ to $\mathbf{v}_s$. Thus $\mathbf{w}_i = \mathbf{v}_i$ for $i \neq s$, $\mathbf{w}_s = \mathbf{v}_s + k\,\mathbf{v}_r$. As before we obtain corresponding vectors in the subspaces generated by S and T by letting $\beta_1 = \alpha_i$ for $i \neq r$ and $\beta_r = \alpha_r - k\,\alpha_s$.

any of these operations produce a set in the same subspace

We have now proved that each of the elementary operations leaves the generated subspace unaltered and it follows that this subspace is unaltered by any sequence of elementary vector operations.

1.8.2 Reduction to echelon form

A set of vectors in R^n are said to be in **echelon form** if each vector in the set has a greater number of 0's in leading positions than the preceding vector. For example, the vectors (1,2,1,1), (0,2,1,0), (0,0,0,3) are in echelon form.

It is left as an exercise for the reader to prove that any set of vectors in R^n can be reduced to echelon form by a sequence of elementary vector operations (see Problem 1.12). This reduction provides a convenient method of calculating the dimension of the subspace generated by a particular set of vectors because the dimension of the space is equal to the number of non-zero vectors in the final echelon-reduced form.

If $[\mathbf{v}_1,\mathbf{v}_2,\ldots,\mathbf{v}_m]$ is a set of non-zero vectors in echelon form and if $\sum_{i=1}^{m} \alpha_i\mathbf{v}_i = (0,0,\ldots,0)$, we can deduce by considering the coefficient of the first non-zero element in $\mathbf{v}_1$ that $\alpha_1 = 0$. Consideration of subsequent coefficients gives $\alpha_2 = \alpha_3 = \ldots = \alpha_m = 0$. From that it follows that the vectors in echelon form must be linearly independent.

Example 1.3 Find the dimension of the subspace of R^4 generated by the vectors [(1,2,1,–1), (2,3,1,0), (–1, –1,2,3), (1,2,3,3)]. Is (2,1,3,4) in this subspace?

Solution. The problem is solved by using elementary vector operations to produce an alternative set of generators in echelon form. From this the dimension of the space is apparent and the problem of determining whether or not a particular vector is in the space is simplified.

The reduction process is described by using $\mathbf{v}_1$, $\mathbf{v}_2$, $\mathbf{v}_3$, $\mathbf{v}_4$ to identify vectors in the appropriate position of the current set. The operations are used systematically to introduce 0's into the first position, then the second position, then the third position of the appropriate vectors.

Vectors	**Operations**	**Vectors**	**Operations**	**Vectors**
(1,2,1,–1)		(1,2,1,–1)		(1,2,1,–1)
(2,3,1,0)	$\mathbf{v}_2 - 2\mathbf{v}_1$	(0,–1,–1,2)		(0,–1,–1,2)
(–1,–1,2,3)	$\mathbf{v}_3 + \mathbf{v}_1$	(0,1,3,2)	$\mathbf{v}_3 + \mathbf{v}_2$	(0,0,2,4)
(1,2,3,3)	$\mathbf{v}_4 - \mathbf{v}_1$	(0,0,2,4)		(0,0,2,4)

The final operation $\mathbf{v}_4 - \mathbf{v}_3$ produces the required set of generators in echelon form.

$$[(1,2,1,-1), (0,-1,-1,2), (0,0,2,4), (0,0,0,0)] = [\mathbf{u}_1,\mathbf{u}_2,\mathbf{u}_3,\mathbf{0}]$$

The dimension of the subspace is 3. To determine whether $(2,1,3,4)$ is in the subspace we attempt to solve for $\alpha_1, \alpha_2, \alpha_3$ the equation

$$\alpha_1 \mathbf{u}_1 + \alpha_2 \mathbf{u}_2 + \alpha_3 \mathbf{u}_3 = (2,1,3,4). \qquad (1.13)$$

After substituting for $\mathbf{u}_1$, $\mathbf{u}_2$ and $\mathbf{u}_3$, Equation 1.13 corresponds to the four simultaneous equations:

$$\begin{aligned}
\alpha_1 &= 2, \\
2\alpha_1 - \alpha_2 &= 1, \\
\alpha_1 - \alpha_2 + 2\alpha_3 &= 3, \\
-\alpha_1 + 2\alpha_2 + 4\alpha_3 &= 4.
\end{aligned}$$

Solving the first three of these equations in order gives $\alpha_1 = 2, \alpha_2 = 3, \alpha_3 = 2$. Substituting these values into the final equation gives the inconsistent result $12 = 4$, hence $(2,1,3,4)$ is not in the subspace.

1.9 THE RANK OF A MATRIX

If A is a real $m \times n$ matrix, each column of A is an ordered set of m real numbers and can be regarded as a vector in R^m. These vectors are usually referred to as the column vectors of A. A particular subspace R^m is the space generated by all the column vectors of A. We shall show in the next Chapter that this space, known as the **column space of** A, plays a significant part in the theory of linear equations. The dimension of the column space of A is called the **column rank of** A. Since the dimension of a subspace coincides with the maximum number of linearly independent vectors in a generating set, the column rank of A could be defined as **the maximum number of linearly independent column vectors in** A. As will be demonstrated in Example 1.4, the column rank of a matrix can be computed by reducing the column vectors to echelon form.

Example 1.4

By applying elementary vector operations to the column vectors of the matrix $A = \begin{pmatrix} 1 & 2 & 3 & 4 \\ 3 & 4 & 7 & 10 \\ 2 & 1 & 3 & 5 \end{pmatrix}$, find its column rank. Use a similar method to determine the row rank (number of linearly independent row vectors) of this matrix.

i.e. what is dimension of subspace generated by these vectors.

Solution

If we denote the ith column vector by C_i, the reduction of the columns to echelon form is achieved by the following sequence of elementary equations.

$$\begin{pmatrix} 1 & 2 & 3 & 4 \\ 3 & 4 & 7 & 10 \\ 2 & 1 & 3 & 5 \end{pmatrix} \quad \begin{matrix} & C_2-2C_1 & C_3-3C_1 & C_4-4C_1 \\ \end{matrix} \begin{pmatrix} 1 & 0 & 0 & 0 \\ 3 & -2 & -2 & -2 \\ 2 & -3 & -3 & -3 \end{pmatrix} \quad \begin{matrix} C_3-C_2 & C_4-C_2 \end{matrix} \begin{pmatrix} 1 & 0 & 0 & 0 \\ 3 & -2 & 0 & 0 \\ 2 & -3 & 0 & 0 \end{pmatrix}$$

It can now be seen by inspection of the final matrix above that the column rank of A is 2.

A sequence of elementary operations applied to the row vectors gives:

$$\begin{pmatrix} 1 & 2 & 3 & 4 \\ 3 & 4 & 7 & 10 \\ 2 & 1 & 3 & 5 \end{pmatrix} \begin{matrix} \\ R_2-3R_1 \\ R_3-2R_1 \end{matrix} \begin{pmatrix} 1 & 2 & 4 & 4 \\ 0 & -2 & -2 & -2 \\ 0 & -3 & -3 & -3 \end{pmatrix} R_3 - 3/2\, R_2 \begin{pmatrix} 1 & 2 & 3 & 4 \\ 0 & -2 & -2 & -2 \\ 0 & 0 & 0 & 0 \end{pmatrix}.$$

The row rank also has the value 2.

This example illustrates a particular case of a theorem which will be proved in Chapter 5, that for any matrix the row rank is equal to the column rank. Another method of defining the rank of a matrix is to find the order of the largest (that is maximum number of rows and columns) non-zero determinant which can be constructed by omitting some rows or columns from the matrix. This is called the **determinantal rank of the matrix** and its value is equal to the row and column ranks. In the above example ever 3X3 determinant obtainable from A is zero but, for example, $\begin{vmatrix} 1 & 2 \\ 3 & 4 \end{vmatrix} = 2$, verifying that the determinantal rank is also 2.

1.10 ELEMENTARY MATRICES

In the previous Section the elementary row and column operations were introduced. In this Section it will be shown that these operations can be performed by pre-, or post-multiplying the matrix by special matrices called **elementary matrices.** In the following paragraphs the existence and properties of the elementary row matrices are proved; it is left as an exercise for the reader to establish the corresponding properties of the post-multiplying elementary column matrices.

If, for a moment, we take for granted the existence of these elementary matrices, it is a simple matter to find their values by considering their effect upon the $m \times m$ identity matrix I. Let ρ be any elementary row operation and denote by $\rho(A)$ the matrix obtained after applying this operation to the $m \times n$ matrix A. If a corresponding elementary matrix E exists then, for any matrix A, we should have the equation $\rho(A) = EA$. Considering the particular case $A = I$ shows that $\rho(I) = EI = E$, or the matrix E can be calculated by applying the appropriate elementary row operation to the identify matrix. Armed with this

EA = A*

P(A) = EA

P(I) = E

prior knowledge of how to calculate the elementary matrices, it is a comparatively simple matter to show that elementary matrices exist corresponding to each type of elementary row operation.

(i) Interchange any two rows

Suppose rows k and ℓ are to be interchanged. Let A be any $m \times n$ matrix and let E be the matrix obtained from I by interchanging rows k and ℓ. The elements of E are given by the equations:

$$\begin{aligned} e_{ij} &= \delta_{ij} \qquad i \neq k \text{ or } \ell \text{ (note } \delta_{ij} = 0, i \neq j; \delta_{ii} = 1) \\ e_{kj} &= \delta_{\ell j} \\ e_{\ell j} &= \delta_{kj} \end{aligned}$$

If $F = EA$ then, from the definition of matrix products:

$$f_{ij} = \sum_{r=1}^{m} e_{ir}\mathbf{a}_{rj}$$

Thus for $i \neq k$ or ℓ,

$$f_{ij} = \sum_{r=1}^{m} \delta_{ir}a_{rj} = a_{ij},$$

$$f_{kj} = \sum_{r=1}^{m} \delta_{\ell r}a_{rj} = a_{\ell j}$$

and

$$f_{\ell j} = \sum_{r=1}^{m} \delta_{kr}a_{rj} = a_{kj}$$

From these equations we see that the elements of F correspond exactly to those of A except for the interchange of rows k and ℓ. Hence, for this matrix E, $EA = F = \rho(A)$.

(ii) Multiply any row by a non-zero constant

Suppose row ℓ is to be multiplied by c. Using the previous notation let E be defined by the equations:

$$\begin{aligned} e_{ij} &= \delta_{ij} \qquad i \neq \ell \\ e_{\ell j} &= c\delta_{\ell j}. \end{aligned}$$

Then if $EA = F$ we have the equations:

$$f_{ij} = \sum_{k=1}^{m} e_{ik}a_{kj} = \sum_{k=1}^{m} \delta_{ik}a_{kj} = a_{ij} \quad \text{for } i \neq \ell$$

and

$$f_{\ell j} = \sum_{k=1}^{m} c\delta_{\ell k}a_{kj} = c\,a_{\ell j}$$

This establishes again that $F = EA = \rho(A)$ for the appropriate elementary matrix E and any matrix A.

(iii) Add a constant multiple of one row to another row

Suppose c times row k is to be added to row ℓ. By considering $\rho(I)$ we obtain the elementary matrix E whose elements are

$$e_{ij} = \delta_{ij} \qquad \text{for } i \neq \ell$$
$$e_{\ell j} = \delta_{\ell j} + c\delta_{kj}.$$

It is left for the reader to confirm that $F = EA$ is the matrix $\rho(A)$.

Example 1.5

Show that the matrix $A = \begin{pmatrix} 1 & -1 & 1 \\ 2 & -2 & 4 \\ 1 & 0 & 1 \end{pmatrix}$ can be reduced to I by a sequence of elementary row operations, and hence obtain an expression for A^{-1} and for A as products of elementary matrices.

Solution

Performing the reduction sequence and noting at the same time the elementary matrices which are obtained by applying the same operations to I gives:

$$A = \begin{pmatrix} 1 & -1 & 1 \\ 2 & -2 & 4 \\ 1 & 0 & 1 \end{pmatrix}$$

$$R_2 - 2R_1 \begin{pmatrix} 1 & -1 & 1 \\ 0 & 0 & 2 \\ 1 & 0 & 1 \end{pmatrix} \qquad E_1 = \begin{pmatrix} 1 & 0 & 0 \\ -2 & 1 & 0 \\ 0 & 0 & 1 \end{pmatrix} \qquad E_1^{-1} = \begin{pmatrix} 1 & 0 & 0 \\ 2 & 1 & 0 \\ 0 & 0 & 1 \end{pmatrix}$$

$$R_3 - R_1 \begin{pmatrix} 1 & -1 & 1 \\ 0 & 0 & 2 \\ 0 & 1 & 0 \end{pmatrix} \qquad E_2 = \begin{pmatrix} 1 & 0 & 0 \\ 0 & 1 & 0 \\ -1 & 0 & 1 \end{pmatrix} \qquad E_2^{-1} = \begin{pmatrix} 1 & 0 & 0 \\ 0 & 1 & 0 \\ 1 & 0 & 1 \end{pmatrix}$$

$$\begin{matrix} \\ R_3 \\ R_2 \end{matrix}\begin{pmatrix} 1 & -1 & 1 \\ 0 & 1 & 0 \\ 0 & 0 & 2 \end{pmatrix} \qquad E_3 = \begin{pmatrix} 1 & 0 & 0 \\ 0 & 0 & 1 \\ 0 & 1 & 0 \end{pmatrix} \qquad E_3^{-1} = \begin{pmatrix} 1 & 0 & 0 \\ 0 & 0 & 1 \\ 0 & 1 & 0 \end{pmatrix}$$

$$R_1+R_2 \begin{pmatrix} 1 & 0 & 1 \\ 0 & 1 & 0 \\ 0 & 0 & 2 \end{pmatrix} \qquad E_4 = \begin{pmatrix} 1 & 1 & 0 \\ 0 & 1 & 0 \\ 0 & 0 & 1 \end{pmatrix} \qquad E_4^{-1} = \begin{pmatrix} 1 & -1 & 0 \\ 0 & 1 & 0 \\ 0 & 0 & 1 \end{pmatrix}$$

$$R_1-\tfrac{1}{2}R_3 \begin{pmatrix} 1 & 0 & 0 \\ 0 & 1 & 0 \\ 0 & 0 & 2 \end{pmatrix} \qquad E_5 = \begin{pmatrix} 1 & 0 & -\tfrac{1}{2} \\ 0 & 1 & 0 \\ 0 & 0 & 1 \end{pmatrix} \qquad E_5^{-1} = \begin{pmatrix} 1 & 0 & 2 \\ 0 & 1 & 0 \\ 0 & 0 & 1 \end{pmatrix}$$

$$\begin{matrix} \\ \\ \tfrac{1}{2}R_3 \end{matrix}\begin{pmatrix} 1 & 0 & 0 \\ 0 & 1 & 0 \\ 0 & 0 & 1 \end{pmatrix} = I \quad E_6 = \begin{pmatrix} 1 & 0 & 0 \\ 0 & 1 & 0 \\ 0 & 0 & \tfrac{1}{2} \end{pmatrix} \qquad E_6^{-1} = \begin{pmatrix} 1 & 0 & 0 \\ 0 & 1 & 0 \\ 0 & 0 & 2 \end{pmatrix}.$$

reduces A to I

Note that the inverses of the elementary matrices above were obtained by determining the inverse of the appropriate elementary row operation and simply writing down the corresponding elementary matrix. Since this sequence of operations reduces A to I we have $E_6E_5E_4E_3E_2E_1A = I$.

Thus, because $A^{-1}A = I$ we obtain $A^{-1} = E_6E_5E_4E_3E_2E_1$.

Also $A = (A^{-1})^{-1} = (A_6A_5A_4A_3A_2A_1)^{-1} = A_1^{-1}A_2^{-1}A_3^{-1}A_4^{-1}A_5^{-1}A_6^{-1}$.

$(E_6E_5E_4E_3E_2E_1)^{-1} = E_1^{-1}E_2^{-1}E_3^{-1}E_4^{-1}E_5^{-1}E_6^{-1}$

Notes

(1) The method above does not of course provide a convenient method of calculating an explicit expression for A^{-1}. Details of how this can be obtained are given in the following Chapter. rows are L.I.

(2) Since any $n \times n$ matrix A of row rank n can be reduced to echelon form with precisely n non-zero row vectors, it follows that the method above could be applied to reduce any such matrix to the $n \times n$ identity matrix I. From this reduction A^{-1} could be calculated and hence we obtain:

Theorem 1.6

Every $n \times n$ matrix of row rank n is non-singular and can be factorised as a product of elementary matrices.

PROBLEMS

1.1 Determine whether or not each of the following is a real vector space. If it is not a vector space, state the axiom which is violated.

(a) The set of all real polynomials in x of degree 2.

(b) The set of all real homogeneous polynomials in x and y of degree 2, together with 0.

(c) The set of all 2X2 matrices A with $a_{11} = 0$.
(d) The set of all 2X2 matrices A with $a_{11} = 1$.

1.2 Show that the set of all real polynomials in x divisible by $x - 2$ is a subspace of the space P^3 of all polynomials of degree $\leqslant 3$. Find a basis of this subspace and extend this to obtain a basis of P^3.

1.3 Prove that a subset S of a real vector space **V** is a subspace if and only if for all **x**, **y** $\in S$ and for all real α, $\mathbf{x} + \alpha\mathbf{y} \in S$.

1.4 Which of the following subsets of R^4 are subspaces?
(a) Set of all (x_1,x_2,x_3,x_4) with $x_1 \leqslant x_2$.
(b) Set of all (x_1,x_2,x_3,x_4) with $x_1 + x_2 = x_3$.
(c) Set of all (x_1,x_2,x_3,x_4) with $x_1^2 + x_2^2 = 0$.
(d) Set of all (x_1,x_2,x_3,x_4) with $x_1^2 - x_4^2 = 0$.

1.5 S and T are subspaces of a real vector space V. State which of the following are subspaces and justify your answer by a proof or a simple counter-example.
(a) Set of all **x** such that $\mathbf{x} \in S$ and $\mathbf{x} \in T$.
(b) Set of all **x** such that $\mathbf{x} \in S$ or $\mathbf{x} \in T$.
(c) Set of all $\mathbf{v} = \mathbf{x} + \mathbf{y}$ with $\mathbf{x} \in S$, $\mathbf{y} \in T$.

1.6 S and T are subspaces of a finite dimensional vector space V such that $\mathbf{x} \in S$ and $\mathbf{x} \in T \Rightarrow \mathbf{x} = \mathbf{0}$ and each vector $\mathbf{v} \in V$ is expressible in the form $\mathbf{v} = \mathbf{s} + \mathbf{t}$ with $\mathbf{s} \in S$ and $\mathbf{t} \in T$.

Prove that dimension S + dimension T = dimension V and that the equation $\mathbf{v} = \mathbf{s} + \mathbf{t}$ determines **s** and **t** uniquely for a given vector **v**.

1.7 Which of the following sets of vectors in R^4 are linearly dependent?
(a) [(1,2,1,2), (2,3,2,3), (1,2,3,4), (1,1,1,1)]
(b) [(1,0,1,0), (0,1,0,1), (1,0,0,0), (0,1,0,0)]
(c) [(2,3,1,2), (1,2,3,1), (4,7,7,4)].

1.8 Prove that the set of all nXn matrices with real elements forms a real vector space of dimension n^2. Determine which of the following subsets of the space of 3X3 matrices are subspaces and, when possible, find the dimension of the subspace.
(a) The set of all diagonal matrices A with $a_{ij} = 0$ for $i \neq j$.
(b) The set of all matrices A with $|A| = 0$.
(c) The set for all upper triangular matrices A with $a_{ij} = 0$ for $i > j$.
(d) The set of all matrices A with trace $A = 0$.

1.9 Prove that the set of all real continuous functions of x which are periodic of period 2π, such that $f(x+2\pi)=f(x)$ for all x, is a real vector space. Is this space finite dimensional?

1.10 S is the subspace of R^3 generated by the vectors [(1,1,0), (2,3,1), (6,8,2)]. T is the subspace of R^3 which consists of all $\mathbf{x}=(x_1,x_2,x_3)$ with $x_1-2x_2-2x_3=0$.

Find bases of S, of T and of $S \cap T$.

($S \cap T$ denotes the intersection of S and T. It is the set of all vectors which are in S and in T).

1.11 Find a matrix P which represents the change from basis $[\mathbf{e}_1,\mathbf{e}_2,\mathbf{e}_3,\mathbf{e}_4]$ of R^4 to the basis $[\mathbf{w}_1=(1,0,0,0), \mathbf{w}_2=(1,-1,0,0), \mathbf{w}_3=(0,1,-1,0), \mathbf{w}_4=(0,0,1,-1)]$. Find expressions for $\mathbf{a}=(4,3,2,1)$ and for $\mathbf{b}=(1,1,1,1)$ in terms of the new basis.

1.12 Prove by induction on n that all sets of vectors in R^n can be reduced to echelon form by a sequence of elementary vector operations.

1.13 By using elementary operations, find the row ranks and column ranks of the following matrices.

$$A=\begin{pmatrix}1&2&3\\2&1&3\\3&3&6\end{pmatrix} \quad B=\begin{pmatrix}1&2&1&3\\-1&2&3&1\\2&1&3&4\end{pmatrix} \quad C=\begin{pmatrix}1&0&1\\2&1&2\\1&-1&0\end{pmatrix}.$$

1.14 Show that the subspace of R^3 generated by the vectors $[(1,2,1), (1,\theta+1,2), (2,1,5-\theta)]$ is of dimension 2 or 3 depending upon the value of θ. Find the values of θ for which the dimension is 2.

1.15 V is a real vector space. Prove that a set of vectors $[\mathbf{v}_1,\mathbf{v}_2,\ldots,\mathbf{v}_n]$ is a basis of V if and only if every $\mathbf{v} \in V$ has a unique expression of the form $\mathbf{v}=\sum_{i=1}^{n}\alpha_i\mathbf{v}_i$.

1.16 V is a real vector space. If all proper subspaces S of V are such that dimension $S \leqslant m$ prove that V is finite dimensional and dimension $V \leqslant m+1$.

1.17 Find the matrix which represents the change of basis in P^2 from $[1,x,x^2]$ to $[1+x,1-x,x^2-1]$. Find an expression x^2+2x+3 in terms of each basis.

1.18 Find the dimensions of the subspaces of R^4 generated by the following sets of vectors.

(a) [(1,2,3,4), (1,1,1,1), (−1,0,1,2)]

(b) [(1,3,2,1), (1,2,3,7), (1,3,4,1), (0,1,2,3)]
(c) [(1,0,1,0), (0,1,0,−1), (0,0,1,−1), (1,1,1,1)]

1.19 $A = \begin{pmatrix} 1 & 1 & 1 \\ 1 & -1 & 2 \\ 0 & 0 & 1 \end{pmatrix}$.

Find expressions for A and for A^{-1} as products of elementary matrices.

1.20 $[\mathbf{v}_1, \mathbf{v}_2, \ldots, \mathbf{v}_m]$ is a set of non-zero linearly dependent vectors in a real vector space V. Prove that at least one of the vectors $\mathbf{v}_1, \mathbf{v}_2, \ldots, \mathbf{v}_m$ is linearly dependent upon the preceding vectors in the set.

Chapter 2

Applications of Linear Dependence

INTRODUCTION

In Chapter 1 vector spaces were introduced together with the important concepts of linear dependence, subspaces and dimension. This Chapter is concerned with the applications of these to the theory of linear equations and the solution of linear programming problems.

A set of linear algebraic equations is a set of equations of the form:

$$\begin{array}{llllll} a_{11}x_1 & + a_{12}x_2 & + & \ldots + a_{2n}x_n & = c_1 \\ a_{21}x_1 & + a_{22}x_2 & + & \ldots + a_{2n}x_n & = c_2 \\ \cdot & & & & \\ \cdot & & & & \\ \cdot & & & & \\ \cdot & & & & \\ a_{m1}x_1 & + a_{m2}x_2 & + & \ldots + a_{mn}x_n & = c_m \end{array} \tag{2.1}$$

This is a set of m equations for the n unknowns $x_1, x_2, \ldots, x_n$. We shall show in the next Section how the existence of uniqueness or otherwise of the solution depends upon the properties of the coefficients $a_{11}, a_{12}, \ldots, a_{mn}$ and upon the constants $c_1, c_2, \ldots, c_m$ from the right hand side of the equations.

Linear programming problems are a special type of optimisation problems in which a linear function of a number of variables is to be maximised subject to certain linear inequalities, or constraints, on the variables. A very simple problem of this type would be to find the values of x_1 and x_2 which maximise the function $f(x_1,x_2) = 3x_1 + x_2$ subject to constraints:

$$\begin{array}{c} x_1 - x_2 \leqslant 1 \\ 2x_1 + x_2 \leqslant 7 \\ x_1 \geqslant 0, x_2 \geqslant 0 \ . \end{array}$$

The later sections of this Chapter will show how such problems can arise, will apply the theory of the previous Chapter to obtain some important properties of the solution of linear programming problems and will give a practical method for solving these problems.

2.1 THE THEORY OF LINEAR EQUATIONS

The set of Equations (2.1) can be associated with the $m \times n$ coefficient matrix A and written $A\mathbf{x} = \mathbf{c}$, or with certain vectors in the real vector space R^m. (We are assuming that the equations have real coefficients; for equations with complex coefficients an exactly parallel theory can be developed.) Some of the properties of these equations are most readily obtained by using matrix properties, others are obtainable from the properties of R^m.

From the equations (2.1) we immediately obtain a column vector $\mathbf{c}$ in R^m. Less obviously we also have column vectors $\mathbf{v}_1, \mathbf{v}_2, \ldots, \mathbf{v}_n$ which are respectively the coefficients of $x_1, x_2, \ldots, x_n$ respectively. For instance, $\mathbf{v}_1 = \begin{pmatrix} a_{11} \\ a_{21} \\ \cdot \\ \cdot \\ a_{m1} \end{pmatrix}$, the first column vector of the coefficient matrix A. In terms of these vectors Equations (2.1) can be re-written:

$$\mathbf{c} = x_1\mathbf{v}_1 + x_2\mathbf{v}_2 + \ldots + x_n\mathbf{v}_n \tag{2.2}$$

In Equation (2.2) all the vectors are known but the coefficients $x_1, x_2, \ldots, x_n$ have to be determined. The problem is now seen to be that of expressing the vector $\mathbf{c}$ as a linear combination of the vectors $\mathbf{v}_1, \mathbf{v}_2, \ldots, \mathbf{v}_n$. With this interpretation the properties of linear equations are clearly closely related to those of the real vector space R^m.

Theorem 2.1

The set of linear equations (2.1) $A\mathbf{x} = \mathbf{c}$ is only soluble if

$$\text{rank }(A,\mathbf{c}) = \text{rank } A.$$

Proof

In the statement of this theorem $(A,\mathbf{c})$ denotes the $m \times (n+1)$ augmented matrix:

$$\left(\begin{array}{cc|c} a_{11} & a_{1n} & c_1 \\ a_{21} & a_{2n} & c_2 \\ \cdot & & \\ \cdot & & \\ \cdot & & \\ a_{m1} & a_{mn} & c_n \end{array}\right)$$

The vertical partition in this matrix is used to separate the coefficients from the constants. The Equations (2.2) are soluble if and only if $\mathbf{c}$ is linearly dependent upon the column vectors $\mathbf{v}_1, \mathbf{v}_2, \ldots, \mathbf{v}_n$ of the matrix A. If rank $(A,\mathbf{c})$ = rank (A) there are sufficient linearly independent vectors in the set $(\mathbf{v}_1, \ldots, \mathbf{v}_n)$ to generate all vectors in the set $(\mathbf{v}_1, \mathbf{v}_2, \ldots, \mathbf{v}_n, \mathbf{c})$. Hence $\mathbf{c}$ is linearly dependent upon some, or all, of the vectors $\mathbf{v}_1, \mathbf{v}_2, \ldots, \mathbf{v}_n$ giving a solution of the equations. Conversely, if rank (A,c) > rank (A), the set $(\mathbf{v}_1, \mathbf{v}_2, \ldots, \mathbf{v}_n, \mathbf{c})$ contains more linearly independent vectors than $(\mathbf{v}_1, \mathbf{v}_2, \ldots, \mathbf{v}_n)$. This can only mean that $\mathbf{c}$ is not dependent upon $\mathbf{v}_1, \mathbf{v}_2, \ldots, \mathbf{v}_n$ and in this case the equations are insoluble.

Corollary

If rank $(A,\mathbf{c})$ = rank $A = n$, the solution of $A\mathbf{x} = \mathbf{c}$ is unique.

Proof

If rank $A = n$ then the vectors $\mathbf{v}_1, \mathbf{v}_2, \ldots, \mathbf{v}_n$ are linearly independent and so form a basis of the column space of A. From Theorem 1.2 the expression for any vector in terms of a basis is unique. The equation $\mathbf{c} = x_1\mathbf{v}_1 + \ldots + x_n\mathbf{v}_n$ hence determines the coefficients $x_1, x_2, \ldots, x_n$ uniquely.

The converse of this result is established after considering the relationship between the equations $A\mathbf{x} = \mathbf{c}$ and the corresponding homogeneous equations $A\mathbf{x} = \mathbf{0}$.

Theorem 2.2

If $\mathbf{x} = \mathbf{y}$ is any solution of $A\mathbf{x} = \mathbf{c}$ and if $\mathbf{x} = \mathbf{z}$ is a solution of the homogeneous equations $A\mathbf{x} = \mathbf{0}$, then for any constant k, $\mathbf{x} = \mathbf{y} + k\mathbf{z}$ is a solution of $A\mathbf{x} = \mathbf{c}$.

Proof

$A\mathbf{y} = \mathbf{c}$ and $A\mathbf{z} = \mathbf{0}$ (given).

Let $\mathbf{x} = \mathbf{y} + k\mathbf{z}$. Then, using the linear properties of matrices,

$$\begin{aligned} A\mathbf{x} &= A(\mathbf{y} + k\mathbf{z}), \\ &= A\mathbf{y} + A(k\mathbf{z}), \\ &= A\mathbf{y} + kA\mathbf{z} \\ &= \mathbf{c} + k\mathbf{0} = \mathbf{c}. \end{aligned}$$

Thus $\mathbf{x} = \mathbf{y} + k\mathbf{z}$ gives a solution of Equations (2.1).

This solution will differ from $\mathbf{x} = \mathbf{y}$ only when $\mathbf{z} \neq \mathbf{0}$ and this case, when $A\mathbf{x} = \mathbf{0}$ has a so-called non-trivial solution, is obviously of considerable importance. In terms of the column vectors $\mathbf{v}_1, \mathbf{v}_2, \ldots, \mathbf{v}_n$, $A\mathbf{x} = \mathbf{0}$ has a non trivial solution whenever the vectors $\mathbf{v}_1, \mathbf{v}_2, \ldots, \mathbf{v}_n$ are linearly dependent.

Theorem 2.3

The set $A\mathbf{x} = \mathbf{0}$ of m homogeneous equations in n unknowns has a non-trivial solution if $m < n$.

if $n >$ rank A (see notes)

Proof

The set $(\mathbf{v}_1, \mathbf{v}_2, \ldots, \mathbf{v}_n)$ is a set of n vectors from the m dimensional space R^m, and such a set must be linearly dependent if $n > m$. Hence we can find $x_1, x_2, \ldots, x_n$ not all zero such that $x_1\mathbf{v}_1 + x_2\mathbf{v}_2 + \ldots + x_n\mathbf{v}_n = \mathbf{0}$. These values x_i provide the required non-trivial solution of $A\mathbf{x} = \mathbf{0}$.

The above Theorems taken together show that the linear Equations (2.1) cannot be expected to possess a unique solution if the number of variables (n) exceeds the number of equations (m). The case where $m = n$ and the number of variables corresponds to the number of equations is of considerable practical importance. Theorem 2.4 gives the appropriate properties in this case.

Theorem 2.4

If A is an $n \times n$ matrix of rank n the equations $A\mathbf{x} = \mathbf{c}$ are soluble for all constants $\mathbf{c}$ and this solution is unique. If rank $A < n$, a solution only exists if rank A = rank $(A, \mathbf{c})$ and in this case infinitely many distinct solutions will exist.

Proof

If rank $A = n$, the column vectors $\mathbf{v}_1, \mathbf{v}_2, \ldots, \mathbf{v}_n$ are linearly independent and provide a basis of R^n. By Theorem 1.2, any vector $\mathbf{c}$ in R^n will have a unique expression $\mathbf{c} = x_1\mathbf{v}_1 + x_2\mathbf{v}_2 + \ldots + x_n\mathbf{v}_n$, hence $A\mathbf{x} = \mathbf{c}$ has a unique solution.

Conversely if rank $A < n$, the vectors $\mathbf{v}_1, \ldots, \mathbf{v}_n$ are linearly dependent. Hence $A\mathbf{x} = \mathbf{0}$ has a non-trivial solution $\mathbf{x} = \mathbf{z}$. A given vector $\mathbf{c}$ is only in the space spanned by $\mathbf{v}_1, \mathbf{v}_2, \ldots, \mathbf{v}_n$ if rank (A, c) = rank A. In this case $A\mathbf{x} = \mathbf{c}$ will possess some particular solution $\mathbf{x} = \mathbf{y}$. The application of Theorem 2.2 then gives infinitely many solutions of the form $\mathbf{x} = \mathbf{y} + k\mathbf{z}$ as the constant k takes different values.

The condition of rank $A = n$ in the first part of Theorem 2.4 corresponds to the determinantal condition $|A| \neq 0$. In terms of determinants the Theorem can be restated as $A\mathbf{x} = \mathbf{c}$, is soluble for all $\mathbf{c}$ if $|A| \neq 0$, but if $|A| = 0$ the solution may not exist and can never be unique. This suggests that before attempting to solve a set of n linear equations in n unknowns, it might be a sensible precaution first to check that the determinant of the matrix of coefficients is non-zero. In practice, the amount of effort involved in evaluating the determinant for values of n larger than 2 is almost as much as that needed to obtain a solution and this precaution is not practicable. The method given in Section 2.2 provides a solution if it exists and gives a clear indication of insoluble equations.

2.2 THE SOLUTION OF LINEAR EQUATIONS

This Section gives details of two of the most widely used practical methods of solving sets of linear equations. The methods are suitable for hand calculation where the number of variables is small or, with slight modifications, can be adopted for solving large systems of equations with a digital computer.

2.2.1 The method of Gaussian elimination

Theorem 2.1 showed that the system of equations $A\mathbf{x} = \mathbf{c}$ is soluble if rank $(A) =$ rank (A,c). The proof of the Theorem gave no indication of how this solution can be obtained. In practice the computation of rank $(A,\mathbf{c})$ can take us a considerable way towards obtaining the solution of the equations when it exists. Section 1.9 gave details of how the rank of a matrix can be calculated either by using elementary column operations or by elementary row operations. If $(A,\mathbf{c})$ is reduced to echelon form by row operations, not only is the rank obtained but the rows of the reduced matrix will represent a set of equations corresponding to the original equations in the sense that they will possess the same solution. The solution of these reduced equations is particularly simple. The method is illustrated in the examples below, while a theoretical explanation of the method is given later.

Example 2.1

Solve the equations:

$$\begin{aligned} x_1 + x_2 + 2x_3 &= 5, \\ 2x_1 + 3x_2 + 2x_3 &= 10, \\ -x_1 + x_2 + x_3 &= 2. \end{aligned}$$

Solution

The first stage in the solution is to reduce the augmented matrix $(A,\mathbf{c})$ to echelon form by a sequence of elementary row operations.

$$(A,\mathbf{c}) = \left(\begin{array}{ccc|c} 1 & 1 & 2 & 5 \\ 2 & 3 & 2 & 10 \\ -1 & 1 & 1 & 2 \end{array}\right)$$

$$\begin{array}{l} \\ R_1 - 2R_2 \\ R_3 + R_1 \end{array} \left(\begin{array}{ccc|c} 1 & 1 & 2 & 5 \\ 0 & 1 & -2 & 0 \\ 0 & 2 & 3 & 7 \end{array}\right),$$

$$\begin{array}{l} \\ \\ R_3 - 2R_2 \end{array} \left(\begin{array}{ccc|c} 1 & 1 & 2 & 5 \\ 0 & 1 & -2 & 0 \\ 0 & 0 & 7 & 7 \end{array}\right).$$

At this stage it is clear that rank (A) = rank $(A,\mathbf{c}) = 3$ and so, by Theorem 2.4, the equations possess a unique solution. If we now re-interpret the rows of this reduced matrix as equations we obtain:

$$\begin{aligned} x_1 + x_2 + 2x_3 &= 5, \\ x_2 - 2x_3 &= 0, \\ 7x_3 &= 7. \end{aligned}$$

Solving these equations in reverse order with back substitution gives:

$$\begin{aligned} &x_3 = 1, \\ &x_2 - 2 = 0 \Rightarrow x_2 = 2, \\ &x_1 + 2 + 2 = 5 \Rightarrow x_1 = 1. \end{aligned}$$

Hence the solution is $(x_1,x_2,x_3) = (1,2,1)$ and it can quickly be verified that this is a solution of the original system of equations.

Example 2.2

Solve, if possible, the equations:

$$\text{(a)}\quad \begin{aligned} x_1 + x_2 + 2x_3 &= 2, \\ 2x_1 + x_2 - x_3 &= 3, \\ 3x_1 + 2x_2 + x_3 &= 7. \end{aligned} \qquad \text{(b)}\quad \begin{aligned} x_1 + x_2 + 2x_3 &= 1, \\ 2x_1 + x_2 - x_3 &= 4, \\ 3x_1 + 2x_2 + x_3 &= 5. \end{aligned}$$

Solution

In this example both systems of equations have the same coefficient matrix A. Denoting the equations $A\mathbf{x} = \mathbf{c}$, $A\mathbf{x} = \mathbf{d}$ respectively, some saving of effort is made if we consider the reduction of the augmented matrix $(A,\mathbf{c},\mathbf{d})$.

$$(A,\mathbf{c},\mathbf{d}) \quad \left(\begin{array}{ccc|c|c} 1 & 1 & 2 & 2 & 1 \\ 2 & 1 & -1 & 3 & 4 \\ 3 & 2 & 1 & 7 & 5 \end{array}\right)$$

$$\begin{array}{l} \\ R_2 - 2R_1 \\ R_3 - 3R_1 \end{array} \quad \left(\begin{array}{ccc|c|c} 1 & 1 & 2 & 2 & 1 \\ 0 & -1 & -5 & -1 & 2 \\ 0 & -1 & -5 & 1 & 2 \end{array}\right)$$

$$\begin{array}{l} \\ \\ R_3 - R_2 \end{array} \quad \left(\begin{array}{ccc|c|c} 1 & 1 & 2 & 2 & 1 \\ 0 & -1 & -5 & -1 & 2 \\ 0 & 0 & 0 & 2 & 0 \end{array}\right).$$

From this it can be seen that rank $(A) = 2$, rank $(A,\mathbf{c}) = 3$ and rank $(A,\mathbf{d}) = 2$. Thus, by Theorem 2.1, $A\mathbf{x} = \mathbf{c}$ is insoluble but solutions to $A\mathbf{x} = \mathbf{d}$ exist. The same result can be deduced from the corresponding equations because the final equations in the reduced form are $0x_1 + 0x_2 + 0x_3 = 2$ and $0x_1 + 0x_2 + 0x_3 = 0$. To solve the system $A\mathbf{x} = \mathbf{d}$ we have only two equivalent equations to solve:

$$\begin{aligned} x_1 + x_2 + 2x_3 &= 1, \\ \text{and} \qquad -x_2 - 5x_3 &= 2. \end{aligned}$$

Letting $x_3 = k$ and using back substitution gives the solution $x_3 = k$, $x_2 = -2-5k$, $x_1 = 3+3k$. This solution can be expressed in vector form as $\mathbf{x} = \mathbf{y} + k\mathbf{z} = \begin{pmatrix} 3 \\ -2 \\ 0 \end{pmatrix} + k \begin{pmatrix} 3 \\ -5 \\ 1 \end{pmatrix}$. Theorem 2.2 can be verified in this particular case because $\mathbf{x} = \mathbf{y}$ is a particular solution of $A\mathbf{x} = \mathbf{d}$ and $A\mathbf{z} = 0$.

2.2.2 Theoretical background to Gaussian elimination

The method of Gaussian elimination used in the above examples can be justified simply by considering each row of the augmented matrix as corresponding to one of the linear equations. In eliminating variables from simultaneous equations it is normal to allow either the interchange of equations, the subtraction of a multiple of one equation from another or the multiplication of an equation by a non-zero constant. The consistent application of any number of these operations will always give an equivalent set of equations with the same solutions. A comparison of these operations on equations and the elementary row operations on an augmented matrix shows that they correspond exactly.

An alternative explanation of Gaussian elimination can be given in terms of the properties of the elementary matrices introduced in Section 1.10. Let the elementary matrices corresponding to the elementary row operations be, in the correct order, $E_1, E_2, \ldots, E_k$. The final echelon form will then be given by $E_k E_{k-1} \ldots E_2 E_1 (A,c) = (E_k \ldots E_2 E_1 A, E_k \ldots E_2 E_1 \mathbf{c})$. This augmented matrix corresponds to the equation:

$$E_k E_{k-1} \ldots\ldots E_2 E_1 A\mathbf{x} = E_k \ldots\ldots E_2 E_1 \mathbf{c}. \tag{2.3}$$

If $\mathbf{x}$ is any solution of $A\mathbf{x} = \mathbf{c}$ it will certainly satisfy Equation (2.3). Conversely, since each of the elementary matrices is non-singular, any solution of 2.3 will give a solution of $A\mathbf{x} = \mathbf{c}$.

2.2.3 Some Practical Considerations

For consistent sets of linear equations with a unique solution, the method of Gaussian elimination described in Section 2.2.1 will always produce the exact solution provided there are no arithmetic errors. When the number of equations is small and the calculation is being performed manually, it is possible to guard against accidental errors by introducing a row sum check into the calculation. This is described in detail in the next paragraph. When a large system of equations is being solved using a computer, the arithmetic will rarely be exact because each answer is expressed in a finite number of digits. However, the method of **partial-pivoting** described at the end of this Section helps to minimise the effect of these errors.

The sum of the numbers in each row of the augmented matrix can be calculated and stored as an additional column. Since the elimination process operates on entire rows, the row sum remains valid provided the corresponding operations are performed on the numbers in the check column. At the end of the elimination process, the row sums can again be calculated and compared with the numbers in the check column. Any discrepancy indicates that an error has been made in that particular row, but it is of course possible that there are two or more mistakes without such a discrepancy.

Example 2.3

This example illustrates the detection of an arithmetic error by a row sum check.

Solve the equations:

$$\begin{aligned} x_1 - x_2 + 2x_3 &= 5, \\ 2x_1 - x_2 + x_3 &= 5, \\ x_1 + x_2 - x_3 &= 1. \end{aligned}$$

The augmented matrix of the system, with a final check column is:

$$\left(\begin{array}{ccc|c|c} 1 & -1 & 2 & 5 & 7 \\ 2 & -1 & 1 & 5 & 7 \\ 1 & 1 & -1 & 1 & 2 \end{array}\right).$$

The use of row operations on this matrix gives:

$$\begin{array}{l} \\ R_2 - 2R_1 \\ R_3 - R_1 \end{array} \left(\begin{array}{ccc|c|c} 1 & -1 & 2 & 5 & 7 \\ 0 & 1 & -3 & -5 & -7 \\ 0 & 2 & 1 & -4 & -5 \end{array}\right),$$

$$\begin{array}{l} \\ \\ R_3 - 2R_2 \end{array} \left(\begin{array}{ccc|c|c} 1 & -1 & 2 & 5 & 7 \\ 0 & 1 & -3 & -5 & -7 \\ 0 & 0 & 7 & 6 & 9 \end{array}\right).$$

Checking the row sums before beginning the back substitution process shows that the final row sum is inconsistent. Further examination of the row sums for this row shows that the mistake occurred in the operation $R_3 - R_1$. The final row of the second matrix should read (0 2 −3 −4 −5). After correcting this mistake, the final row of the third matrix becomes (0 0 3 6 9). From this the solution $x_3 = 2$ is obtained and the process of back substitution gives the complete solution $x_3 = 2, x_2 = 1, x_1 = 2$.

When using a digital computer, errors arise because each number is stored as a finite number of digits, usually in binary form. Hence the computer works with approximations to the numbers in the real problem because even a simple finite decimal number may not have a finite binary representation. Moreover, at each step in the calculation the answer is also given as a finite approximation. These 'rounding errors' can have a cumulative effect and the final answer may contain an error much larger than the relative error at each stage of the calculation. For a large computer, the effective accuracy of storing a single number may be equivalent to 10 or 11 decimal digits, but for some calculations the final answer could only contain a few correct digits. Example 2.4 below is worked to a relative accuracy of 4 digits to illustrate the cumulative effect of rounding errors and to show how some of these effects can be minimised by modifying the calculating algorithm.

Example 2.4

Find the approximate solution of:

$$\begin{aligned} 1.7x_1 + 2.3x_2 + 1.5x_3 &= 5.5, \\ 3.5x_1 + 4.7x_2 + 2.3x_3 &= 10.5, \\ 0.7x_1 + 3.1x_2 - 1.2x_3 &- 2.6, \end{aligned}$$

[exact solution $x_1 = x_2 = x_3 = 1$].

Using the method of Gaussian elimination and with an accuracy of 4 significant figures at each step we obtain:

$$\left(\begin{array}{ccc|c} \textcircled{1.7} & 2.3 & 1.5 & 5.5 \\ 3.5 & 4.7 & 2.3 & 10.5 \\ 0.7 & 3.1 & -1.2 & 2.6 \end{array}\right),$$

$$\begin{array}{l} \\ R_2 - 2.059R_1 \\ R_3 - 0.4118R_1 \end{array} \left(\begin{array}{ccc|c} 1.7 & 2.3 & 1.5 & 5.5 \\ 0 & \boxed{-0.036} & -0.789 & -0.82 \\ 0 & 2.153 & -1.818 & 0.335 \end{array}\right),$$

$$\begin{array}{l} \\ \\ R_3 + 59.81R_2 \end{array} \left(\begin{array}{ccc|c} 1.7 & 2.3 & 1.5 & 5.5 \\ 0 & -0.036 & -0.789 & -0.82 \\ 0 & 0 & -49.01 & -48.70 \end{array}\right).$$

From the final reduced matrix we obtain by back substitution $x_3 = 0.9937$, $x_2 = 0.9992$, $x_1 = 1.006$. In the reduction process the pivotal elements have been ringed. These are the elements which to a large extent determine the row multipliers to be used in the next stage of the calculation. In this particular example, most of the error relates to the very small pivot -0.036 and the related multiplier 59.81. This means that any small rounding errors present in the second row will be magnified at the next stage of the calculation. The method of partial pivoting avoids this magnification effect by ensuring that the largest available element is used as a pivot, so giving row multipliers of modulus less than 1. Using partial pivoting we obtain:

$$\left(\begin{array}{ccc|c} 1.7 & 2.3 & 1.5 & 5.5 \\ \boxed{3.5} & 4.7 & 2.3 & 10.5 \\ 0.7 & 3.1 & -1.2 & 2.6 \end{array}\right),$$

$$\begin{array}{l} R_2 \\ R_1 - 0.4857R_2 \\ R_3 - 0.2R_2 \end{array} \left(\begin{array}{ccc|c} 3.5 & 4.7 & 2.3 & 10.5 \\ 0 & 0.017 & 0.383 & 0.4 \\ 0 & \boxed{2.16} & -1.66 & 0.5 \end{array}\right),$$

$$\begin{array}{l} \\ R_3 \\ R_2 - .00787R_3 \end{array} \left(\begin{array}{ccc|c} 3.5 & 4.7 & 2.3 & 10.5 \\ 0 & 2.16 & -1.66 & 0.5 \\ 0 & 0 & 0.3961 & 0.396 \end{array}\right).$$

The final solution is now $x_3 = 0.9997, x_2 = 0.9998, x_1 = 1.0005$ and these differ from the accurate solution only in the fourth significant digit.

Further information about rounding errors and accurate numerical methods of solving linear equations can be found in [Goult, Hoskins, Milner, Pratt, 1974].

2.2.4 Matrix Inversion

The Gaussian elimination method can be adapted to find the inverse of a non-singular matrix A. The matrix inverse A^{-1} is required to satisfy the matrix equation $AA^{-1} = I$. Since, in a matrix product, the columns of the second matrix are multiplied by the rows of the first, the ith column vector $\mathbf{x}_i$ of A^{-1} must satisfy the equation $A\mathbf{x}_i = \mathbf{e}_i$ where $\mathbf{e}_i$ is the ith column vector of the identity matrix I. This argument suggests that the individual columns of A^{-1} could be found by using Gaussian elimination to solve:

$$A\mathbf{x}_1 = \mathbf{e}_1, A\mathbf{x}_2 = \mathbf{e}_2 \ldots\ldots, A\mathbf{x}_n = \mathbf{e}_n \tag{2.4}$$

These n sets of equations need not be solved individually because they all have the same coefficient matrix A on the left hand side and the same sequence of elementary row operations can be applied to each set. This reduction is achieved in a compact way if the individual vectors $\mathbf{e}_1, \mathbf{e}_2, \ldots, \mathbf{e}_n$ are written as consecutive columns of the augmented matrix. The need for back substitution is avoided if A is fully reduced to produce an identity matrix rather than the usual triangular form. Example 2.5 below illustrates the suggested method.

Example 2.5

Find the inverse of the matrix $A = \begin{pmatrix} 1 & 2 & -2 \\ 1 & 3 & -1 \\ 2 & 1 & -5 \end{pmatrix}$.

Using the notation of Equation (2.4) we wish to find the vectors $\mathbf{x}_1$, $\mathbf{x}_2$ and $\mathbf{x}_3$. The method of Gaussian elimination gives:

$$\left(\begin{array}{ccc|ccc} 1 & 2 & -2 & 1 & 0 & 0 \\ 1 & 3 & -1 & 0 & 1 & 0 \\ 2 & 1 & -5 & 0 & 0 & 1 \end{array}\right),$$

$$\begin{array}{l} \\ R_2 - R_1 \\ R_3 - 2R_1 \end{array} \left(\begin{array}{ccc|ccc} 1 & 2 & -2 & 1 & 0 & 0 \\ 0 & 1 & 1 & -1 & 1 & 0 \\ 0 & -3 & -1 & -2 & 0 & 1 \end{array}\right),$$

$$\begin{array}{l} R_1 - 2R_2 \\ \\ R_3 + 3R_2 \end{array} \left(\begin{array}{ccc|ccc} 1 & 0 & -4 & 3 & -2 & 0 \\ 0 & 1 & 1 & -1 & 1 & 0 \\ 0 & 0 & 2 & -5 & 3 & 1 \end{array}\right),$$

$$\begin{array}{l} R_3 + 2R_3 \\ R_2 - \tfrac{1}{2}R_3 \\ \tfrac{1}{2}R_3 \end{array} \left(\begin{array}{ccc|ccc} 1 & 0 & 0 & -7 & 4 & 2 \\ 0 & 1 & 0 & 3/2 & -1/2 & -1/2 \\ 0 & 0 & 1 & -5/2 & 3/2 & 1/2 \end{array}\right).$$

At this stage the solutions can be read off. Since, for example, the equation $A\mathbf{x}_1 = \mathbf{e}_1$ is equivalent to $I\mathbf{x}_1 = (-7, 3/2, -5/2)'$, we have immediately $\mathbf{x}_1 = (-7, 3/2, -5/2)'$. Combining $\mathbf{x}_1$, $\mathbf{x}_2$ and $\mathbf{x}_3$ together gives the required matrix $A^{-1} = \begin{pmatrix} -7 & 4 & 2 \\ 3/2 & -1/2 & -1/2 \\ -5/2 & 3/2 & 1/2 \end{pmatrix}$, which was the matrix finally obtained on the right hand side after completely reducing A to I.

In practice the vectors $\mathbf{x}_1$, $\mathbf{x}_2$ and $\mathbf{x}_3$ need never have been introduced. Their sole purpose was to illustrate the relationship between the problems of matrix inversion and the solution of linear equations. The method of inversion used here can also be explained in terms of the elementary matrices described in Section 1.10. In effect the right hand side of the augmented matrix above stores a running total of the product of the elementary matrices corresponding to the row operations performed. If these matrices are, in the correct order, $E_1, E_2, \ldots, E_7$, we have $E_7E_6E_5E_4E_3E_2E_1A = I$. Hence $A^{-1} = E_7E_6 \ldots E_1$, which should appear as the final matrix on the right hand side.

2.3 LINEAR PROGRAMMING PROBLEMS

Linear programming problems, in which a linear function of the variables is required to be maximised or minimised subject to a number of linear constraints, arise in many different contexts. Problems from fields as diverse as production planning, transportation and dietetics can all be formulated as standard linear programming problems. In practice the number of variables and constraints can be very large but the paragraphs below give some simplified problems in order to illustrate the potential applications of linear programming.

Example 2.6 (A production planning problem)

A manufacturer produces electric motors and gearboxes in a small workshop. Because of sales difficulties, the number of motors produced must never exceed the number of gearboxes by more than one per day. Each motor takes 2 hours to produce and each gearbox 1 hour. The profit on a motor is 3 times that on a gearbox. Find the daily production rates of motors and of gearboxes in order to maximise the profit in a 7 hour working day.

This problem can be expressed in simple mathematical terms if we let x_1 denote the number of motors produced daily and x_2 be the daily production of gearboxes. If one unit of profit is made on a gearbox, the daily profit will be $3x_1 + x_2$ units.

The restriction imposed by the length of the working day is expressed by the inequality:

$$2x_1 + x_2 \leqslant 7.$$

The sales restriction on the number of motors produced becomes:

$$x_1 - x_2 \leqslant 1.$$

The remaining constraints are the commonsense ones that the number of articles produced can never be negative, that is $x_1 \geqslant 0$ and $x_2 \geqslant 0$.

We have now obtained our linear programming problem:

Maximise $$f(x_1,x_2) = 3x_1 + x_2,$$

subject to constraints:

$$\begin{aligned} 2x_1 + x_2 &\leqslant 7,\\ x_1 - x_2 &\leqslant 1,\\ x_1 &\geqslant 0,\\ x_2 &\geqslant 0. \end{aligned}$$

Example 2.7 (A transporation problem)

A chemical company has 2 factories and 3 wholesale depots to be supplied. The daily outputs of the factories are respectively 60 tons and 100 tons. The daily requirements at the depots are 40 tons, 60 tons and 60 tons. How should the product be distributed if the transportation costs (£ per ton) between the factories and the depots are given in the table below?

	Depot A	Depot B	Depot C
Factory 1	10	15	30
Factory 2	20	40	10

The objective is clearly to minimise the total cost of transportation. If x_1, x_2, x_3 denote the daily distributions from Factory 1 to the 3 Depots and x_4, x_5, x_6 similarly denote the daily distributions in tons from Factory 2, the problem becomes the linear programming problem:

$$\text{Minimise: } 10x_1 + 15x_2 + 30x_3 + 20x_4 + 40x_5 + 10x_6,$$

subject to constraints:

$$\begin{aligned} x_1 + x_4 &= 40 \text{ (requirement of Depot A)} \\ x_2 + x_5 &= 60, \\ x_3 + x_6 &= 60, \\ x_1 + x_2 + x_3 &= 60 \text{ (output of Factory 1)}, \\ x_4 + x_5 + x_6 &= 100, \end{aligned}$$

$$x_1 \geqslant 0, x_2 \geqslant 0, x_3 \geqslant 0, x_4 \geqslant 0, x_5 \geqslant 0, x_6 \geqslant 0.$$

This problem differs from the previous example because the main constraints are now equalities and the linear function is required to be minimised rather than maximised. However it can still be solved by the methods given later in this Chapter.

Example 2.8 (A dietary problem)

Suppose a number of foods are available and that the ith food contains c_i calories, p_i units of protein and a_i, b_i units of vitamins A and B per unit weight. Suppose also that the minimum daily requirements for a balanced diet are C calories, P units of protein, and α, β units of vitamins A and B respectively. The problem of providing nourishment at minimum cost can be simply expressed mathematically.

Let x_i be the weight of the daily intake of the ith food. If there are n foods, costing $y_1, y_2, \ldots, y_n$ per unit weight, we require to minimise $x_1y_1 + x_2y_2 + \ldots + x_ny_n$ subject to the constraints:

$$\begin{aligned}
a_1x_1 &+ a_2x_2 + \ldots + a_nx_n \geqslant \alpha,\\
b_1x_1 &+ b_2x_2 + \ldots + b_nx_n \geqslant \beta,\\
c_1x_1 &+ c_2x_2 + \ldots + c_nx_n \geqslant C,\\
p_1x_1 &+ p_2x_2 + \ldots + p_nx_n \geqslant P.
\end{aligned}$$

The above examples illustrate the formulation of some typical linear programming problems. Before attempting to solve these problems it is necessary to introduce some of the underlying theory and this is done in the next Section.

2.3.1 Convex sets and linear programming theory

Let V be a real vector space and S a subset of V. S is said to be a **convex set** if whenever $\mathbf{v}_1 \in S$ and $\mathbf{v}_2 \in S$, then $\alpha_1\mathbf{v} + \alpha_2\mathbf{v}_2 \in S$ for all $\alpha_1, \alpha_2 \geqslant 0$ such that $\alpha_1 + \alpha_2 = 1$.

If V is the real vector space R^3 the above definition is geometrically equivalent to the requirement that whenever P_1 (corresponding to $\mathbf{v}_1$) and P_2 (corresponding to $\mathbf{v}_2$) are in the set S, then all points on the line P_1P_2 and between P_1 and P_2 should also be contained in S. Geometrically any point on the line P_1P_2 is represented by the vector $\alpha_1\mathbf{v}_1 + \alpha_2\mathbf{v}_2$ with $\alpha_1 + \alpha_2 = 1$. For interior points of this line there is the additional requirement that α_1 and α_2 should be positive. The diagrams below show examples of sets in two dimensional space. Sets A and C are convex but B is not a convex set because it is possible to find points between the illustrated points P_1 and P_2 which are not in the set B. These diagrams show that the formal definition given for convex sets corresponds to the normal usage of the word convex.

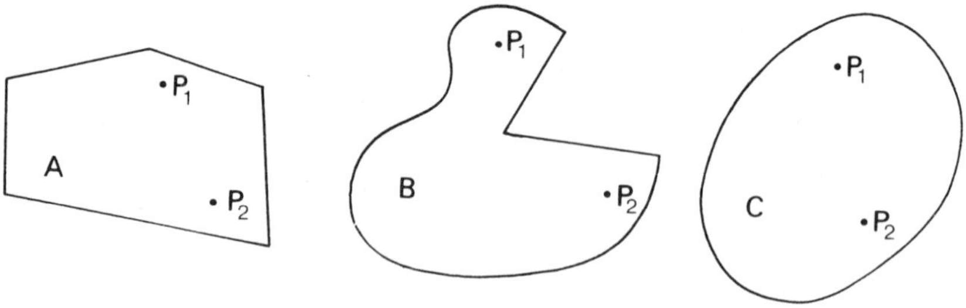

Figure 2.1

Theorem 2.5

The intersection of any two convex sets is a convex set.

Proof

Let C and D be any convex sets in a real vector space V. Suppose $\mathbf{v}_1 \in C \cap D$ and $\mathbf{v}_2 \in C \cap D$. Then for all α_1, α_2 with $\alpha_1 > 0, \alpha_2 > 0$ and $\alpha_1 + \alpha_2 = 1$ we have:

$$\alpha_1\mathbf{v}_1 + \alpha_2\mathbf{v}_2 \in C,$$

since C is convex,

and $$\alpha_1\mathbf{v}_1 + \alpha_2\mathbf{v}_2 \in D,$$

since D is convex.

Thus, $$\alpha_1\mathbf{v}_1 + \alpha_2\mathbf{v}_2 \in C \cap D.$$

Hence, $C \cap D$ is also a convex set.

Theorem 2.5 enables new convex sets to be constructed by taking the intersections of one or more simple convex sets. The reader is invited to verify for himself that the examples below are all convex sets in accordance with the given definition.

(i) In 3-dimensional space, the interior and boundary of the sphere $x_1^2 + x_2^2 + x_3^2 \leqslant r^2$ is a convex set.

(ii) In R^n the set of all $\mathbf{x}$ with $x_1 \geqslant 0$ is a convex set. Geometrically this is the set of all points on or above the plane $x_1 = 0$.

(iii) As a generalisation of the above example, for any integer i the set of all $\mathbf{x}$ with $x_i \geqslant 0$ is a convex set.

(iv) For given values of $(a_1, a_2, \ldots, a_n)$ the set of all $\mathbf{x} \in R^n$ with $\sum_{i=1}^{n} a_i x_i = C$ is a convex set.

(v) For given $(a_1, a_2, \ldots, a_n)$ the set of all $\mathbf{x} \in R^n$ with $\sum_{i=1}^{n} a_i x_i \leqslant k$ is also a convex set.

The relationship between convex sets and the standard linear programming problem is established by applying Theorem 2.5. to Examples (iii), (iv) and (v) above. A standard linear programming problem is to find $\mathbf{x} = (x_1, x_2, \ldots, x_n)$ which maximises the linear function:

$$f(\mathbf{x}) = \sum_{i=1}^{n} c_i x_i = \mathbf{c}'\mathbf{x}$$

subject to constraints:

$$x_i \geqslant 0 \qquad \text{for } i = 1, \ldots, n,$$

and $$\sum_{j=1}^{n} a_{ij} x_j \leqslant b_i \qquad \text{for } i = 1, \ldots, n \text{ (or } A\mathbf{x} \leqslant \mathbf{b}).$$

Any point which satisfies the constraints of a linear programming problem is called a **feasible point**. The combination of Theorem 2.5 with Examples (iii) and (v) above shows that the set of feasible points for a linear programming problem is a convex set. If some or all of the constraints are equalities rather than inequalities, the same result is established by making use of Example (iv). If the problem is one of minimising a linear function rather than of maximising, this is reduced to standard form by noting that $-f(\mathbf{x})$ has a minimum value at any point where $f(\mathbf{x})$ has a maximum value.

Now that we have established that the set of feasible points for a linear programming problem forms a convex set, it remains to determine which of the points in this set will maximise the linear function $f(\mathbf{x})$. In general the set of feasible points will be infinite but the application of Theorem 2.6 below restricts the search for an optimum solution to one of a finite number of points called vertices.

A point $\mathbf{x}$ of a convex set S is said to be a **vertex** of S if we cannot find $\mathbf{x}_1, \mathbf{x}_2$ both in S such that $\mathbf{x} = \alpha_1\mathbf{x}_1 + \alpha_2\mathbf{x}_2$ with $\alpha_i > 0$ and $\alpha_1 + \alpha_2 = 1$. This definition is equivalent to the geometric statement that P, corresponding to $\mathbf{x}$, is not an interior point of some line P_1P_2 inside S. This definition accords with the normal meaning of vertex since for a convex polygon in R^2 the only vertices so defined are vertices in the ordinary geometric sense (see Figure 2.1, A).

Theorem 2.6

Let S be a convex set in R^n and $f(\mathbf{x}) = \sum_{i=1}^{n} c_i x_i$ a real linear function. Then at least one of the points of S which maximises $f(\mathbf{x})$ is a vertex of S.

Proof

Let θ denote the maximum value of $f(\mathbf{x})$ for all $\mathbf{x}$ in the convex set S. If T denotes the set of all $\mathbf{x}$ in S with $f(\mathbf{x}) = \theta$ then, by Example (iv) and Theorem 2.5, T is also a convex set. Suppose, if possible, that no point of T is a vertex of S, then, in particular, no vertex of T is a vertex of S.

Let $\mathbf{x}_0$ be any vertex of T, then because $\mathbf{x}_0$ is not a vertex of S, for some $\mathbf{x}_1$ and $\mathbf{x}_2$ in S $\mathbf{x}_0$ is on the line $\mathbf{x}_1\mathbf{x}_2$. Hence for some α_1, α_2 with $\alpha_1 > 0$ $\alpha_2 > 0$ and $\alpha_1 + \alpha_2 = 1$, $\mathbf{x}_0 = \alpha_1\mathbf{x}_1 + \alpha_2\mathbf{x}_2$. Because $\mathbf{x}_0$ is a vertex of T $\mathbf{x}_1$, $\mathbf{x}_2$ cannot both be in T; assume $\mathbf{x}_1 \in T$.

Then $\qquad f(\mathbf{x}_1) < \theta.$

But
$$\begin{aligned} \theta = f(\mathbf{x}_0) &= f(\alpha_1\mathbf{x}_1 + \alpha_2\mathbf{x}_2) \\ &= \alpha_1 f(\mathbf{x}_1) + \alpha_2 f(\mathbf{x}_2) \\ &< \alpha_1\theta + \alpha_2 f(\mathbf{x}_2) \\ &\leqslant (\alpha_1 + \alpha_2)\theta \\ &= \theta. \end{aligned}$$

We have thus obtained the contradiction $\theta < \theta$, hence our original assumption that $\mathbf{x}_0$ is not a vertex of S must be false, and one of the maximum values of $f(\mathbf{x})$ must occur at a vertex.

This theorem can be demonstrated in a simple case if we consider the geometric interpretation of a simple linear programming problem.

Example 2.9

Find graphically the maximum value of:

$$f(\mathbf{x}) = 3x_1 + x_2$$

with constraints

$$2x_1 + x_2 \leqslant 7,$$
$$x_1 - x_2 \leqslant 1,$$
$$x_1 \geqslant 0,$$
$$x_2 \geqslant 0.$$

[See example 2.7 for the formulation of this problem.]

Solution

$2x_1 + x_2 = 7$ defines a line in the plane of x_1 and x_2. The set of all points such that $2x_1 + x_2 \leqslant 7$ corresponds to the set of all points on, or below, this line.

In a similar way the remaining three inequalities define regions in the plane. Taking the intersection of these regions gives the set of feasible points which are inside or on the quadrilateral OABC in Figure 2.2 below.

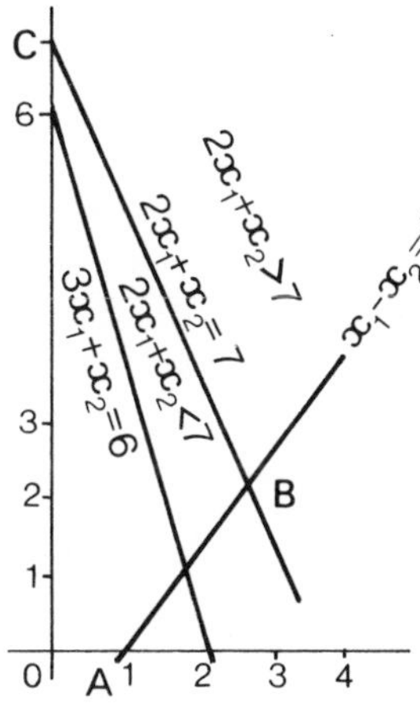

Figure 2.2

The function $f(\mathbf{x}) = 3x_1 + x_2$ has a constant value along any line $3x_1 + x_2 = k$. The line $3x_1 + x_2 = 6$ is illustrated on the diagram. All other lines of constant profit k, $3x_1 + x_2 = k$, will be parallel to this, the profit increasing as the lines move further out from 0. The maximum profit is obtained by finding the line $3x_1 + x_2 = k$ which just passes through the vertex B. The point B is found by solving:

$$x_1 - x_2 = 1,$$
$$2x_1 + x_2 = 7.$$

B is the point (8/3,5/3) and the corresponding maximum value of f is 29/3.

The geometric method of solution used above clearly illustrates the way in which the maximum function value occurs at a vertex, but it is of course unsuitable for solving linear programming problems involving a large number of variables. What is needed for these problems is some algebraic method of solution and the first requirement for this is to have an algebraic method of identifying vertices. The search for a maximum value of $f(\mathbf{x})$ can then be confined to the vertices of the set of feasible points. As the number of variables in the problem increases, the number of vertices increases even more rapidly and it is not practicable to evaluate $f(\mathbf{x})$ at every vertex. A more realistic method (as used in the Simplex algorithm) is to start the search at any vertex and always move to an adjacent vertex at which the value of the function is increased. When no such adjacent vertex can be found, the search is terminated.

Theorem 2.7

Let P be an $m \times k$ matrix of rank m. Then the vertices of the convex set S defined by,

$$P\mathbf{x} = \mathbf{b}, \quad x_i \geqslant 0 \quad \text{for } i = 1, \ldots, k,$$

all correspond to vectors $\mathbf{x}$ with at least $(k - m)$ zero components.

Proof

Suppose, if possible, that $\mathbf{x}_0$ is a vertex of S with more than m non-zero components. Let the column vectors of P corresponding to these non-zero components be $\mathbf{v}_1, \mathbf{v}_2, \ldots, \mathbf{v}_r$ $(r > m)$. Because rank $p = m$ these vectors are linearly dependent and we can find $(y_1, y_2, \ldots, y_r)$ not all zero, such that $\sum_{i=1}^{r} y_i \mathbf{v}_i = 0$.

Taking the non-zero components of $\mathbf{x}_0$ we have the equation:

$$\sum_{i=1}^{r} x_i^0 \mathbf{v}_i = \mathbf{b}.$$

Let $$x_i^1 = x_i^0 - \epsilon y_i \quad \text{for } i = 1, \ldots, r,$$

and $$x_i^2 = x_i^0 + \epsilon y_i \quad \text{for } i = 1, \ldots, r.$$

Then, because $x_i^0 > 0$ for all i, we can find a small but non-zero value of ϵ such that x_i^1 and x_i^2 are both positive for all values of i.

For this value of ϵ we have

$$\sum_{i=1}^{r} x_i^1 \mathbf{v}_i = \sum_{i=1}^{r} x_i^0 \mathbf{v}_i - \epsilon \sum_{i=1}^{r} y_i \mathbf{v}_i = \mathbf{b} - \epsilon \mathbf{O} = \mathbf{b},$$

and $$\sum_{i=1}^{r} x_i^2 \mathbf{v}_i = \sum_{i=1}^{r} x_i^0 \mathbf{v}_i + \epsilon \sum_{i=1}^{r} y_i \mathbf{v}_i = \mathbf{b} + \epsilon \mathbf{O} = \mathbf{b}.$$

The corresponding points $\mathbf{x}_1$ and $\mathbf{x}_2$ are both feasible points of S with the same zero components as $\mathbf{x}_0$. However, clearly $\mathbf{x}_0 = ½\mathbf{x}_1 + ½\mathbf{x}_2$ and $\mathbf{x}_0$ is the midpoint of the line $\mathbf{x}_1\mathbf{x}_2$. This contradicts the definition of $\mathbf{x}_0$ as a vertex of S and our assumption that $\mathbf{x}_0$ could have more than m non-zero components was false.

The conclusion is that each vertex of S must have no more than m non-zero components. Such a point is often referred to as a **basic feasible point.** Theorem 2.7 provides an algebraic solution to the problem of identifying vertices, but it would appear to be restricted to the special case when all the linear constraints are equalities. In the following Section we shall show how, in the case of linear ineqaulities, extra variables can be introduced to re-formulate the problem with equality constraints.

2.3.2 The Simplex method in Linear programming

The simplex method is essentially an algebraic method of moving progressively from vertex to vertex in the set of feasible points in such a way that the value of the function to be maximised is always increased. When no neighbouring vertex can be found which avoids a decrease in the function value, then, by applying Theorem 2.6, the optimum has been attained. For a problem with m linearly independent equality constraints, the process starts with a basic feasible solution containing precisely m non-zero variables and systematically replaces one variable at a time until the maximum is reached. This algorithm relies upon Theorem 2.7, which ensures that any solution containing m or less non-zero variables will correspond to a vertex in the set of feasible points. At each step of the calculation, the new variable to be introduced is chosen as the one giving the largest possible increase in the function value. For problems with ineqaulity constraints, the preliminary stage of the calculation is to introduce new variables called **slack variables** in order to re-write the constraints as equalities. For hand calculation the working is normally set out in a **simplex tableau** which reduces the working to a simple mechanical process but which tends to obscure the simple geometric interpretation of what is being done. The use of slack variables and of the simplex tableau is demonstrated in Example 2.10 below.

Example 2.10

Find the maximum value of $f(\mathbf{x}) = 3x_1 + x_2$ with constraints:

$$\begin{aligned} 2x_1 + x_2 &\leqslant 7, \\ x_1 - x_2 &\leqslant 1, \\ x_1 \geqslant 0, x_2 &\geqslant 0. \end{aligned}$$

(See Examples 2.6 and 2.9).

Solution

The introduction of slack variables x_3, x_4 enables us to replace the inequality constraints by:

$$\begin{aligned} 2x_1 + x_2 + x_3 &= 7, \\ x_1 - x_2 + x_4 &= 1. \end{aligned}$$

Referring to the formulation in Example 2.6, these slack variables are readily interpreted as under-used capacity. For example, x_3 represents non-productive hours in the working-day. These constraint equations can be written in vector form as:

$$x_1 \begin{pmatrix} 2 \\ 1 \end{pmatrix} + x_2 \begin{pmatrix} 1 \\ -1 \end{pmatrix} + x_3 \begin{pmatrix} 1 \\ 0 \end{pmatrix} + x_4 \begin{pmatrix} 0 \\ 1 \end{pmatrix} = \begin{pmatrix} 7 \\ 1 \end{pmatrix},$$

or

$$\sum_{i=1}^{4} x_i \mathbf{v}_i = \mathbf{v}_0.$$

Each feasible point corresponds to some non-negative solution of this equation, while each basic feasible point, or vertex of the convex set, corresponds to a solution with only two non-zero variables present. For such a basic feasible point we have in effect chosen precisely two of the vectors $\mathbf{v}_1, \mathbf{v}_2, \mathbf{v}_3, \mathbf{v}_4$ as a basis of R^2 and expressed $\mathbf{v}_0$ in terms of the chosen basis. In the simplex tableau below, the second column gives the chosen basis at each stage of the working.

		Tableau					*Comments*
c_j	0	0	3	1	0	0	c_j is the coefficient of x_j in $f(\mathbf{x})$.
	Basis	$\mathbf{v}_0$	$\mathbf{v}_1$	$\mathbf{v}_2$	$\mathbf{v}_3$	$\mathbf{v}_4$	
0	$\mathbf{v}_3$	7	2	1	1	0	
0	$\mathbf{v}_4$	1	(1)	−1	0	1	The pivot element is ringed.
z_j		0	0	0	0	0	z_j = the sum of products of
$c_j - z_j$		0	3	1	0	0	elements of $\mathbf{v}_j$ and coefficients from the c_j column.
3	$\mathbf{v}_1$	1	1	−1	1	1	
0	$\mathbf{v}_3$	1	0	(3)	1	−2	$\mathbf{v}_1$ has replaced $\mathbf{v}_4$ in basis.
z_j		3	0	−3	0	3	
$c_j - z_j$		−3	0	4	0	−3	
1	$\mathbf{v}_2$	5/3	0	1	1/3	−2/3	$\mathbf{v}_2$ has replaced $\mathbf{v}_3$ in basis.
3	$\mathbf{v}_1$	8/3	1	0	1/3	1/3	
z_j		29/3	3	1	4/3	1/3	
$c_j - z_j$		−29/3	0	0	−4/3	−1/3	The optimum is attained since $c_j - z_j$ is negative for all vectors not in the basis.

Optimum solution $x_1 = 8/3, x_2 = 5/3,$
$f = 29/3.$

The simplex method requires a basic feasible point as starting point. The simplest of these is $x_3 = 7, x_4 = 1$ corresponding to basis vectors $\mathbf{v}_3$ and $\mathbf{v}_4$. In the initial tableau, c_j is the coefficient of x_j in the linear function $f(\mathbf{x}) = \sum_{j=1} c_j x_j$ being maximised. The sum of the products of the components of $\mathbf{v}_j$ with the numbers in the left hand column which give the weightings in $f(\mathbf{x})$ of the variables corresponding to the current basis is z_j. At each stage of the calculation the pivot element is ringed. This identifies the vector to be introduced to the basis at the next step.

Computational Algorithm

The pivotal column is the column with the largest positive value of $c_j - z_j$; this indicates the new vector to be introduced in the basis. The pivotal row is the row giving the smallest positive value to the quotient (element of $\mathbf{v}_0$)/(element of pivotal column); this indicates the vector to be omitted from the basis. Once the pivot has been determined the new tableau is calculated by using row operations.

The pivotal row is divided by the pivot to give the replacement row (row labelled $\mathbf{v}_1$ in second tableau).

From each of the other rows the product of the replacement row and the corresponding element in the pivotal column above is subtracted. This method is also applied to the calculation of the new $c_j - z_j$ row, but the z_j row cannot be obtained by row operations. In practice, after the first stage of the computation the z_j row and the c_j column can be omitted. They are included in this example only as an aid to explain the method.

The algorithm terminates when no suitable pivotal column can be found. At this stage the maximum value of f is given by changing the sign of the entry in column $\mathbf{v}_0$ and row $c_j - z_j$.

Explanation of Algorithm

The columns of the table give the coefficients expressing the vectors $\mathbf{v}_i$, including the constraint vector $\mathbf{v}_0$, in terms of the chosen basis vectors. c_j is the coefficient of x_j in $f(\mathbf{x})$ and represents the potential contribution to f of $\mathbf{v}_j$ if included in the basis. z_j represents the contribution of f of $\mathbf{v}_j$ when expressed in terms of the current basis. Hence, $c_j - z_j$ represents the difference between the potential and actual contributions to f of $\mathbf{v}_j$. If $c_j - z_j$ is positive, f will be increased by including $\mathbf{v}_j$ in the basis. The pivotal column is normally chosen as the one with the largest positive value of $c_j - z_j$.

The choice of pivotal column determines which new vector is to be included in the basis; the final choice of pivot element indicates the vector to be omitted. In the first stage of the above calculation this choice is determined by the equation:

$$x_1 \begin{pmatrix}2\\1\end{pmatrix} + x_3 \begin{pmatrix}1\\0\end{pmatrix} + x_4 \begin{pmatrix}0\\1\end{pmatrix} = \begin{pmatrix}7\\1\end{pmatrix}$$

Clearly, as x_1 increases from zero both x_3 and x_4 must decrease, but x_4 will be the first variable to violate the constraint $x_i \geqslant 0$, hence $\mathbf{v}_4$ must be omitted from the basis. In practice the pivotal row is the row giving the smallest positive value to the ratio (element in $\mathbf{v}_0$ column)/(element in pivot column) because this determines the value of the newly introduced variable at which the first sign change will occur amongst the other variables. Once the pivot element has been determined the row operations performed on the tableau can be interpreted either in terms of vector spaces or in terms of augmented matrices.

In vector space terms, the columns in the table gives expressions for all the vectors $\mathbf{v}_j$ in terms of the chosen basis vectors, $\mathbf{v}_j = \sum_i t_{ij}\mathbf{v}_i$ where the summation is over the current basis vectors.

If we assume that the rth column is pivotal and that $\mathbf{v}_s$ is the vector being replaced, then the pivot element is $p = t_{sr}$. The expression for the replacement vector $\mathbf{v}_r$ in terms of the original basis is:

$$\mathbf{v}_r = t_{sr}\mathbf{v}_s + \sum_{i \neq s} t_{ir}\mathbf{v}_r.$$

Solving this equation for $\mathbf{v}_s$ gives $\mathbf{v}_s = \dfrac{1}{p}\mathbf{v}_r - \sum_{i \neq s} \dfrac{t_{ir}}{p}\mathbf{v}_i.$

Substituting this value for $\mathbf{v}_s$ into the expression for the other vectors $\mathbf{v}_j$ gives:

$$\mathbf{v}_j = t_{sj}\mathbf{v}_s + \sum_{i \neq s} t_{ij}\mathbf{v}_i$$

$$= \frac{t_{sj}}{p}\mathbf{v}_r + \sum_{i \neq s} (t_{ij} - \frac{t_{ir}}{p} t_{si})\mathbf{v}_i. \tag{2.5}$$

Equation 2.5 shows how the coefficients of the new tableau can be obtained from the previous tableau by the row operations of the computational algorithm.

In terms of augmented matrices the initial simplex tableau corresponds to an augmented matrix for solving the equations $\mathbf{b} = A\mathbf{x}$. Since this is a set of m equations in $m + n$ unknowns, the solution will not be unique but a basic solution can be read off when m columns of this matrix coincide with the elementary vectors $\mathbf{e}_i$ (the column vectors of I). The row operations performed on the simplex tableau are precisely those which will reduce the pivotal column to $\mathbf{e}_s$. The value of $c_r - z_r$ must be reduced to zero because $\mathbf{v}_r$ is now included in the basis and there can be no difference between its actual and potential contributions to f.

Geometric interpretation

It is instructive to relate the various stages of the above solution to the geometric solution of the same problem obtained in Example 2.9. Using the notation of Figure 2.2, each boundary line of the feasible region can be identified with a zero value for one of the variables x_1, x_2, or one of the slack variables x_3, x_4. For example the line AB corresponds to $x_4 = 0$. At the first step of the simplex algorithm the basic feasible point $x_1 = x_2 = 0, x_3 = 7, x_4 = 1$ is represented by the point 0 of the diagram. The introduction of vector **v** into the basis corresponds to traversing 0A in search of the next vertex. The fact that vertex A corresponds to the omission of $\mathbf{v}_3$ rather than of $\mathbf{v}_4$ from the basis is indicated on the diagram by the fact that line 0A intersects the line $x_1 - x_2 = 1$ before it meets the line $2x_1 + x_2 = 7$. In the second stage of the solution $\mathbf{v}_2$ replaces $\mathbf{v}_3$ in the basis and this replacement corresponds to progress in the diagram from A to B. The final negative values of $c_j - z_j$ in the tableau indicate that the function cannot be increased by traversing BC or BA.

Note that (i): when solving problems with inequality constraints by the simplex algorithm it is conventional to start with the basic solution including all the slack variables because this point is immediately available without any preliminary working. For problems with equality constraints, the simplex algorithm can still be employed but it is necessary to do some preliminary working to find a basic feasible point as starting point (see Problem 2.17).

(ii): for problems where the function is to be minimised rather than maximised, either the simplex algorithm can be employed to maximise the value of $-f(\mathbf{x})$ or the criteria used in the simplex algorithm can be changed, the search terminating when all values of $c_j - z_j$ are positive.

(iii): the simplex algorithm is closely related to the solution of systems of linear equations. For linear programming problems with a large number of variables, some of the techniques used for solving large sets of linear equations can be employed. These techniques give rise to the **revised simplex method** and methods based on the LU factorisation of matrices [Luenberger, 1973].

Example 2.11

Maximise $f(\mathbf{x}) = 2x_1 + 4x_2 = \Sigma c_i x_i$

subject to constraints:

$$x_1 + 3x_2 \leqslant 21, \quad x_1 \geqslant 0, x_2 \geqslant 0.$$
$$2x_1 + 3x_2 \leqslant 24,$$
$$x_1 + x_2 \leqslant 10\tfrac{1}{2}.$$

Solution

The introduction of slack variables x_3, x_4, x_5 gives the constraints:

$$x_1 \begin{pmatrix}1\\2\\1\end{pmatrix} + x_2 \begin{pmatrix}3\\3\\1\end{pmatrix} + x_3 \begin{pmatrix}1\\0\\0\end{pmatrix} + x_4 \begin{pmatrix}0\\1\\0\end{pmatrix} + x_5 \begin{pmatrix}0\\0\\1\end{pmatrix} = \begin{pmatrix}21\\24\\10\tfrac{1}{2}\end{pmatrix},$$

$x_i \geqslant 0, i = 1, \ldots, 5.$

Starting from the basic feasible point with $x_1 = x_2 = 0$, we obtain the simplex tableau below:

c_j		0	2	4	0	0	0
	Basis	$\mathbf{v}_0$	$\mathbf{v}_1$	$\mathbf{v}_2$	$\mathbf{v}_3$	$\mathbf{v}_4$	$\mathbf{v}_5$
0	$\mathbf{v}_3$	21	1	③	1	0	0
0	$\mathbf{v}_4$	24	2	3	1	1	0
0	$\mathbf{v}_5$	10½	1	1	0	0	1
z_j		0	0	0	0	0	0
$c_j - z_j$		0	2	4	0	0	0
	$\mathbf{v}_2$	7	1/3	1	1/3	0	0
	$\mathbf{v}_4$	3	①	0	−1	1	0
	$\mathbf{v}_5$	3½	2/3	0	−1/3	0	1
$c_j - z_j$		−28	2/3	0	−4/3	0	0
	$\mathbf{v}_1$	3	1	0	−1	1	0
	$\mathbf{v}_2$	6	0	1	2/3	−1/3	0
	$\mathbf{v}_5$	1½	0	0	1/3	−2/3	1
$c_j - z_j$		−30	0	0	−2/3	−2/3	0

The pivot element is ringed.

Values of c_j corresponding to the basis vectors are not needed after the first stage. z_j row can be omitted also,

The optimum solution is $f(\mathbf{x}) = 30$ at $x_1 = 3, x_2 = 6$ ($x_3 = 1\tfrac{1}{2}$).

PROBLEMS

2.1 A is an $m \times n$ matrix of column rank n with $m > n$. Prove that the equations $A\mathbf{x} = \mathbf{b}$ are either insoluble or have a unique solution depending on the value of the constant vector $\mathbf{b}$.

Find a value of $\mathbf{b}$ for which the equations $A\mathbf{x} = \mathbf{b}$ are insoluble if:

$$A = \begin{pmatrix}1 & 2 & 1\\2 & 1 & 2\\1 & 1 & 0\\0 & 1 & 1\end{pmatrix}.$$

2.2 Solve the equations:

$$\begin{aligned} x_1 + 3x_2 + x_3 &= 2, \\ x_1 + 2x_2 - x_3 &= 0, \\ 2x_1 + 4x_2 + 5x_3 &= 7. \end{aligned}$$

2.3 Prove, without assuming any of the theoretical results in Section 2.1, that if A is a real $m \times n$ matrix, the set of all vectors $\mathbf{b}$ for which the equations $A\mathbf{x} = \mathbf{b}$ are soluble is a real vector space. Find a basis of this space if:

$$A = \begin{pmatrix} 1 & 2 & 3 \\ 0 & 1 & 1 \\ 1 & -1 & 0 \end{pmatrix}.$$

2.4 Find the general solution of the equations:

$$\begin{aligned} x_1 - x_2 + 2x_3 + x_4 &= 1, \\ 2x_1 - x_2 + x_3 + 2x_4 &= 3, \\ x_1 - x_3 + x_4 &= 2, \\ 3x_1 - x_2 + 3x_4 &= 5. \end{aligned}$$

Hence find all the solutions satisfying the additional condition $x_1^2 = x_2^2$.

2.5 Find a linear condition on the values of c_1, c_2, c_3, c_4 which ensures that the equations below are soluble.

$$\begin{aligned} x_1 + 2x_2 - 3x_3 &= c_1, \\ x_1 - x_2 + x_3 &= c_2, \\ 2x_1 - x_2 + x_3 &= c_3, \\ x_1 + 2x_2 + 2x_3 &= c_4. \end{aligned}$$

2.6 Use the method of Gaussian elimination (a) without pivoting, (b) with partial pivoting, to solve the equations:

$$\begin{aligned} 1.3x_1 + 4.1x_2 + 1.7x_3 &= 4.5, \\ 2.7x_1 + 8.3x_2 + 1.8x_3 &= 5.6, \\ 1.2x_1 + 2.1x_2 - 1.3x_3 &= 3.8. \end{aligned}$$

Work in each case to an accuracy of 4 significant figures at all stages of the calculation. Compare the accuracy of the answers obtained by calculating the residual vector $\mathbf{r} = \mathbf{b} - A\mathbf{x}$ where $\mathbf{x}$ is the solution obtained ($\mathbf{r}$ must be calculated using exact arithmetic).

2.7 Find in terms of n the number of multiplications or divisions required to solve a system of n equations in n unknowns (a) by Gaussian elimination, (b) by computing the inverse of the matrix of coefficients and calculating $\mathbf{x}=A^{-1}\mathbf{b}$.

2.8 Find the inverses of the matrices below:

$$A = \begin{pmatrix} 1 & 3 \\ 1 & 4 \end{pmatrix} \quad B = \begin{pmatrix} 1 & 3 & 1 \\ 1 & 2 & -1 \\ 2 & 4 & 5 \end{pmatrix} \quad C = \begin{pmatrix} 1 & 2 & 0 & 0 \\ 2 & 1 & 1 & 0 \\ 0 & 1 & 1 & -1 \\ 0 & 0 & -1 & 1 \end{pmatrix}.$$

2.9 Use the method of Gaussian elimination with partial pivoting to solve the equations below. All the working should be carried out to an accuracy of 4 significant figures.

$$\begin{aligned} 1.1x_1 + 1.3x_2 - 1.4x_3 &= 2.4, \\ 0.7x_1 + 0.8x_2 - 1.1x_3 &= 1.5, \\ 2.3x_1 + 1.2x_2 + 2.1x_3 &= 4.6. \end{aligned}$$

2.10 Show that for all values of θ the equations below have a unique solution except for one critical value of t. For this critical value of t find the value of θ which ensures that the equations are still soluble.

$$\begin{aligned} x_1 - x_2 + 2x_3 &= 1, \\ 2x_1 - x_2 + tx_3 &= 2, \\ -x_1 + 2x_2 + x_3 &= \theta. \end{aligned}$$

2.11 An $n \times n$ matrix A is said to be non-negative if $a_{ij} \geqslant 0$ for $i = 1, \ldots, n$, $j = 1, \ldots, n$. Prove that the set of all non-negative matrices is a convex set. Is this set a subspace of the space of all $n \times n$ matrices?

2.12 S and T are convex subsets of a real vector space V. For each of the following sets either prove it is a convex set or provide a counter example to disprove the statement.

(a) $S \cup T$ = set of all $\mathbf{x}$ such that $\mathbf{x} \in S$ or $\mathbf{x} \in T$.
(b) Set of all $\mathbf{x}$ such that $\mathbf{x} \in S$, $\mathbf{x} \notin T$.
(c) Set of all $\mathbf{v} \in V$ such that $\mathbf{v} = \mathbf{s} + \mathbf{t}$ with $\mathbf{s} \in S$, $\mathbf{t} \in T$.

2.13 Prove that every subspace of a real vector space V is a convex set. Is every convex subset of V a subspace of V?

2.14 Illustrate graphically the set of feasible points defined by the constraints:

$$\begin{aligned} x_1 + x_2 &\leqslant 8, \\ 2x_1 + x_2 &\leqslant 10, \\ 2x_1 - x_2 &\leqslant 6, \\ x_1 &\geqslant 0, \\ x_2 &\geqslant 0. \end{aligned}$$

Plot on the same graph the curves

$$f(x_1,x_2) = 3x_1 + 2x_2 = \text{constant}$$
$$\text{and } g(x_1,x_2) = 8x_1 + 8x_2 - x_1^2 - x_2^2 = \text{constant}$$

Hence find the maximum values of f and of g subject to the above constraints.

Deduce that Theorem 2.6 cannot be extended to apply to quadratic functions.

2.15 Use the simplex algorithm to maximise $f(x_1,x_2) = 3x_1 + 2x_2$ subject to the constraints given in Problem 2.14.

2.16 Show that the constraint equations in the transportation problem (Example 2.7) are linearly dependent but that a linearly independent set of constraints is obtained by removing the last constraint equation. Show that $x_1 = x_2 = 0$ gives a basic feasible point for this problem and apply the simplex algorithm with this as the starting point to find the optimum solution.

Give reasons why the constraints in a transportation problem will always be linearly dependent.

2.17 Maximise $f(x_1,x_2,x_3) = 3x_1 + 5x_2 + x_3$
subject to the constraints

$$x_1 > 0, x_2 > 0, x_3 > 0,$$
$$x_1 + x_2 + x_3 \leqslant 10,$$
$$2x_1 - x_2 - x_3 \leqslant 5,$$
$$4x_1 + x_2 + 3x_3 = 24.$$

(Hint: show that a basic feasible point is given by $x_1 = x_2 = 0, x_3 = 8$ and apply the simplex algorithm.)

2.18 Show that the unrestricted variable x_1 can be eliminated from the problem below to obtain a standard linear programming problem with 2 linear constraints. Hence find the solution.

Maximise $\quad f(x_1,x_2,x_3) = 10x_1 + 5x_2 + 4x_3,$

subject to the constraints:

$$x_2 \geqslant 0,\ x_3 \geqslant 0,$$
$$x_1 + 2x_2 - x_3 = 10,$$
$$2x_1 + 3x_2 + x_3 < 40,$$
$$x_1 - 2x_2 + 4x_3 < 15.$$

2.19 A toy manufacturer has a range of three products made of metal and plastic. The profit margins and material and machine time requirements for the products are given in the table below. Find the daily output of each product which maximises the profit if his maximum daily supplies of plastic and metal are respectively 60 kg and 12 kg, and if the machine shop works an 8 hour day.

	Profit per 100	Plastic (kg per 100)	Metal (kg per 100)	Machine Time per 100
Product A	£7	6	2	0.6 hrs.
Product B	£10	8	1	1.1 hrs.
Product C	£12	10	1.5	0.9 hrs.

2.20 A motor manufacturer has two factories supplying four wholesalers. The factories each have a daily output of 200 cars. Find how the cars should be distributed to minimise the transportation costs if the daily requirements of the wholesalers and their geographical location are as given in the table below.

Number of Wholesaler	Daily Requirement	Dist. to Factory A	Dist. to Factory B
1	90 cars	60 miles	50 miles
2	80 cars	100 miles	30 miles
3	100 cars	25 miles	90 miles
4	130 cars	40 miles	80 miles

Chapter 3

Scalar Products, Norms and Quadratic Forms

INTRODUCTION

We have already defined the operations of addition and multiplication by a real scalar for vectors in the n dimensional real space R^n. The chosen definition is analagous to that used in the ordinary 3-dimensional vector space familiar to all those who have studied 3-dimensional geometry or mechanics. However, there are two further algebraic operations which can be performed on the vectors in 3-dimensional space. These are the operation of taking the scalar product **a.b** of two vectors **a** and **b** and that of taking the vector or cross product **a** $\times$ **b**. It is an obvious question to ask whether these operations can be generalised and usefully applied to the vectors in R^n. The short answer is that the idea of a scalar product can be quickly adapted to R^n but that the vector product cannot be readily generalised.

3.1 SCALAR PRODUCT IN R^n

3.1.1 Definitions

If **a** and **b** are vectors in the ordinary 3-dimensional vector space, the scalar product **a.b** is usually defined to be the real number $ab \cos\theta$, where a and b are the lengths of **a** and **b** respectively and θ is the angle between their directions.

From this definition, it is a simple matter to obtain the alternative expression $\mathbf{a.b} = a_1b_1 + a_2b_2 + a_3b_3$, where the components of **a** and **b** are given relative to a set of mutually perpendicular coordinate axes. This second expression provides the motivation for defining the scalar product in R^n as:

$$\mathbf{v.w} = v_1w_1 + v_2w_2 + \ldots + v_nw_n = \mathbf{v}'\mathbf{w} \qquad (3.1)$$

where $(v_1, \ldots v_n)$ & $(w_1 \ldots w_n)$ are the coords. of v & w respectively wrt to the standard basis for $\mathbb{R}^n$

From Equation (3.1), which defines the scalar product, we can formally derive definitions of length and angle in R^n.

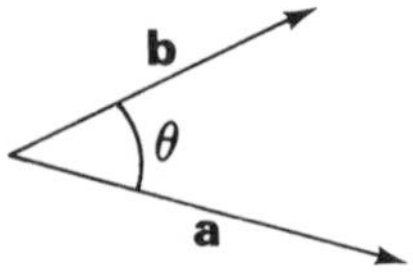

Figure 3.1

The length or modulus of **v** is defined as:

$$|\mathbf{v}| = \sqrt{(\mathbf{v}.\mathbf{v})} = \sqrt{(v_1^2 + v_2^2 + \ldots + v_n^2)} \tag{3.2}$$

Note that the notation used here for length is the same as that used for the modulus of a real number. This should not lead to any confusion because the modulus of the real number $\alpha = |\alpha| = \sqrt{(\alpha^2)}$ coincides with the length of the vector α in R^1.

The angle θ between non-zero vectors **v** and **w** in R^n is then obtained from the equation:

$$\cos\theta = \frac{\mathbf{v}.\mathbf{w}}{|\mathbf{v}|\,|\mathbf{w}|} \tag{3.3}$$

v.w = |v||w| cos θ

3.1.2 Properties of the Scalar product

From the definition (3.1), the following fundamantal properties of the scalar product in R^n can be deduced. Their verification is left as an easy exercise for the reader. For all vectors **v**, **w** in R^n.

$S1$; the product **v.w** is an unambiguously defined real number,
$S2$; **v.w** = **w.v** (the symmetirc property),
$S3$; for any real α, $(\alpha\mathbf{v}).\mathbf{w} = \alpha(\mathbf{v}.\mathbf{w})$,
$S4$; for any vector **x**, $(\mathbf{v} + \mathbf{w}).\mathbf{x} = \mathbf{v}.\mathbf{x} + \mathbf{w}.\mathbf{x}$,
$S5$; $\mathbf{v}.\mathbf{v} \geqslant 0$ for all **v** in R^n and $\mathbf{v}.\mathbf{v} = 0$ only if $\mathbf{v} = 0$.

different operations — 1st is addition of 2 vectors, 2nd is addition of 2 real nos

From the symmetric property $S2$ and the properties $S3$ and $S4$ we obtain immediately:

$S3'$; for any real α, $\mathbf{v}.(\alpha\mathbf{w}) = \alpha(\mathbf{v}.\mathbf{w})$,
$S4'$; for any vector **x**, $\mathbf{x}.(\mathbf{v} + \mathbf{w}) = \mathbf{x}.\mathbf{v} + \mathbf{x}.\mathbf{w}$.

These properties, together with $S3$ and $S4$, form the so-called bilinear properties of the scalar product. They define the manner in which the scalar product interacts with the vector space operations of addition and multiplication by scalars.

Theorem 3.1 (Cauchy-Schwarz Inequality)

For any vectors **v**, **w** in R^n, $|\mathbf{v}.\mathbf{w}| \leqslant |\mathbf{v}|\,|\mathbf{w}|$, where $|\mathbf{v}.\mathbf{w}|$ denotes the modulus of the real number **v.w**.

but does in fact apply to any vector space with any inner product

Proof

For any real number θ, $(\mathbf{v}.\mathbf{w})\theta\ \mathbf{v} - \mathbf{w}$ is a vector in R^n, hence, by *S*5, $0 \leqslant [(\mathbf{v}.\mathbf{w})\theta\ \mathbf{v} - \mathbf{w}] \cdot [(\mathbf{v}.\mathbf{w})\theta\ \mathbf{v} - \mathbf{w}]$. Thus,

$$0 \leqslant (\mathbf{v}.\mathbf{w})^2\theta^2\ |\mathbf{v}|^2 - 2\theta(\mathbf{v}.\mathbf{w})^2 + |\mathbf{w}|^2. \tag{3.4}$$

If $\mathbf{v} = \mathbf{0}$, the Cauchy-Schwarz inequality is clearly satisfied. Otherwise let $\theta = \dfrac{1}{|\mathbf{v}|^2}$ in (3.4). This gives:

$$0 \leqslant (\mathbf{v}.\mathbf{w})^2 \cdot \frac{1}{|\mathbf{v}|^2} - \frac{2}{|\mathbf{v}|^2}(\mathbf{v}.\mathbf{w})^2 + |\mathbf{w}|^2,$$

or, after re-arranging and simplifying,

$$(\mathbf{v}.\mathbf{w})^2 \leqslant |\mathbf{v}|^2\ |\mathbf{w}|^2 \cdot$$

Hence

$$|\mathbf{v}.\mathbf{w}| \leqslant |\mathbf{v}|\ |\mathbf{w}| \cdot \tag{3.5}$$

Note that:

(i) The inequality (3.5) ensures that for all non-zero vectors in R^n Equation (3.3) defines a proper angle.

(ii) The substitution $\theta = \dfrac{1}{|\mathbf{v}|^2}$ into the second line of the above proof shows that the inequality becomes an equality if $\mathbf{w} = \dfrac{(\mathbf{v}.\mathbf{w})}{|\mathbf{v}|^2}\mathbf{v}$; that is when $\mathbf{v}$ and $\mathbf{w}$ are parallel vectors.

3.1.3 Worked Examples

Example 3.1

$\mathbf{a} = (1,2,-1,3)'$, $\mathbf{b} = (2,-2,3,1)'$, $\mathbf{c} = (-3,1,2,1)'$ are vectors in R^4. Verify that $\mathbf{a} \cdot (\mathbf{b} + \mathbf{c}) = \mathbf{a} \cdot \mathbf{b} + \mathbf{a} \cdot \mathbf{c}$.

Solution

$$\mathbf{b} + \mathbf{c} = (2,-2,3,1)' + (-3,1,2,1)' = (-1,-1,5,2)'.$$

Thus,

$$\mathbf{a}.(\mathbf{b} + \mathbf{c}) = (1,2,-1,3)' \cdot (-1,-1,5,2)' = -1 -2 -5 +6 = -2,$$
$$\mathbf{a}.\mathbf{b} = (1,2,-1,3)' \cdot (2,-2,3,1)' = -2,$$
$$\mathbf{a}.\mathbf{c} = (1,2,-1,3)' \cdot (-3,1,2,1) = 0.$$

Thus,

$$\mathbf{a}.(\mathbf{b} + \mathbf{c}) = \mathbf{a}.\mathbf{b} + \mathbf{a}.\mathbf{c}.$$

Note that $\mathbf{a}$ and $\mathbf{c}$ are examples of **orthogonal vectors** (since $\mathbf{a}.\mathbf{c} = 0$) which will be considered in the following Section.

Example 3.2

Triangle Inequality. Deduce, from the Cauchy-Schwarz inequality, that

$|v + w| \leqslant |v| + |w|$, for any vectors v and w in R^n. *— again a general result*
— can also be applied to any vector space

Solution

$$\begin{aligned}
|v + w|^2 &= (v + w) \cdot (v + w), \\
&= v.v + 2v.w + w.w, \\
&\leqslant |v|^2 + 2|v| \cdot |w| + |w|^2 \quad \text{(by (3.5))}, \\
&= (|v| + |w|)^2.
\end{aligned}$$

Hence, after taking positive square roots, $|v + w| \leqslant |v| + |w|$.

Note that the above ineaquality is usually known as the **triangle inequality**. In 2 or 3 dimensions it is simply stating the fact that the length of the third side of a triangle is no greater than the sum of the lengths of the other two sides (see Figure 3.2).

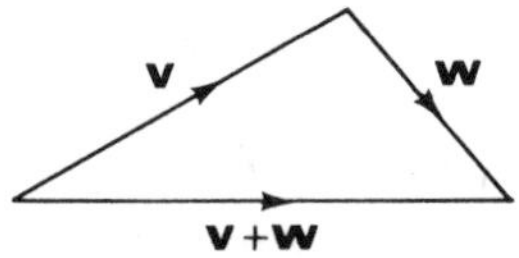

Figure 3.2

3.2 ORTHOGONALITY

again can be applied generally not just in R^n

3.2.1 Definition

Vectors v and w in R^n are said to be orthogonal if $v.w = 0$.

Note that it is an immediate consequence of this definition that the zero vector **0** is orthogonal to every vector in R^n and this is the only vector with this property.

The idea of orthogonality is an obvious generalisation of that of perpendicular directions which occurs in two and three dimensional geometry. Corres-ponding as they do to the geometric concept of mutually orthogonal reference axes, sets of mutually orthogonal vectors are of particular practical importance. As can be easily verified, the elementary basis $e_1, e_2, \ldots, e_n$ of R^n is a set of mutually orthogonal vectors, though it is by no means the only such set.

Theorem 3.2

If the non-zero vectors $v_1, \ldots, v_k$ are mutually orthogonal (that is if $v_i.v_j = 0$ for all $i \neq j$) then they are linearly independent.

Proof

Suppose, if possible, $\sum_{i=1}^{k} \alpha_i v_i = 0$ with some $\alpha_j \neq 0$. Taking the scalar product of the above equation with v_j we obtain:

$$v_j \cdot \sum_{i=1}^{k} \alpha_i v_i = v_j.0. \quad = 0$$

not 0

Hence,
$$\sum_{i=1}^{k} \alpha_i \mathbf{v}_j.\mathbf{v}_i = 0.$$

Using the orthogonality property, $\mathbf{v}_j.\mathbf{v}_i = 0$ if $i \neq j$.

Hence,
$$\alpha_j \mathbf{v}_j.\mathbf{v}_j = 0.$$

Thus,
$$\alpha_j = 0 \text{ since } |\mathbf{v}_j| \neq 0.$$

This contradicts our initial assumption of linear dependence. Hence $[\mathbf{v}_1, \ldots, \mathbf{v}_k]$ form a set of linearly independent vectors.

The above theorem can be combined with our knowledge of the dimension of R^n to state that any set of n mutually orthogonal vectors is a basis of R^n. In such a basis, each vector can be scaled or normalised by dividing by its own length to obtain a basis consisting of mutually orthogonal vectors of unit length. This is called **orthonormal basis.** The properties of an orthonormal basis enable the coefficients of any vector $\mathbf{v}$ when expressed in the terms of the orthonormal basis to be calculated simply by taking scalar products.

Let $\mathbf{u}_1, \mathbf{u}_2, \ldots, \mathbf{u}_n$ be an orthonormal basis of R^n. Then if $\mathbf{v} = \sum_{i=1}^{n} \alpha_i \mathbf{u}_i$ is any vector in R^n, the scalar product with $\mathbf{u}_j$ gives $\mathbf{v}.\mathbf{u}_j = \alpha_j \mathbf{u}_j.\mathbf{u}_j$. Since $|\mathbf{u}_j| = 1$, we obtain $\alpha_j = \mathbf{v}.\mathbf{u}_j$.

Example 3.3

Show that the vectors $\mathbf{v}_1 = (1,0,-1)'$, $\mathbf{v}_2 = (1,0,1)'$, $\mathbf{v}_3 = (0,1,0)'$ are mutually orthogonal. Use these vectors to obtain an orthonormal basis of R^3 and express $\mathbf{v} = (1,2,3)'$ in terms of this basis.

Solution

Clearly $\mathbf{v}_1 \cdot \mathbf{v}_2 = \mathbf{v}_1 \cdot \mathbf{v}_3 = \mathbf{v}_2 \cdot \mathbf{v}_3 = 0$, verifying the orthogonality.

Each unit vector $\mathbf{u}_i$ is given as $\mathbf{u}_i = \dfrac{1}{|\mathbf{v}_i|} \cdot \mathbf{v}_i$.

Thus,
$$\mathbf{u}_1 = \frac{1}{\sqrt{2}}(1,0,-1)', \ \mathbf{u}_2 = \frac{1}{\sqrt{2}}(1,0,1), \ \mathbf{u}_3 = (0,1,0)$$

If $\mathbf{v} = \alpha_1 \mathbf{u}_1 + \alpha_2 \mathbf{u}_2 + \alpha_3 \mathbf{u}_3$ then:

$$\alpha_1 = \mathbf{v}.\mathbf{u}_1 = -\sqrt{2}, \ \alpha_2 = \mathbf{v}.\mathbf{u}_2 = 2\sqrt{2}, \ \alpha_3 = 2.$$

Thus
$$\mathbf{v} = -\frac{\sqrt{2}}{\sqrt{2}}(1,0,-1)' + \frac{2\sqrt{2}}{\sqrt{2}}(1,0,1)' + 2(0,1,0)'$$

or $$(1,2,3)' = -(1,0,-1)' + 2(1,0,1)' + 2(0,1,0)'.$$

3.2.2 The Gram-Schmidt Algorithm

The above example shows that an orthonormal basis is in many ways preferable to a basis of non-orthogonal vectors. The Gram-Schmidt Algorithm provides a simple method of obtaining an orthonormal basis of S from an arbitrary basis of a subspace S of R^n.

Let $\mathbf{b}_1, \ldots, \mathbf{b}_k$ be a basis of S.

Let $\mathbf{v}_1 = \mathbf{b}_1$, define a unit vector $\mathbf{u}_1$ as $\mathbf{u}_1 = \frac{1}{|\mathbf{v}_1|}.\mathbf{v}_1$.

Let $\mathbf{v}_2 = \mathbf{b}_2 - (\mathbf{u}_1.\mathbf{b}_2)\mathbf{u}_1$ define $\mathbf{u}_2 = \frac{1}{|\mathbf{v}_2|}\mathbf{v}_2$ (note that $\mathbf{v}_2$ could only be zero if $\mathbf{b}_1$ and $\mathbf{b}_2$ were linearly dependent.

Then the vectors $\mathbf{u}_1$ and $\mathbf{u}_2$ are mutually orthogonal unit vectors which generate the same subspace as $\mathbf{b}_1$ and $\mathbf{b}_2$. The algorithm continues to define successively the orthonormal vectors $\mathbf{u}_1, \mathbf{u}_2, \ldots, \mathbf{u}_k$. At each stage,

$$\mathbf{v}_i = \mathbf{b}_i - \sum_{j=1}^{i-1} (\mathbf{b}_i.\mathbf{u}_j)\mathbf{u}_j,$$

and $$\mathbf{u}_i = \frac{1}{|\mathbf{v}_i|}\mathbf{v}_i.$$

$[\mathbf{u}_1, \ldots, \mathbf{u}_i]$ are then linearly dependent upon $[\mathbf{b}_1, \ldots, \mathbf{b}_i]$ and conversely. Finally, we obtain an orthonormal basis $[\mathbf{u}_1, \mathbf{u}_2, \ldots, \mathbf{u}_k]$ of S.

Example 3.4

Find an orthonormal basis of the subspace of R^4 generated by the linearly independent vectors $\mathbf{a}_1 = (1,1,-1,1)'$, $\mathbf{a}_2 = (1,2,0,1)'$, $\mathbf{a}_3 = (1,0,0,1)'$.

Solution

Applying the Gram-Schmidt algorithm gives:

$$\begin{aligned}
\mathbf{u}_1 &= \tfrac{1}{2}(1,1,-1,1)', \\
\mathbf{v}_2 &= \mathbf{a}_2 - (\mathbf{a}_2 . \mathbf{u}_1)\mathbf{u}_1 = (1,2,0,1)' - 2(\tfrac{1}{2},\tfrac{1}{2},-\tfrac{1}{2},\tfrac{1}{2})', \\
&= (0,1,1,0)'. \\
\mathbf{u}_2 &= \frac{1}{|\mathbf{v}_2|}\mathbf{v}_2 = \frac{1}{\sqrt{2}}(0,1,1,0)', \\
\mathbf{v}_3 &= \mathbf{a}_3 - (\mathbf{a}_3 . \mathbf{u}_1)\mathbf{u}_1 - (\mathbf{a}_3 . \mathbf{u}_2)\mathbf{u}_2, \\
&= (1,0,0,1)' - (\tfrac{1}{2},\tfrac{1}{2},-\tfrac{1}{2},\tfrac{1}{2})' - 0.\mathbf{u}_2. \\
&= (\tfrac{1}{2},-\tfrac{1}{2},\tfrac{1}{2},\tfrac{1}{2})',
\end{aligned}$$

$$\mathbf{u}_3 = \frac{1}{|\mathbf{v}_3|}\mathbf{v}_3 = (\tfrac12,-\tfrac12,\tfrac12,\tfrac12)'$$

Basis required is $[\tfrac12(1,1,-1,1)', \frac{1}{\sqrt{2}}(0,1,1,0)', \tfrac12(1,-1,1,1)']$.

3.2.3 Change of orthonormal basis

As defined in 3.1, the scalar product appears to be closely related to the particular basis $[\mathbf{e}_1, \mathbf{e}_2, \ldots, \mathbf{e}_n]$ of R^n, since the scalar product is defined in terms of the coefficients of the vectors for this basis. Suppose $[\mathbf{u}_1, \ldots, \mathbf{u}_n]$ is an alternative orthonormal basis of R^n, and that $\mathbf{a} = \sum_{i=1}^{n} \alpha_i\mathbf{u}_i$, $\mathbf{b} = \sum_{i=1}^{n} \beta_i\mathbf{u}_i$ are any vectors in R^n. Then using the properties of the scalar product and of the orthonormal basis, we obtain:

$$\begin{aligned}
\mathbf{a}.\mathbf{b} &= \left(\sum_{i=1}^{n} \alpha_i\mathbf{u}_i\right) \cdot \left(\sum_{j=1}^{n} \beta_j\mathbf{u}_j\right) \\
&= \sum_{i=1}^{n}\sum_{j=1}^{n} \alpha_i\beta_j\mathbf{u}_i.\mathbf{u}_j \\
&= \sum_{i=1}^{n} \alpha_i\beta_i\mathbf{u}_i.\mathbf{u}_i, \text{ since } \mathbf{u}_i.\mathbf{u}_j = \text{if } i \neq j. \\
&= \sum_{i=1}^{n} \alpha_i\beta_i
\end{aligned}$$

Hence the scalar product can be computed by taking products of corresponding coefficients relative to any orthonormal basis, and the definition is not critically dependent upon the elementary basis $[\mathbf{e}_1, \ldots, \mathbf{e}_n]$.

Note that the matrix P which represents the change from basis $[\mathbf{e}_1, \ldots, \mathbf{e}_n]$ to $[\mathbf{u}_1, \ldots, \mathbf{u}_n]$ has column vectors which form an orthonormal set. Such a matrix is called orthogonal and has the property $P'P = I$. Orthogonal matrices are of particular importance in geometrical and physical problems in R^3 since it is only those changes of bases (or changes of coordinate axes, which is the geometrical equivalent) corresponding to orthogonal matrices which leave the lengths of all vectors invariant. If $\mathbf{x} = P\mathbf{y}$ where P is an orthogonal matrix, then $\mathbf{x}.\mathbf{x} = \mathbf{x}'\mathbf{x} = \mathbf{y}'P'P\mathbf{y} = \mathbf{y}'\mathbf{y} = \mathbf{y}.\mathbf{y}$. In particular, every rotation of axes in 3-dimensional space corresponds to a particular type of orthogonal matrix.

3.3 INNER PRODUCT SPACES

3.3.1 Definition

The scalar product has so far only been defined for R^n. In other more general vector spaces it is sometimes possible to associate with each pair of vectors a scalar which has properties similar to the scalar product of two vectors in R^n. Suppose V is a real vector space and, for vectors $\mathbf{v},\mathbf{w} \in V$,$(\mathbf{v},\mathbf{w})$ denotes the associated real number which we shall refer to as the inner product of $\mathbf{v}$ and $\mathbf{w}$. V is called an inner product space, or Euclidean space in the finite dimensional case, if the inner product has the following properties, for vectors $\mathbf{v}$ and $\mathbf{w}$ in V:

$S1$; $(\mathbf{v},\mathbf{w})$ is a well defined real number,
$S2$; $(\mathbf{v},\mathbf{w}) = (\mathbf{w},\mathbf{v})$,
$S3$; for any real α, $(\alpha\mathbf{v},\mathbf{w}) = \alpha(\mathbf{v},\mathbf{w}) = (\mathbf{v},\alpha\mathbf{w})$,
$S4$; for any vector $\mathbf{x}$, $(\mathbf{x},\mathbf{v}+\mathbf{w}) = (\mathbf{x},\mathbf{v}) + (\mathbf{x},\mathbf{w}) = (\mathbf{v}+\mathbf{w},\mathbf{x})$
$S5$; $(\mathbf{v},\mathbf{v}) \geqslant 0$ for all $\mathbf{v}$ in V and $(\mathbf{v},\mathbf{v}) = 0$ only if $\mathbf{v} = 0$.

Note that the above properties which define a real inner product space correspond exactly to the properties of R^n obtained in 3.1.2. Any properties of R^n deduced from those of Section 3.1.2 will thus apply more generally to any real inner product space, in particular the ideas of orthogonality and of orthonormal sets of vectors can be immediately extended to inner product spaces.

3.3.2 Examples of inner product spaces

Example 1

Let P^n be the vector space of all real polynomials $f(x)$ of degree less than or equal n (a space of dimension n+1). An inner product can be defined as $(f(x), g(x)) = \int_0^1 f(x)\, g(x)\, dx$. The linearity of the integration process ensures that properties $S2$ to $S4$ are satisfied for this inner product and since $(f(x))^2$is always greater than or equal to zero for any x in the interval $0 < x < 1$ we have $(f(x), f(x)) \geqslant 0$ for all $f(x)$ in P^n. The inner product $(f(x), f(x))$ will only vanish for the polynomial which is identically zero in $0 \leqslant x \leqslant 1$, that is for $f(x) = 0$. In P^n, for $n > 1$, $f(x) = 1$ and $g(x) = 1 - 2x$ are examples of orthogonal polynomials for this inner product. The inner product opperation suggested here for P^n is by no means unique. A suitable inner product could be defined as

$(f(x), g(x)) = K \int_a^b f(x)\, g(x) dx$ where $b > a$ and K is any positive constant.

Alternatively by analogy with R^n, an inner product could be defined as the sum of the products of corresponding coefficients in $f(x)$ and $g(x)$, see Problem 3.14. No matter how the inner product is defined, provided axioms $S1$ to $S5$ are satisfied, basic properties such as the Cauchy-Schwarz inequality and the linear independence of orthogonal vectors will still apply to the resulting inner product space.

The examples of scalar and inner products studied so far have all been finite dimensional. The following Example will show that it is possible to have an infinite dimensional inner product space.

Example 2

Let S be the set of all real functions $f(x)$ which are continuous, differentiable and periodic of period 2π (that is $f(x + 2\pi) = f(x)$ for all x). Clearly, if $f(x)$ and $g(x)$ are in S so is $af(x) + bg(x)$ for all real numbers a and b. hence S is a real vector space. We define our inner product in S as

$(f(x), g(x)) = \frac{1}{\pi}\int_{-\pi}^{\pi} f(x)\, g(x)dx$. This inner product satisfies the axioms $S1$ to $S5$ as the reader can easily verify. The infinite set of functions:

$$\left[\frac{1}{\sqrt{2}}, \sin x, \cos x, \sin 2x, \cos 2x, \ldots, \sin nx, \cos nx, \ldots\right]$$

is a set of mutually orthogonal functions because:

$$\int_{-\pi}^{\pi} \sin nx\, dx = \int_{-\pi}^{\pi} \cos nx\, dx = 0 \text{ for all integers } n,$$

$$\int_{-\pi}^{\pi} \sin nx \sin mx\, dx = 0 = \int_{-\pi}^{\pi} \cos nx \cos mx\, dx \text{ if } m \neq n,$$

$$\int_{-\pi}^{\pi} \sin nx \cos mx\, dx = 0 \text{ for all integers } m \text{ and } n.$$

(These results can be verified by evaluating the integrals using the appropriate trigonometric identities.)

Also $$\frac{1}{\pi}\int_{-\pi}^{\pi} \frac{1}{2}\, dx = 1,$$

$$\frac{1}{\pi}\int_{-\pi}^{\pi} \sin^2 nx\, dx = \frac{1}{\pi}\int_{-\pi}^{\pi} \frac{1}{2}(1 - \cos 2nx)dx = 1,$$

and $$\frac{1}{\pi}\int_{-\pi}^{\pi} \cos^2 nx\, dx = \frac{1}{\pi}\int_{-\pi}^{\pi} \frac{1}{2}(1 + \cos 2nx)dx = 1,$$

showing that each function in the set is a unit vector for our inner product. The set thus constitutes an orthonormal set in S and, in a sense which will be clarified in the next Chapter when Fourier series are introduced, forms an orthonormal basis for the infinite dimensional space S. (The dimension of S must be infinite because we have an infinite set of orthogonal, and hence linearly independent, vectors.)

3.3.3 Complex Inner Product Spaces

For complex vector spaces, that is vector spaces for which the associated scalars are complex numbers rather than real numbers, the axioms $S1$ to $S5$ defining an inner product space need to be modified, and $S5$ in particular is inappropriate. For example, if we consider C^2, the space of ordered pairs of complex numbers, and attempt to define a scalar product in C^2 as in Section 3.1, we obtain $|(1,i)'|^2 = (1,i)'\cdot(1,i)' = 1 - 1 = 0$. This is a very simple example of a non-zero vector with zero length. The modified axioms for a complex inner product space are:

or $= \bar{\alpha}(v,w)$ *in some books*
\alpha conjugate

$SC1$; (v,w) is a well defined scalar (complex number),
$SC2$; $(v,w) = \overline{(w,v)}$, where $\overline{}$ denotes the complex conjugate,
$SC3$; for any complex α, $(\alpha v,w) = \alpha(v,w)$, ($= (v,\bar{\alpha}w)$ by $SC2$),
$SC4$; for any vector x, $(x,v+w) = (x,v) + (x,w)$,
$SC5$; $(v,v) \geqslant 0$ and $(v,v) = 0$ only if $v = 0$.

Note that:

(i) $SC2$ ensures that for any vector v in the complex space, (v,v) is a real number and $SC5$ is thus a valid inequality.

(ii) If we restrict our scalars to be real rather than complex, axioms $SC1$ to $SC5$ reduce to $S1$ to $S5$.

The usual definition of an inner product in C^n is to define:

$$(z,w) = ((z_1,z_2,\ldots,z_n)', (w_1,w_2,\ldots,w_n)') = \sum_{i=1}^{n} z_i \bar{w}_i.$$

Then $(z,z) = \sum_{i=1}^{n} z_i \bar{z}_i = \sum_{i=1}^{n} |z_i|^2$, which is clearly positive for all non-zero z.

3.4 NORMED VECTOR SPACES

All inner product spaces have the property that the length of a vector can be defined as $|x| = \sqrt{(x,x)}$. For many applications, particularly in the fields of functional analysis and numerical analysis, the ability to measure 'lengths' is of much greater importance than the concept of the inner product. A **normed vector space**, defined below, is **one in which lengths can be defined in some reasonable and consistent way.**

3.4.1 Definition

Let V be a vector space such that for any vector x in V, $\| x \|$, called the norm of x, is a real number with the properties:

$N1$; $\|\alpha\mathbf{x}\| = |\alpha|\,\|\mathbf{x}\|$ for any scalar α.
$N2$; $\|\mathbf{x}\| \geqslant 0$ and $\|\mathbf{x}\| = 0$ only if $\mathbf{x} = 0$,
$N3$; $\|\mathbf{x} + \mathbf{v}\| \leqslant \|\mathbf{x}\| + \|\mathbf{v}\|$ for any $\mathbf{x},\mathbf{v}$ in $\mathbf{V}$.

V is then said to be a normed vector space with norm $\|\mathbf{x}\|$.

The properties of the inner product ensure that every inner product space is also a normed space with norm $\|\mathbf{x}\| = \sqrt{(\mathbf{x},\mathbf{x})}$. This particular norm is for infinite dimensional spaces usually referred to as the **Euclidean Norm,** it is denoted $\|\mathbf{x}\|$. In R^2 or R^3 the Euclidean norm of a vector coincides with the ordinary geometric concept of length. As the examples below will show, there are many other possible ways of defining a suitable norm for R^n.

3.4.2 Examples of Normed Vector Spaces

Example 1

Let R^n be the real n dimensional vector space. A norm of R^n which is particularly simple to calculate is the so-called **maximum element norm.**

Let $\mathbf{x} = (x_1, x_2, \ldots, x_n)'$ be a vector in R^n, define $\|\mathbf{x}\|_M = \max_{i=1,\ldots n} |x_i|$.

Then $\|\alpha\mathbf{x}\|_M = \max_{i=1,\ldots n} |\alpha x_i| = |\alpha| \max_{i=1,\ldots n} |x_i| = |\alpha| \cdot \|\mathbf{x}\|$,

$$\|\mathbf{x} + \mathbf{y}\|_M = \max_{i=1,\ldots n} |x_i + y_i| \leqslant \max_{i=1,\ldots n} |x_i| + \max_{i=1,\ldots n} |y_i| = \|\mathbf{x}\|_M + \|\mathbf{y}\|_M,$$

and $\|\mathbf{x}\|_M = 0$ only if $\max_{i=1,\ldots n} |x_i| = 0 \Rightarrow \mathbf{x} = \mathbf{0}$.

We have thus verified axioms $N1$ to $N3$, showing that the maximum element norm is a proper norm on R^n. Unlike the Euclidean norm, there is no inner product $(\mathbf{x},\mathbf{y})$ on R^n which can be associated with the maximum element norm in the sense that $\|\mathbf{x}\|_M = \sqrt{(\mathbf{x},\mathbf{x})}$.

For particular vectors in R^n, the Euclidean norm and the maximum element norm will generally have different numerical values, but both will successfully distinguish between 'large' and 'small' vectors. For example, in R^3 if $\mathbf{a} = (12,5,0)$, $\mathbf{b} = (0.1, 0.01, 0.02)$ then:

$$\|\mathbf{a}\|_E = 13, \quad \|\mathbf{a}\|_M = 12,$$

$$\|\mathbf{b}\|_E \simeq 0.1025, \quad \|\mathbf{b}\|_M = 0.1.$$

Example 2

Once more taking R^n as our vector space, we can define an infinite family of norms in terms of the so-called ℓ_p norm. For any $p > 1$ define:

$$\|\mathbf{x}\|_p = \sqrt[p]{\left(\sum_{i=1}^{n} |x_i|^p\right)}.$$

It can be quickly verified that the ℓ_p norm so defined satisfies axioms $N1$ to $N3$ thus making R^n a normed space for any value of p. This family of norms includes our two previous examples since $\|\mathbf{x}\|_E = \sqrt{\left(\sum_{i=1}^{n} x_i^2\right)} = \|\mathbf{x}\|_2$ and since it can be shown that $\lim_{p\to\infty} \sqrt[p]{\left(\sum_{i=1}^{n} |x_i|^p\right)} = \max_{i=1,\dots n} |x_i|, \|\mathbf{x}\|_M$ can be formally identified with $\|\mathbf{x}\|_\infty$ and the maximum element norm is usually referred to as the **infinity norm**. For values of p other than 1, 2 or ∞, the ℓ_p norm is little practical significance. Because the ℓ_1 and ℓ_∞ norms are particularly simple to compute, they are frequently used in numerical analysis (see Chapter 4).

3.4.3 Metric Spaces

is there a difference between a norm space and a metric space?

In any normed vector space V we can immediately define the distance between two vectors $\mathbf{x}$ and $\mathbf{v}$ as $d(\mathbf{x},\mathbf{y}) = \|\mathbf{x} - \mathbf{y}\|$. $d(\mathbf{x},\mathbf{y})$ is then a positive quantity which vanishes only if $\mathbf{x} = \mathbf{y}$.

use the norm to define a distance

$d(\mathbf{x},\mathbf{y})$ has the additional properties:

(i) $d(\mathbf{x},\mathbf{y}) = d(\mathbf{y},\mathbf{x})$, and

(ii) $d(\mathbf{x},\mathbf{y}) \leqslant d(\mathbf{x},\mathbf{z}) + d(\mathbf{z},\mathbf{y})$ for any $\mathbf{z}$ in V, this triangle inequality being an immediate consequence of $N3$.

Any space with a distance or metric function having these properties is called a **metric space**. In a metric space, concepts such as continuity of functions and convergence of sequences can be given a precise meaning. For this reason, the study of metric spaces is a fundamental part of real analysis and of functional analysis, but is beyond the scope of this book. (More information in [Bachman, Narici, 1968], [Copson, 1966] or [White, 1968]).

3.5 QUADRATIC FORMS

Many mathematical problems of physical and geometrical origin involve homogeneous quadratic functions in a number of variables. That is, expressions of the form:

$$Q(x_1, x_2, \dots, x_n) = a_{11}x_1^2 + a_{22}x_2^2 + \dots + a_{nn}x_n^2 + 2a_{12}x_1x_2 + \dots$$
$$+ 2a_{nn-1}x_nx_{n-1}.$$

If the coefficients are real, such an expression can be readily associated with a vector $\mathbf{x}$ in R^n and the properties of the quadratic form are in many ways similar to those of an inner product.

3.5.1 Definitions

order n → order of Q = no. of variables

$$Q(x_1, x_2, \ldots, x_n) = a_{11}x_1^2 + \ldots + a_{nn}x_n^2 + 2a_{12}x_1x_2 + \ldots + 2a_{n-1n}x_{n-1}x_n$$

is called a quadratic form in the variables $x_1, \ldots, x_n$. If the coefficients $a_{11}, \ldots,$ a_{n-1n} are all real, Q is called a real quadratic form. It is real quadratic forms which will be studied throughout this Chapter.

Since $Q(x_1 \ldots x_n) = (x_1, \ldots x_n) \begin{pmatrix} a_{11} & a_{12} & \cdots & a_{1n} \\ a_{21} & a_{22} & \cdots & a_{2n} \\ & & & \vdots \\ a_{n1} & & \cdots & a_{nn} \end{pmatrix} \begin{pmatrix} x_1 \\ \vdots \\ x_n \end{pmatrix} = x'A\,x$, where A

rank of Q = rank of A → $= x^TAx$

is a real symmetric matrix (that is $A' = A$), each quadratic form in n variables can be associated with an $n \times n$ symmetric matrix. The **rank of Q** is defined to be equal to the rank of the associated matrix A. If the rank of Q is less than n, there will be some non-zero vectors x for which $Ax = \mathbf{0}$, hence for corresponding values of $(x_1, \ldots, x_n)$, $Q(x_1, \ldots, x_n)$ will be zero.

The quadratic form Q is said to be **positive definite** if, for all $(x_1, \ldots, x_n) \neq (0, \ldots, 0)$, $Q(x_1, \ldots, x_n) > 0$. *i.e. its value is always +ve*

A matrix A is said to be positive definite **if its associated quadratic form is positive definite**. In simple cases, the positive definite property can be established by direct algebraic manipulation of the quadratic form.

3.5.2 Worked Examples

rank = no. of squared terms

Example 3.5

Show that $Q_1(x_1, x_2, x_3) = x_1^2 + 2x_2^2 + 6x_3^2 + 2x_1x_2 - 2x_1x_3 + 2x_2x_3$ is a positive definite quadratic form. What is the associated positive definite matrix?

Solution

Completing the square on all terms involving x_1 we obtain:

$$\begin{aligned} Q_1(x_1, x_2, x_3) &= x_1^2 + 2x_1x_2 - 2x_1x_3 + 2x_2^2 + 6x_3^2 + 2x_2x_3 \\ &= (x_1^2 + 2x_1x_2 - 2x_1x_3 - 2x_2x_3 + x_2^2 + x_3^2) + x_2^2 + 4x_2x_3 \\ &\quad + 5x_3^2 \\ &= (x_1 + x_2 - x_3)^2 + (x_2 + 2x_3)^2 + x_3^2. \end{aligned}$$

$2x_1 x_2 \to 1, x_2 x_1$

Q is thus a positive definite quadratic form because $x_1 + x_2 - x_3, x_2 + 2x_3$ and x_3 can only be simultaneously zero if $x_1 = x_2 = x_3 = 0$. Because Q_1 is positive definite, the matrix $A = \begin{pmatrix} 1 & 1 & -1 \\ 1 & 2 & 1 \\ -1 & 1 & 6 \end{pmatrix}$ is a positive definite matrix.

$1 x_1 x_2$

Example 3.6

Show that $Q_2(x_1, x_2, x_3) = x_1^2 + 3x_2^2 + 9x_3^2 + 4x_1x_2 + 6x_1x_3 + 10x_2x_3$ is not a positive definite quadratic form.

Solution

Completing the square as above gives:

$$\begin{aligned} Q_2(x_1,x_2,x_3) &= (x_1 + 2x_2 + 3x_3)^2 - x_2^2 - 2x_2x_3 \\ &= (x_1 + 2x_2 + 3x_3)^2 - (x_2 + x_3)^2 + x_3^2 . \end{aligned}$$

Q_2 can thus take either positive or negative values depending upon the values of (x_1, x_2, x_3). For example, $x_1 = 2, x_2 = -1, x_3 = 0$ gives $Q_2 = -1$,
$x_1 = 1, x_2 = 0, x_3 = 0$ gives $Q_2 = 1$.
The associated matrix $A = \begin{pmatrix} 1 & 2 & 3 \\ 2 & 3 & 5 \\ 3 & 5 & 9 \end{pmatrix}$ is said to be indefinite.

3.5.3 Positive Definite Quadratic Forms:

The above examples illustrate a simple method of determining, for a small number of variables, whether a quadratic form is positive definite. There are two simple tests for positive definiteness which can be applied directly to the associated matrix. The first test involves the use of determinants. A proof of this method can be found in [Archbold, 1964] or [Wilkinson, 1964]. The second test depends upon the properties of eigenvalues and will be proved in Chapter 5.

Test 1

A real symmetric matrix A is positive definite if $|A| > 0$ and if all the leading principal minors (that is all the determinants formed by removing the last row and column, the last two rows and columns, and so on, from A) are positive.

In Example 1 of 3.5.2 the determinants to be evaluated are:

$$\begin{vmatrix} 1 & 1 & -1 \\ 1 & 2 & 1 \\ -1 & 1 & 6 \end{vmatrix} = 1, \quad \begin{vmatrix} 1 & 1 \\ 1 & 2 \end{vmatrix} = 1, \quad |\,1\,| = 1.$$

In Example 2, the relevant determinants are:

$$\begin{vmatrix} 1 & 2 & 3 \\ 2 & 3 & 5 \\ 3 & 5 & 9 \end{vmatrix} = -1, \quad \begin{vmatrix} 1 & 2 \\ 2 & 3 \end{vmatrix} = -1 \quad |\,1\,| = 1.$$

Test 2

A real symmetric matrix A is positive definite if all its eigenvalues are positive. In Example 3.5 the approximate eigenvalues of A at 0.06, 2.59, 6.35. In Example 3.6, the eigenvalues are approximately −0.24, 0.32, 12.92. The reader unfamiliar with eigenvalues will be able to confirm these values after reading Chapter 5.

The properties of a positive definite quadratic form are in many ways similar to those of the inner product. If A is a positive definite real symmetric $n \times n$ matrix we have, for all vectors $\mathbf{x}, \mathbf{y}$ in R^n.

(i) $\mathbf{x}'A\ \mathbf{y}$ is a real number (the product of a row vector, an $n \times n$ matrix and a column vector).

(ii) $\mathbf{x}'A\ \mathbf{y} = \mathbf{y}'A\ \mathbf{x}$ (by symmetry of A).

(iii) For any real α, $(\alpha\mathbf{x})'A\ \mathbf{y} = \alpha(\mathbf{x}'A\ \mathbf{y}) = \mathbf{x}'A\ (\alpha\mathbf{y})$.

(iv) For any vector $\mathbf{z}$, $\mathbf{x}'A(\mathbf{y} + \mathbf{z}) = \mathbf{x}'A\ \mathbf{y} + \mathbf{x}'A\ \mathbf{z}$.

[(iii) and (iv) are consequences of the linear properties of a matrix product.]

(v) For any vector $\mathbf{x}$, $\mathbf{x}'A\ \mathbf{x} \geqslant 0$, and $\mathbf{x}'A\ \mathbf{x} = 0$ only if $\mathbf{x} = 0$(the positive definitive property).

A comparison of the above properties with axioms $S1$ to $S5$ of Section 3.3.1 shows that any positive definite matrix could be used to define an inner product in R^n by setting $(\mathbf{x},\mathbf{y}) = \mathbf{x}'A\ \mathbf{y}$. The conventional scalar product in R^n is in fact related to the positive definite symmetric matrix I because $\mathbf{x} \cdot \mathbf{y} = \mathbf{x}'\mathbf{y} = \mathbf{x}'I\mathbf{y}$.

By analogy with the definition of orthogonal vectors, we define vectors $\mathbf{x}, \mathbf{y}$ to be **conjugate** with respect to A if $\mathbf{x}'A\ \mathbf{y} = 0$.

If A is positive definite, the results on orthogonal vectors can be extended to prove that mutually conjugate vectors are linearly independent and the Gram-Schmidt algorithm can be adapted to generate a mutually conjugate basis of R^n (see Problem 3.10). Conjugate vectors have a significant application to the problem of minimising a quadratic function.

If A is not positive definite, conjugate vectors are still defined in the same way but their linear independence is not assured.

3.5.4 Worked examples

Example 3.6

Show that $A = \begin{pmatrix} 2 & 1 & -1 \\ 1 & 3 & 2 \\ -1 & 2 & 4 \end{pmatrix}$ is a positive definite matrix.

$\mathbf{x} = (1,0,0)'$, find vectors $\mathbf{y}$ and $\mathbf{z}$ such that $[\mathbf{x}, \mathbf{y}, \mathbf{z}]$ is a set of mutually conjugate directions for A. Verify that $\mathbf{x}, \mathbf{y}$, and $\mathbf{z}$ are linearly independent.

Solution

Using Test 1 of 3.5.3:

$$|\mathrm{A}| = \begin{vmatrix} 2 & 1 & -1 \\ -1 & 2 & 2 \\ -1 & 2 & 4 \end{vmatrix} = 5, \quad \begin{vmatrix} 2 & 1 \\ 1 & 3 \end{vmatrix} = 5 \quad \text{and } |\,2\,| = 2.$$

Thus A is positive definite.

Let $\mathbf{y} = \begin{pmatrix} y_1 \\ y_2 \\ y_3 \end{pmatrix}$, $\mathbf{y}$ is conjugate to $\mathbf{x}$ if $\mathbf{x}'A\,\mathbf{y} = 0$.

Hence: $$(1 \quad 0 \quad 0) \begin{pmatrix} 2y_1 + y_2 - y_3 \\ y_1 + 2y_2 + 2y_3 \\ y_1 + 2y_2 + 4y_3 \end{pmatrix} = 0,$$

$$\text{or} \quad 2y_1 + y_2 - y_3 = 0.$$

$\mathbf{y}$ is not uniquely determined by this equation, but one solution is $\mathbf{y} = (0,1,1,)'$.

Let $\mathbf{z} = (z_1, z_2, z_3)'$, the conditions for conjugacy $\mathbf{x}'A\,\mathbf{z} = 0$, $\mathbf{y}'A\,\mathbf{z} = 0$ give:

$$2z_1 + z_2 - z_3 = 0,$$ z conjugate to x

and $$5z_2 + 6z_3 = 0.$$ z conjugate to y

The solution is $\mathbf{z} = \alpha(-11/2, 6, -5)'$, where α is an arbitrary scalar.

Note that once $\mathbf{y}$ has been chosen, the direction of $\mathbf{z}$ is uniquely determined. $\mathbf{x}, \mathbf{y}, \mathbf{z}$ are linearly independent because:

$$|(\mathbf{x},\mathbf{y},\mathbf{z})| = \begin{vmatrix} 1 & 0 & -11/2 \\ 0 & 1 & 6 \\ 0 & 1 & -5 \end{vmatrix} = -11 \neq 0.$$

Example 3.7

Show that for $A = \begin{pmatrix} 1 & 2 & -1 \\ 2 & 2 & -4 \\ -1 & -4 & 0 \end{pmatrix}$, the vector $\mathbf{x} = \begin{pmatrix} 2 \\ 0 \\ 1 \end{pmatrix}$ is conjugate to itself. Verify, by completing the square, that the corresponding quadratic form is indefinite.

Solution

$$\mathbf{x}'A\,\mathbf{x} = (2 \quad 0 \quad 1) \begin{pmatrix} 1 & 2 & -1 \\ 2 & 2 & -4 \\ -1 & -4 & 0 \end{pmatrix} \begin{pmatrix} 2 \\ 0 \\ 1 \end{pmatrix} = (2 \quad 0 \quad 1) \begin{pmatrix} 1 \\ 0 \\ -2 \end{pmatrix} = 0.$$

Thus $\mathbf{x}$ is self conjugate. This means that the set of vectors $[\mathbf{x}, -\mathbf{x}]$ is a simple example of a linearly dependent, mutually conjugate set, something which is impossible for a positive definite matrix.

The quadratic form associated with A is:

$$Q(x_1, x_2, x_3) = x_1^2 + 2x_2^2 + 4x_1x_2 - 2x_1x_3 - 8x_2x_3.$$

Completing the square gives:

$$Q(x_1, x_2, x_3) = (x_1 + 2x_2 - x_3)^2 - 2(x_2+x_3)^2 + x_3^2.$$

From this expression, we see that any vector $\mathbf{x}$ for which $(x_1 + 2x_2 - x_3)^2 + x_3^2 = 2(x_2 + x_3)^2$ will be self conjugate.. For example, the vector $\mathbf{x} = (0, 0, 1)'$ is also self conjugate.

PROBLEMS

3.1 Prove that if $\mathbf{v}$ and $\mathbf{w}$ are vectors in R^n with $|\mathbf{v}| > |\mathbf{w}|$,

$$|\mathbf{v}| - |\mathbf{w}| \leqslant |(\mathbf{v} - \mathbf{w})| \leqslant |\mathbf{v}| + |\mathbf{w}|.$$

(Hint: use the Cauchy-Schwarz inequality.)

3.2 $\mathbf{v}_1, \mathbf{v}_2, \ldots, \mathbf{v}_m$ are vectors in R^n. An $m \times m$ matrix A is defined by the equations:

$$a_{ij} = \mathbf{v}_i . \mathbf{v}_j \text{ for } i,j = 1, \ldots, m.$$

Prove that the columns vectors of A are linearly dependent if and only if $\mathbf{v}_1, \mathbf{v}_2, \ldots, \mathbf{v}_m$ is a linearly dependent set of vectors. Use this result to show that $(1,2,1,-1)'$, $(1,0,1,1)'$ and $(1,4,1,-3)'$ are linearly dependent vectors in R^4.

3.3 A bilinear scalar function in R^3 is defined by the equation:

$$\phi(\mathbf{x},\mathbf{y}) = x_1y_2 + x_2y_1 + x_2y_3 + x_3y_2 + x_3y_1 + x_1y_3.$$

Show that ϕ satisfies all the axioms of an inner product except $S5$. Find a set of linearly dependent vectors which are mutually orthogonal with respect to ϕ. Deduce that Theorem 3.2 cannot be extended to apply to spaces for which the scalar product is not positive definite.

3.4 The vectors $\mathbf{v}_1, \mathbf{v}_2, \ldots, \mathbf{v}_m$ are mutually orthogonal vectors in R^n. Prove that $|\mathbf{v}_1 + \mathbf{v}_2 + \ldots + \mathbf{v}_m|^2 = |\mathbf{v}_1|^2 + |\mathbf{v}_2|^2 + \ldots + |\mathbf{v}_m|^2$.

3.5 (a) S is a proper subspace of R^n. Prove that the set T of all vectors orthogonal to every vector $\mathbf{s}$ in S is also a subspace of R^n. (T is called the orthogonal complement of S.)
(b) S is the subspace of R^4 generated by $[(1\ 1\ 0\ 0)', (0\ 1\ 1\ 0)']$. Use the Gram-Schmidt algorithm to find orthogonal bases of S and its orthogonal complement.

3.6 V is the space of all periodic functions of period 2π. An inner product on

V is defined as $(f(x),g(x)) = \int_{-\pi}^{\pi} f(x)g(x)dx$. Find an orthogonal basis for the subspace of V generated by $\sin x$, $\cos x$, $\sin^2 x$, $\cos^2 x$.

3.7 V is a finite dimensional vector space with a scalar product. S is a proper subspace of V and T is the orthogonal complement of S. (See Problem 3.5). Prove that dimension S + dimension T = dimension V. Deduce that every vector in V has a unique expression of the form $\mathbf{v} = \mathbf{s} + \mathbf{t}$ with $\mathbf{s} \in S$ and $\mathbf{t} \in T$. If s has an orthonormal basis $[\mathbf{s}_1,\mathbf{s}_2,\ldots,\mathbf{s}_m]$ find an expression for $\mathbf{t}$ in terms of $\mathbf{v}$ and this basis.

3.8 Use the Gram-Schmidt algorithm to find an orthonormal basis of the subspace of R generated by $[(1,0,1,0)', (1,1,1,1)', (0,1,0,1)']$.

3.9 An nXn orthogonal matrix P is any real matrix with the property that $PP' = I = P'P$. Prove that the column vectors of P form an orthonormal basis of R^n. Do the row vectors of P possess the same property?

3.10 (a) If A is a positive definite symmetric matrix, prove that any set of mutually conjugate vectors with respect to A is a linearly independent set.
(b) if $A = \begin{pmatrix} 1 & 1 & 0 \\ 1 & 2 & -1 \\ 0 & -1 & 5 \end{pmatrix}$ use a modification of the Gram-Schmidt algorithm starting with $[\mathbf{e}_1,\mathbf{e}_2,\mathbf{e}_3]$ to find a mutually conjugate basis of R^3. (A 'unit' vector will be one for which $\mathbf{x}'A\mathbf{x} = 1$.)

3.11 Use the Gram-Schmidt algorithm to find an orthonormal basis of the subspace of C^4 generated by $[(1,i,0,1)', (1+i,-i,1,i)', (0,1,0,i)']$. C^4 denotes the space of complex 4-vectors with inner product $(\mathbf{v},\mathbf{w}) = \sum_{i=1}^{4} v_i\bar{w}_i$.

3.12 A is a real nXn matrix. Prove that $(\mathbf{x},\mathbf{y}) = \mathbf{x}'A\mathbf{y}$ defines an inner product on R^n if and only if A is a symmetric positive definite matrix.

3.13 V is a Euclidean space of dimension n with inner product denoted $(\mathbf{v},\mathbf{w})$. If $[\mathbf{v}_1,\ldots,\mathbf{v}_n]$ is a basis of V and if $a_{ij} = (\mathbf{v}_i,\mathbf{v}_j)$ prove that for any vectors $\mathbf{v}$ and $\mathbf{w}$ in V with representations $\mathbf{v} = \sum_{i=1}^{n} x_i\mathbf{v}_i$, $\mathbf{w} = \sum_{i=1}^{n} y_i\mathbf{w}_i$ the inner product is given by $(\mathbf{v},\mathbf{w}) = \mathbf{x}'A\mathbf{y}$. Deduce that A is a positive definite matrix. What will be the form of A if the chosen basis is orthogonal?

3.14 Find the matrix A, as defined in Problem 3.13 which represents the inner

product $(f(x),g(x)) = \int_{-1}^{1} f(x)g(x)dx$ in P^2 with respect to the basis $[1,x,x^2]$
Use this matrix to calculate $\int_{-1}^{1} (x^3 - 1)dx$.

3.15 P^2 denotes the real vector space of all polynomials of degree $\leqslant 2$. An inner product is defined in P^2 as $(f(x),g(x)) = \int_{-1}^{1} f(x)g(x)dx$. Show that $f(x) = 1$, $g(x) = x$ are orthogonal for this inner product and find a polynomial $h(x)$ orthogonal to $f(x)$ and to $g(x)$. What is the corresponding orthonormal basis of P^2?

3.16 V is a real vector space. The 'discrete metric' on V is defined by the equations:

$$d(\mathbf{x},\mathbf{y}) = 0 \text{ if } \mathbf{x} \neq \mathbf{y}$$

$$d(\mathbf{x},\mathbf{y}) = 1 \text{ if } \mathbf{x} = \mathbf{y}.$$

Show that with this metric V is a metric space.

3.17 For a given vector norm $\|\mathbf{x}\|$ on R^n, a subordinate matrix norm for an $n \times n$ matrix A is defined as:

$$\|A\| = \text{maximum } \|A\mathbf{x}\|, \text{ for all } \mathbf{x} \text{ with } \|\mathbf{x}\| = 1.$$

If $\|\mathbf{x}\|_\infty$ denotes the maximum element norm, prove that

$$\|A\|_\infty = \underset{\text{for all } i}{\text{maximum}} \sum_{j=1}^{n} |a_{ij}|.$$

Prove that $\|A + B\|_\infty \leqslant \|A\|_\infty + \|B\|_\infty$.

3.18 If $\mathbf{x} = (1,-2,1,3)'$, find the values of the ℓ_p norms $\|\mathbf{x}\|_1$, $\|\mathbf{x}\|_2$, $\|\mathbf{x}\|_3$ and $\|\mathbf{x}\|_\infty$.

3.19 The quadratic form $Q(x_1,x_2,\ldots,x_n)$ is associated with $n \times n$ matrix A. Prove that if the variables are changed by a linear substitution $\mathbf{x} = P\mathbf{y}$, the corresponding quadratic form $Q^*(y_1,y_2,\ldots,y_n)$ is associated with a matrix $B = P'AP$. By completing the square in the corresponding quadratic form find a matrix P such that $P'AP$ is a diagonal matrix when $A = \begin{pmatrix} 1 & 2 & -2 \\ 2 & 4 & 1 \\ -2 & 1 & 9 \end{pmatrix}$.

3.20 If A is a real $n \times n$ matrix, prove that AA' is a symmetric matrix and is positive definite if rank $A = n$.

3.21 Determine which of the following matrices are positive definite.

$$A = \begin{pmatrix} 2 & 1 \\ 1 & 1 \end{pmatrix} \quad B = \begin{pmatrix} 2 & 1 & 3 \\ 1 & 2 & -1 \\ 3 & -1 & 1 \end{pmatrix} \quad C = \begin{pmatrix} 1 & 1 & 0 & 0 \\ 1 & 2 & 0 & 0 \\ 0 & 0 & 2 & 2 \\ 0 & 0 & 2 & 3 \end{pmatrix}.$$

3.22 Prove that if $Q(x_1, x_2, \ldots, x_n)$ is a positive definite quadratic form, then $Q^*(y_1, y_2, \ldots, y_m)$ is also positive definite if Q^* is obtained from Q by letting $n-m$ of the variables have value 0 and substituting $y_1, \ldots, y_m$ for the remaining variables. Deduce from Test 1 for positive definite matrices that if A is positive definite then all the principal minors of A are positive. [The principal minors of A are the determinants obtained after deleting any rows and corresponding columns from A].

Chapter 4

Applications of Scalar Products

INTRODUCTION

The algebraic concepts of scalar products, orthogonality, norms and quadratic forms already introduced have applications in many branches of mathematics. In this Chapter, we introduce a few of these applications. Section 4.1 shows how a judicious use of orthogonal properties can simplify the problem of approximating to functions by polynomials. Section 4.2 introduces Fourier Series and provides an illustration of orthogonality in an infinite dimensional vector space. Section 4.3 shows how vector norms can be used to quantify the errors liable to be introduced in computing the solution of a set of linear equations. Section 4.4 contains an introduction to the problem of minimising a function of several variables. In this Section use is made of orthogonality and of the theory of quadratic forms.

4.1 ORTHOGONAL POLYNOMIALS

Compared to most other functions, polynomials have a number of practical advantages; they are continuous and differentiable and easy to evaluate for all finite values of the argument. Consequently a common problem is that of finding for a given given function $f(x)$ a polynomial function $p(x)$ which approximates closely to it over a suitable range of values of x. $f(x)$ itself may be an explicit but not easily computed function, such as $\log(1 + e^{\sqrt{x}})$, or may be given only by a table of values, as in the case of experimental data. In either case, particularly when using a digital computer, it is more convenient to replace $f(x)$ by the approximating polynomial. Once the degree of the approximating polynomial has been determined, the polynomial itself could be found in a number of ways. For some functions $f(x)$ we could take the first few terms of a Taylor Series, but this may not give a particularly close approximation of the function because in some cases the sum of the neglected terms can be considerable (see Ex. 4.1.4, p.87). An alternative approach, which is used in this Chapter, is to decide some suitable criteria of 'goodness-of-fit' and to determine for any fixed value of n the polynomial of degree n which gives the 'best fit' to the given function.

4.1.1 Least Squares Approximation and Normal Equations

Suppose we wish to approximate aver the range $a < x < b$ to the function $f(x)$ by a polynomial $p(x)$ of degree n. Assuming $f(x)$ to be an integrable function, a reasonable criterion for a good fit is that $S = \int_a^b (f(x) - p(x))^2 dx$ should be minimised. This is the well known **least squares criterion.** A direct approach to the problem is to let $p(x) = a_0 + a_1 x + \ldots + a_n x^n$, be an arbitrary polynomial of degree n and to attempt to adjust the coefficients $a_0, a_1, \ldots, a_n$ so that S is minimised.

$$S = \int_a^b (f(x) - \sum_{i=0}^{n} a_i x^i)^2 dx. \tag{4.1}$$

Considering S as a function of the variables $(a_0, \ldots, a_n)$, S can only be a minimum if, for $i = 0, \ldots, n$, we have:

$$\frac{\partial S}{\partial a_i} = 0 \tag{4.2}$$

From (4.1) and (4.2) we obtain:

$$\int_a^b x^i (f(x) - \sum_{j=0}^{n} a_j x^j) dx = 0, \text{ for } i = 0, \ldots, n. \tag{4.3}$$

After the appropriate integrals have been evaluated, (4.3) is a system of $n+1$ linear equations (the **normal equations**) with constant coefficients which can be solved for $a_0, a_1, \ldots, a_n$.

This direct approach has a number of practical disadvantages:

(i) The Normal Equations are a full set of $n+1$ equations in $n+1$ unknowns and are not particularly simple to solve.

(ii) The Normal Equations frequently turn out to be ill-conditioned for solution by digital computer.

(iii) If, for some reason, a polynomial of higher degree than n is required, the entire computation must be repeated because all the coefficients are liable to change.

In effect the direct approach is using the polynomials $1, x, x^2 \ldots, x^n$ as a basis of $P^n(x)$. If instead a suitable orthogonal basis of $P^n(x)$ is used, all of the above disadvantages are avoided.

4.1.2 Use of Orthogonal Polynomials

Suppose, again, that we wish to approximate over the range $a < x < b$ to the function $f(x)$. Let $p_0(x), p_1(x), \ldots, p_n(x)$ be polynomials of degress $0, 1, \ldots, n$, which are orthogonal in the sense that $\int_a^b p_i(x)\, p_j(x)\mathrm{d}x = 0$, if $i \neq j$. These poly-nomials can be used as a basis of $P^n(x)$ and the polynomial $p(x)$ which approximates to $f(x)$ has a unique expression.

$$p(x) = \sum_{i=1}^{n} b_i p_i(x). \tag{4.4}$$

Applying the least squares criterion:

$$S = \int_a^b (f(x) - \sum_{i=1}^{n} b_i p_i(x))^2 \mathrm{d}x. \tag{4.5}$$

Using the orthogonal property (4.5) can be immediately simplified to give:

$$S = \int_a^b [(f(x))^2 - 2\sum_{i=1}^{n} f(x) b_i\, p_i(x) + \sum_{i=0}^{n} b_i^2\, p_i^2(x)]\, \mathrm{d}x. \tag{4.6}$$

Differentiating (4.6) with respect to b_i we obtain:

$$\frac{\partial S}{\partial b_i} = -2\int_a^b f(x)\, p_i(x)\mathrm{d}x + 2b_i \int_a^b (p_i(x))^2 \mathrm{d}x = 0. \tag{4.7}$$

Equations (4.7), which correspond to the Normal Equations, can be immediately solved to give:

$$b_i = \frac{\int_a^b f(x)\, p_i(x)\mathrm{d}x}{\int_a^b (p_i(x))^2 \mathrm{d}x}, \quad i = 0, \ldots, n. \tag{4.8}$$

The use of orthogonal polynomials has thus overcome all the difficulties in-herent in solving the Normal Equations. Moreover, if we wish to increase the degree of $p(x)$ to $n+1$, the only modification we need make is to add to (4.7) the additional equation:

$$-2\int_a^b f(x)\, p_{n+1}(x)\mathrm{d}x + 2b_{n+1}\int_a^b (p_{n+1}(x))^2 \mathrm{d}x = 0.$$

The previously computed coefficients $b_0, b_1, \ldots, b_n$ are thus unaltered.

The preceding paragraph shows how the problem of approximating to a function can be simplified by the use of orthogonal polynomials. The actual value of the polynomials $p_0(x), p_1(x), \ldots, p_n(x)$ will depend upon the interval (a,b) over which the approximation is required. One particularly frequently used interval is $(-1,1)$, which gives rise to the **Legendre polynomials** described below.

4.1.3 Legendre Polynomials

We require to find a family of polynomials $p_0(x), p_1(x), \ldots, p_n(x)$ for which $\int_{-1}^{1} p_i(x)\, p_j(x)\mathrm{d}x = 0$ if $i \neq j$. Following the method of Section 3.2.3 we could start with the basis, $1, x, \ldots, x^n$ of $P^n(x)$ and use the Gram-Schmidt algorithm to generate an orthonormal basis of $P^n(x)$.

In practice, a slight modification of the Gram-Schmidt process can considerably simplify the computation. Suppose we have found orthogonal polynomials $[p_0(x), p_1(x), \ldots, p_m(x)]$ such that every polynomial of degree m or less is linearly dependent upon this set, $xp_m(x)$ will then be a polynomial of degree $m+1$ not dependent upon the above set. Applying the Gram-Schmidt algorithm, an orthogonal polynomial will be:

$$q_{m+1}(x) = xp_m(x) - \sum_{i=1}^{m} \frac{\left(\int_{-1}^{1} xp_m(x)p_i(x)\mathrm{d}x\right)p_i(x)}{\int_{-1}^{1} p_i^2(x)\mathrm{d}x} \tag{4.9}$$

However for $i \leqslant m\text{-}2$, $\int_{-1}^{1} p_m(x)\, xp_i(x)\mathrm{d}x = 0$ because $xp_i(x)$ is a polynomial of degree $i+1$ and $p_m(x)$ being orthogonal to each of $p_0(x), p_1(x), \ldots, p_{m-1}(x)$ is orthogonal to every polynomial of degree $\leqslant m-1$.

Equation (4.9) can thus be simplified to give:

$$q_{m+1}(x) = xp_m(x) - \frac{\int_{-1}^{1} xp_m^2(x)\mathrm{d}x}{\int_{-1}^{1} p_m^2(x)\mathrm{d}x} \cdot p_m(x) - \frac{\int_{-1}^{1} xp_m(x)p_{m-1}(x)\mathrm{d}x}{\int_{-1}^{1} p_{m-1}^2(x)\mathrm{d}x} p_{m-1}(x) \tag{4.10}$$

The Legendre polynomial $p_{m+1}(x)$ is obtained from $q_{m+1}(x)$ by dividing by an appropriate constant to scale it. In the standard formulation the Legendre polynomials are scaled so that $p_m(1)=1$ for all integers m. This gives:

$$p_0(x) = 1,\ p_1(x) = x.$$

Equation (4.10) together with the scaling requirement can be used to find successively all the Legendre Polynomials. In fact, with the chosen scaling $\int_{-1}^{1} p_m^2(x)\mathrm{d}x = \dfrac{2}{2m+1}$ and (4.10) reduces to the standard recurrence relation:

$$p_{m+1}(x) = \frac{2m+1}{m+1}\,x\,p_m(x) - \frac{m}{m+1}\,p_{m-1}(x). \tag{4.11}$$

i.e. 3 term generating process.

Note that from (4.10) we obtain immediately that $\int_{-1}^{1} x p_m{}^2(x)\mathrm{d}x = 0$ because the integrand is an odd function of x. This explains the apparent disparity of terms between (4.10) and (4.11). The method used here to derive the recurrence relation (4.11) is readily adapted to other families of polynomials orthogonal over different ranges.

4.1.4 Worked Example

Use Legendre polynomials to find a polynomial approximation of degree 2 to e^{-x} over the range $-1 < x < 1$. Compare the approximate value of e^{-1} with that obtained by taking the first three terms of the Maclaurin series.

Solution

$$p_0(x) = 1,\ p_1(x) = x.$$

using (4.11) $$p_2(x) = \frac{3}{2}x p_1(x) - \frac{1}{2}p_0(x) = \frac{3}{2}x^2 - \frac{1}{2}.$$

If $e^{-x} \cong b_0 p_0 + b_1 p_1(x) + b_2 p_2(x)$ we have, from (4.8) using the orthogonality,

$$b_i = \frac{\int_{-1}^{1} e^{-x} p_i(x)\mathrm{d}x}{\int_{-1}^{1} p_i^2(x)\mathrm{d}x}.$$

Thus $$b_0 = \frac{\int_{-1}^{1} e^{-x}\mathrm{d}x}{2} = \frac{1}{2}(e - e^{-1}) \cong 1.1752,$$

$$b_1 = \frac{3}{2}\int_{-1}^{1} x e^{-x}\mathrm{d}x = \frac{3}{2}\Big[-xe^{-x} - e^{-x}\Big]_{-1}^{1} = -3e^{-1} \cong -1.1036,$$

$$b_2 = \frac{5}{2}\int_{-1}^{1}(\frac{3}{2}x^2 - \frac{1}{2})e^{-x}dx = \frac{5}{4}\Big[-3x^2e^{-x} - 6xe^{-x} - 5e^{-x}\Big]_{-1}^{1} = \frac{5e}{2} - \frac{35e^{-1}}{2},$$

$$\cong 0.3578.$$

The approximating polynomial is thus:

$$e^{-x} \cong +1.1752 - 1.1036x + 0.3578(\frac{3}{2}x^2 - \frac{1}{2}),$$

$$= 0.9963 - 1.1036x + 0.5367x^2. \quad (4.12)$$

Letting $x = 1$ in (4.12) gives $e^{-1} \cong 0.4294$. By comparison the Maclaurin series for e^{-x} is:

$$e^{-x} = 1 - x + \frac{x^2}{2} - \frac{x^3}{6} + \ldots$$

Taking the first three terms gives the approximation:

$$e^{-1} \cong 0.5.$$

(The correct value is $e^{-1} = 0.3678$).

4.1.5 Weighted Orthogonal Polynomials

Let $w(x)$ by any function such that $w(x) > 0$ for all x in the interval $a < x < b$. $w(x)$ can be used as a weighting function to modify slightly the definition of the inner product in $P^n(x)$ in such a way that $P^n(x)$ ramains an inner product space.

For $f(x), g(x)$ in $P^n(x)$ we define the weighted inner product as:

$$(f(x), g(x)) = \int_a^b w(x)\ f(x)\ g(x)dx. \quad (4.13)$$

The reader can quickly verify that axioms $S1$ to $S5$ of Section 3.3.1 are satisfied by this inner product, in particular $S5$ is a consequence of the positive property of the weighting function $w(x)$.

With the inner product defined by Equation (4.13), polynomials $p_i(x)$ and $p_j(x)$ are now orthogonal if:

$$\int_a^b w(x)\ p_i(x)\ p_j(x)dx = 0. \quad (4.14)$$

A large number of different families of orthogonal polynomials can be obtained depending upon the choice of range of integration and of weighting function.

Example 4.1 (Chebyshev Polynomials)

Let $a = -1, b = 1, w(x) = \dfrac{1}{\sqrt{(1-x^2)}}$

The inner product is now defined as:

$$(f(x), g(x)) = \int_{-1}^{1} \frac{f(x)\, g(x)}{\sqrt{(1-x^2)}}\, dx.$$

The corresponding family of orthogonal polynomials are the **Chebyshev polynomials.** These are ususally denoted $T_i(x)$ and satisfy the orthogonality condition:

$$\int_{-1}^{1} \frac{T_i(x)\, T_j(x) dx}{\sqrt{(1-x^2)}} = 0 \quad \text{if } i \neq j. \tag{4.15}$$

The polynomials are scaled so that

$$\int_{-1}^{1} \frac{(T_i(x))^2}{\sqrt{(1-x^2)}}\, dx = \frac{\pi}{2}, \text{ for } i \neq 0; \int_{-1}^{1} \frac{(T_0(x))^2}{\sqrt{(1-x^2)}}\, dx = \pi. \tag{4.16}$$

Conditions (4.15) and (4.16) are sufficient to define the Chebyshev polynomials uniquely. They can be computed by orthonormalisation of the set $(1, x^2, x^2, \ldots, x^n)$ or, in a similar method to that used for the legendre Polynomials, we can obtain a recurrence formula:

$$T_{m+1}(x) = 2xT_m(x) - T_{m-1}(x). \tag{4.17}$$

Using either of these methods the resulting polynomials are:

$$\begin{aligned} T_0(x) &= 1, \\ T_1(x) &= x, \\ T_2(x) &= 2x^2 - 1, \\ T_3(x) &= 4x^3 - 3x. \\ T_4(x) &= 8x^4 - 8x^2 + 1 \text{ etc.} \end{aligned}$$

Because of the properties of the weighting function, $w(x) = \dfrac{1}{\sqrt{(1-x^2)}}$, the

Chebyshev polynomials are particularly useful for function approximation or the solution of differential equations over the range $-1 < x < 1$ where it is more important to have a good fit near the ends of the range than towards the mid point.

Example 4.2 (Laguerre Polynomials)

The range of integration used to define the inner product need not be finite provided the weighting function is suitably chosen. If we take the range as $0 < x < \infty$ and the weighting function was $w(x) = e^{-x}$ we obtain the **Laguerre Polynomials.** (Note that since $\int_0^\infty x^n e^{-x}\, dx = n!$, then for any polynomial $f(x)$, $\int_0^\infty f(x)e^{-x}\, dx$ is finite). The Laguerre polynomials are defined by the orthogonality condition:

$$\int_0^\infty e^{-x}\; L_i(x)\; L_j(x) dx = 0. \tag{4.18}$$

Conventionally, the polynomials are usually scaled by requiring the coefficient of the highest power of x to be 1. The resulting polynomials are:

$$\begin{aligned} L_0(x) &= 1. \\ L_1(x) &= x - 1, \\ L_2(x) &= x^2 - 4x + 2 \\ L_3(x) &= x^3 - 9x^2 + 18x - 6, \\ L_4(x) &= x^4 - 16x^2 + 72x^2 - 96x + 24 \text{ etc.} \end{aligned}$$

These polynomials satisfy the recurrence relation:

$$L_{m+1}(x) = (x - 2m - 1)\; L_m(x) + m^2 L_{m-1}(x), \tag{4.19}$$

and for each integer m we have:

$$\int_0^\infty e^{-x}(L_m(x))^2\; dx = (m!)^2.$$

4.2 FOURIER SERIES

In the previous Section, the vector space being considered was the finite dimensional vector space $P^n(x)$ of polynomials of degree less than or equal to n. By a suitable definition of an inner product we were able to obtain convenient orthogonal bases for this space. In this Section, we extend the idea of an orthogonal basis to the infinite dimensional space V consisting of all continuous periodic functions of period 2π. V is clearly a real vector space because the sum of two such functions will also be periodic and continuous, as will the product of any such function with a scalar. V is an inner product space if we define the inner product of two functions in V as:

$$(f(x), g(x)) = \frac{1}{\pi}\int_{-\pi}^{\pi} f(x)\, g(x)\mathrm{d}x. \tag{4.20}$$

4.2.1 Fourier Series Expansion

In Section 3.3.2 Example 2, we established the fact that the set $S = [\frac{1}{\sqrt{2}}, \sin x, \cos x, \sin 2x, \cos 2x, \ldots, \sin nx, \cos nx, \ldots]$ is a set of orthonormal vectors in V. Let $f(x)$ be any function in V which is linearly dependent upon the functions in this set (note that we are not justified in assuming that every $f(x)$ in V will have this property).

Then
$$f(x) = \frac{K}{\sqrt{2}} + \sum_{n=1}^{\infty} a_n \cos nx + \sum_{n=1}^{\infty} b_n \sin nx. \tag{4.21}$$

The coefficients in this expression can be imediately found by exploiting the orthonormal properties of the set S.
Thus:

See page 71

$$\frac{1}{\pi}\int_{-\pi}^{\pi} f(x)\,\frac{1}{\sqrt{2}}\mathrm{d}x = (f(x), \frac{1}{\sqrt{2}}) = K, \tag{4.22}$$

$$\frac{1}{\pi}\int_{-\pi}^{\pi} f(x)\cos nx\, \mathrm{d}x = (f(x), \cos nx) = a_n \tag{4.23}$$

and
$$\frac{1}{\pi}\int_{-\pi}^{\pi} f(x)\sin nx\, \mathrm{d}x = (f(x), \sin nx) = b_n. \tag{4.24}$$

The first term $\frac{1}{\sqrt{2}}$ in the orthonormal basis is a little inconvenient and it is convenient to replace this by $\frac{1}{2}$, which is not of course a 'unit' vector. With this slight modification Equation (4.21) becomes:

$$f(x) = \frac{a_0}{2} + \sum_{n=1}^{\infty} a_n \cos nx + \sum_{n=1}^{\infty} b_n \sin nx, \tag{4.25}$$

and the comparison of (4.21) and (4.25) shows that

$$a_0 = K\sqrt{2} = \frac{\sqrt{2}}{\pi}\int_{-\pi}^{\pi} f(x)\frac{1}{\sqrt{2}}\,dx = \frac{1}{\pi}\int_{-\pi}^{\pi} f(x)dx \quad \text{[using (4.22)]}.$$

This expression can be formally identified with $\frac{1}{\pi}\int_{-\pi}^{\pi} f(x)\cos 0x\,dx$ and the expressions for the coefficients are reduced to:

$$a_n = \frac{1}{\pi}\int_{-\pi}^{\pi} f(x)\cos nx\,dx \text{ for } n = 0, 1, 2, \ldots, \tag{4.23a}$$

$$b_n = \frac{1}{\pi}\int_{-\pi}^{\pi} f(x)\sin nx\,dx, \text{ for } n = 1, 2, \ldots \tag{4.24a}$$

To prove conclusively that the set of functions S forms a basis of our space is equivalent to establishing **Fourier's Theorem.** Though a proof of this Theorem is beyond the scope of this book, the interested reader will find one in [Whittaker and Watson, 1927].

4.2.2 Fourier's Theorem

If $f(x)$ is a periodic function of period 2π which is finite for all x in $-\pi < x < \pi$, and if $f(x)$ has only a finite number of discontinuities and a finite number of maxima and minima in this interval, then the series (4.25) converges to the sum $\frac{1}{2}[f(x+) + f(x-)]$ for all x in $-\pi < x < \pi$.

Note that $\quad f(x+)$ denotes $\lim_{\delta x \to 0} f(x + \delta x), \delta x > 0,$

and $\quad f(x-)$ denotes $\lim_{\delta x \to 0} f(x - \delta x), \delta x > 0.$

At any point where $f(x)$ is continuous, $f(x) = \frac{1}{2}(f(x+) + f(x-))$ and the sum of the series coincides with the value of the function. At any point where the function has a jump discontinuity (such as $x = x_0$ in Fig. 4.1), the sum of the series is the mean of the values on either side of the discontinuity.

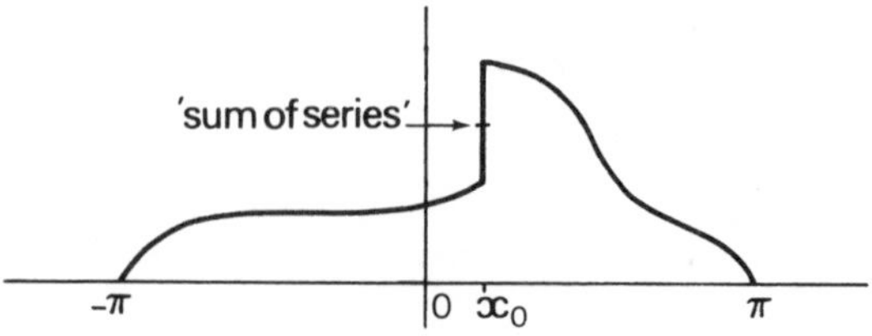

Figure 4.1

4.2.3 Worked Examples

Example 1

$f(t)$ is a periodic function of period 2π defined by the equations:

$$f(t) = 1, \quad 0 < t < \pi.$$

$$f(t) = -1, \quad -\pi < t < 0.$$

an odd function $f(-x) = -f(x)$

Find the Fourier series for $f(t)$. ($f(t)$ is the square wave illustrated in Fig. 4.2).

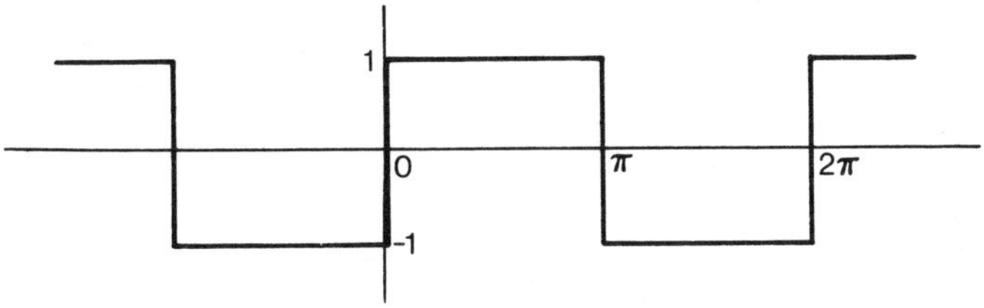

Figure 4.2

Solution

Let
$$f(t) = \frac{1}{2}a_0 + \sum_{n=1}^{\infty} (a_n \cos nt + b_n \sin nt).$$

Then, using the orthogonal property of the trigonometric functions, we have (4.23a) and (4.24a).

$$a_n = \frac{1}{\pi}\int_{-\pi}^{\pi} f(t) \cos nt \, \mathrm{d}t, \; n=0, 1, 2, \ldots,$$

$$b_n = \frac{1}{\pi}\int_{-\pi}^{\pi} f(t) \sin nt \, \mathrm{d}t, n=1,2, \ldots .$$

Thus
$$a_n = \frac{1}{\pi}\int_{-\pi}^{0} -\cos nt \, \mathrm{d}t + \frac{1}{\pi}\int_{0}^{\pi} \cos nt \, \mathrm{d}t$$

$$= 0 \text{ for all } n \text{ because } \cos(-T) = \cos T.$$

$$b_n = \frac{1}{\pi}\int_{-\pi}^{0} - \sin nt \, \mathrm{d}t + \frac{1}{\pi}\int_{0}^{\pi} \sin nt \, \mathrm{d}t$$

$$= \frac{2}{\pi} \int_0^{\pi} \sin nt \, dt, \text{ because } \sin(-T) = -\sin T.$$

$$= \frac{2}{\pi} \left[-\cos nt \right]_0^{\pi}$$

$$= \frac{2}{\pi} (1 - \cos n\pi).$$

Thus, $b_n = 0$ for n even, $b_n = \dfrac{4}{\pi}$ for n odd.

The series is: $$\frac{4}{\pi} \sin t + \frac{4}{\pi} \sin 3t + \frac{4}{\pi} \sin 5t + \ldots,$$

or $$\sum_{n=1}^{\infty} \frac{4}{\pi} \sin(2n-1)t.$$

Note that at $t = 0$ where $f(t)$ is discontinuous, the sum of the series is $0 = ½(1 + -1) = ½(f(0+) + f(0-))$.

Example 2

Find the Fourier series which represents the saw toothed wave $f(t) = t$, $-\pi < t < \pi$.

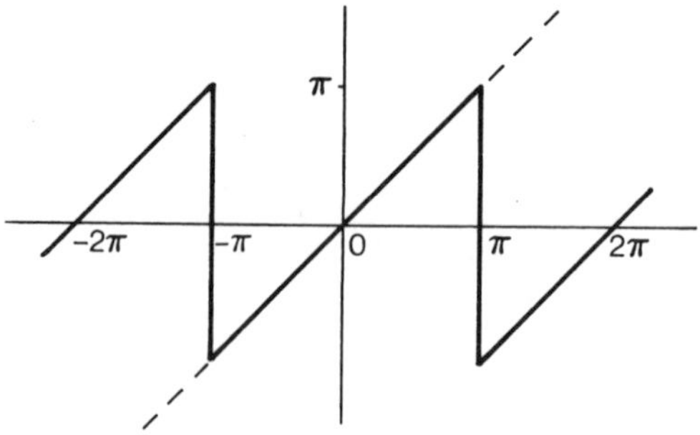

Figure 4.3

This periodic function is illustrated in Fig. 4.3.

Solution

Let $$f(t) = ½a_0 + \sum_{n=1}^{\infty} (a_n \cos nt + b_n \sin nt).$$

Then, from (4.23a) and (4.24a):

$$a_n = \frac{1}{\pi}\int_{-\pi}^{\pi} t \cos nt \, dt = 0 \text{ for all } n \text{ because } \cos(-T) = \cos T.$$

$$b_n = \frac{1}{\pi}\int_{-\pi}^{\pi} t \sin nt \, dt = \frac{1}{\pi}\left[\frac{1}{n^2}\sin nt - \frac{t}{n}\cos nt\right]_{-\pi}^{\pi}$$

$$= -\frac{2}{n}\cos n\pi, n = 1, 2, \ldots$$

$$= \frac{2}{n}(-1)^{n+1}$$

The resulting series is:

$$\sum_{n=1}^{\infty} \frac{2}{n}(-1)^{n+1}\sin nt.$$

Note that the above example illustrates the manner in which Fourier series can be used to represent non-periodic functions. The above series represents the periodic saw-tooth wave illustrated in Fig. 4.3, but it also represents the non-periodic function $f(t) = t$, though only for values of t in the range $-\pi < t < \pi$ is this representation valid. For values of t outside this range, the series gives the saw-tooth wave whilst $f(t) = t$ takes values shown by the dotted lines in Fig. 4.3.

Example 3

Find the Fourier series which represents the half rectified cosine wave:

$$f(x) = \cos x, \qquad -\frac{\pi}{2} \leqslant x \leqslant \frac{\pi}{2}.$$

$$f(x) = 0, \qquad -\pi < x < -\frac{\pi}{2}, \frac{\pi}{2} < x \leqslant \pi.$$

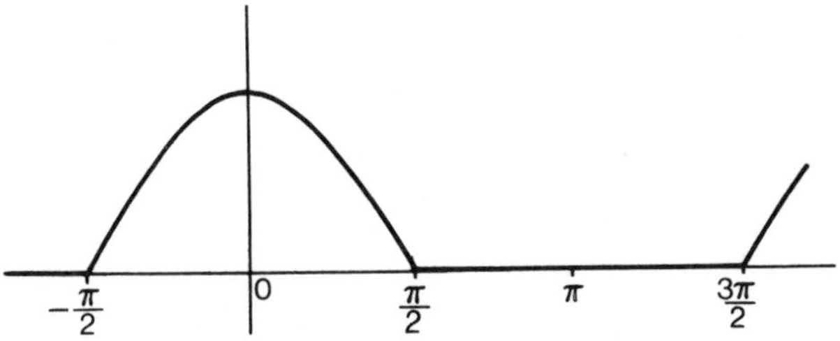

Figure 4.4

Solution

The function is illustrated in Fig. 4.4.
As before, we have:

$$a_n = \frac{1}{\pi}\int_{-\pi}^{\pi} f(x)\cos nx\,dx = \frac{1}{\pi}\int_{-\pi/2}^{\pi/2}\cos x\cos nx\,dx$$

$$= \frac{1}{\pi}\int_{-\pi/2}^{\pi/2}\frac{1}{2}(\cos(n+1)x + \cos(n-1)x)dx$$

$$= \frac{1}{2\pi}\left[\frac{\sin(n+1)x}{n+1} + \frac{\sin(n-1)x}{n-1}\right]_{-\pi/2}^{\pi/2}$$

When n is odd ($n \neq 1$), $n+1$ and $n-1$ are both even and $a_n = 0$.
When n is even we have

$$a_n = a_{2m} = \frac{1}{\pi}\left(\frac{\sin(2m+1)\pi/2}{2m+1} + \frac{\sin(2m-1)\pi/2}{2m-1}\right),$$

but when m is even $\sin(2m+1)\pi/2 = 1, \quad \sin(2m-1)\pi/2 = -1,$

when m is odd $\sin(2m+1)\pi/2 = -1, \sin(2m-1)\pi/2 = 1.$

Thus, $$a_{2m} = \frac{-2.(-1)^m}{\pi(4m^2-1)}.$$

Also, $$a_1 = \frac{1}{\pi}\int_{-\pi/2}^{\pi/2}\cos^2 x\,dx = \frac{1}{2\pi}\left[x + \frac{1}{2}\sin 2x\right]_{-\pi/2}^{\pi/2} = \frac{1}{2}.$$

$$b_n = \frac{1}{\pi}\int_{-\pi/2}^{\pi/2}\cos x\sin nx\,dx = \frac{1}{2\pi}\int_{-\pi/2}^{\pi/2}(\sin(n+1)x + \sin(n-1)x)dx = 0,$$

(for all integers n). Because for all T, $\sin(-T) = -\sin T$.

The resulting series is thus:

$$\frac{2}{\pi} + \frac{1}{2}\cos t + \sum_{m=1}^{\infty}\frac{-2.(-1)^m}{\pi(4m^2-1)}\cos 2mt.$$

4.2.4 Even and Odd Functions

The reader will observe that in Examples 1 and 2 above only the sine terms appear in the series, whereas in Example 3 only the cosine terms are present. This could have been deduced from the fact that the functions in Examples 1 and 2 were odd functions (that is $f(-x) = -f(x)$ for all x) and the function in the final Example was an even function (that is $f(-x) = f(x)$ for all x). Since our inner product is defined as $\frac{1}{\pi}\int_{-\pi}^{\pi} f(x)\, g(x)dx$, it is obvious that any odd function is orthogonal to any even function. For example, if $f(x)$ is odd and $g(x)$ is even we have:

$$\frac{1}{\pi}\int_{-\pi}^{\pi} f(x)\, g(x)dx$$

$$= \frac{1}{\pi}\int_{-\pi}^{0} f(x)\, g(x)dx + \frac{1}{\pi}\int_{0}^{\pi} f(x)\, g(x)dx$$

$$= \frac{1}{\pi}\int_{0}^{\pi} f(-t)\, g(-t)dt + \frac{1}{\pi}\int_{0}^{\pi} f(x)\, g(x)dx \text{ (letting } x = -t\text{)},$$

$$= \frac{1}{\pi}\int_{0}^{\pi} -f(t)\, g(t)dt + \frac{1}{\pi}\int_{0}^{\pi} f(x)\, g(x)dx = 0.$$

Because the Fourier series coefficients are obtained by taking inner products and because (½, cos x, cos $2x$, . . .) are even functions whereas (sin x, sin $2x$, . . .) are odd functions, the Fourier series expansion of any odd function will have $a_n = 0$ for all n. The Fourier series expansion for any even function will have $b_n = 0$, for all n.

In the cases of odd and even functions, the integrals to determine the non-vanishing coefficients in the Fourier series can be further simplified. If $g(x)$ is an even function, the values of $g(x)$ cos nx in the range $-\pi < x < 0$ will match those in the range $0 < x < \pi$. Thus

$$a_n = \frac{1}{\pi}\int_{-\pi}^{\pi} g(x) \cos nx\, dx = \frac{2}{\pi}\int_{0}^{\pi} g(x) \cos nx\, dx$$

Similarly if $f(x)$ is an odd function, the values of $f(x)$sin nx negative for values of x will match those for positive values of x ($f(-x)\sin(-nx) = f(x)\sin nx$), hence:

$$b_n = \frac{1}{\pi}\int_{-\pi}^{\pi} f(x)\sin nx\, dx = \frac{2}{\pi}\int_{0}^{\pi} f(x)\sin nx\, dx.$$

Not all functions can be classified as either odd or even (for example $f(x) = 1+x$), and the Fourier series for such a function will contain both sine and cosine terms (see Problem 4.6).

4.3 VECTOR AND MATRIX NORMS

We won't look at this section – it's

In Section 3.4, the concept of vector norms was introduced. These vector norms enable us to generalise the idea of the 'length' of a vector and hence to decide when a particular vector is 'small' or when two vectors are 'close'. Vector norms enable us to establish rigorous criteria for the termination of an iterative vector process such as the solution of a set of linear equations (4.3.1) or the calculation of eigenvectors (Chapter 6). With each of the common vector norms, we are able to associate a norm for $n \times n$ matrices and these are used in Section 4.3.2 to analyse the possible errors in solving sets of linear equations.

4.3.1. Iterative Methods

Suppose A is a non-singular $n \times n$ matrix. In Chapter 2 direct methods of solving the system of linear equations $A\mathbf{x} = \mathbf{b}$, where $\mathbf{b}$ is an $n \times 1$ constant vector, were introduced. For some applications, particularly where the coefficient matrix is large and sparse (that is has only a few non-zero elements) some iterative method of solution may be preferable. In an iterative method, rather than finding directly the solution $\mathbf{x}$, of $A\mathbf{x} = \mathbf{b}$, we produce a succession $\mathbf{x}_0, \mathbf{x}_1, \ldots, \mathbf{x}_n$ of approximate solutions. If the iterative method is successful, the final approximation $\mathbf{x}_N$ will be very close to the exact solution $\mathbf{x}$. In practice, we need some method of deciding:

(a) whether the iterative method is successful,
(b) if successful, how many iterations are necessary before we obtain a sufficiently good approximation to the exact solution?

The vector norm can be used in one of two ways to make these decisions. Either we can compute the residual vector $\mathbf{r} = \mathbf{b} - A\mathbf{x}_n$, and if $\|\mathbf{r}\|$ is then found to be very small we should, provided the equations are well conditioned, have a good approximate solution. Alternatively, when the process is converging, the results of two consecutive iterations will be very close. We can test this by computing $\|\mathbf{x}_n - \mathbf{x}_{n-1}\|$ but this test is less satisfactory than computing the residual vector. Any of the vector norms can be used in these tests because in each case a small value of the norm means that the vector being tested is close to zero. In practice, the most frequently used norms for this purpose are $\|\mathbf{r}\|_\infty$ and $\|\mathbf{r}\|_2$ because these are readily computed.

Many different iterative methods, such as the Gauss-Seidel method, the Jacobi method, the S.O.R. method [Goult *et al*, 1974], are available for solving linear equations. A typical method is the Gauss-Seidel method illustrated below. The convergence of this method is assured if the matrix is diagonally dominant, that is if the modulus of the coefficient a_{ii} is, for all i, greater than the sum of the moduli of all other coefficients in the ith row of the matrix. In this method the equations $A\mathbf{x} = \mathbf{b}$ are first re-written to provide the iteration formula. The ith equation is re-written with x_i isolated on the left-hand side:

$$x_i = \frac{1}{a_{ii}}(b_i - a_{i1}\,x_1^* - \ldots - a_{ii-1}\,x_{i-1}^* - a_{ii+1}\,x_{i+1} \ldots - a_{in}\,x_n) \qquad (4.26)$$

The method starts with some assumed initial value $\mathbf{x}_0$ for $\mathbf{x}$, and frequently $\mathbf{x}_0 = \mathbf{0}$ is the starting approximation. The first equation is then used to compute the revised value of x_1.

The second equation is then used to compute the revised value of x_2, but in this computation the updated value of x_1 is used. The calculation continues in this way, in computing x_i all the components marked with * in (4.26) are revised values, while the remainder keep their original values.

When finally x_n has been computed in this way, we have completed the first step of the iteration and obtained the complete revised vector $\mathbf{x}_1$. $\mathbf{x}_2$ is then computed in a similar way using $\mathbf{x}_1$ as the vector of initial values.

If a computer is being used for the calculation, the maximum number M (probably 50 or 100) of iterations allowed must be predetermined and the iterations continue until either this number is reached without convergence or until the computation of the appropriate norm indicates that the process has converged. A possible criterion for accepting $\mathbf{x}_N$ as a solution, for some $N < M$, would be if:

$$\frac{\|\mathbf{x}_N - \mathbf{x}_{N-1}\|}{\|\mathbf{x}_N\|} < 10^{-8}$$

Example 4.3

Use the Gauss-Seidel iterative method to find the approximate solution of:

$$\begin{aligned} 10x_1 - x_2 + 2x_3 &= 2, \\ x_1 - 10x_2 + 3x_3 &= 5, \\ x_1 - x_2 + 5x_3 &= 4. \end{aligned}$$

The coefficient matrix is clearly diagonally dominant, and rearranging the equations gives the ite-ative formulae:

$$\begin{aligned} x_1 &= \frac{1}{10}(\;2 + x_2 - 2x_3), \\ x_2 &= \frac{1}{10}(-5 + x_1 + 3x_3), \\ x_3 &= \frac{1}{5}(\;4 - x_1 + x_2). \end{aligned}$$

Computing the iterative vectors and residuals to 7 decimal places gives:

$$
\begin{aligned}
\mathbf{x}_1' &= (0.2, & -0.48, && 0.664)\\
\mathbf{x}_2' &= (0.0192, & -0.2988, && 0.736384)\\
\mathbf{x}_3' &= (0.0228432, & -0.2768005, && 0.7400713)\\
\mathbf{x}_4' &= (0.0243057, & -0.2755480, && 0.7400293)\\
\mathbf{x}_5' &= (0.0244394, & -0.2755473, && 0.7400027)\\
\mathbf{x}_6' &= (0.0244474, & -0.2755547, && 0.7399996)\\
\mathbf{x}_7' &= (0.0244446, & -0.2755557, && 0.7399999)
\end{aligned}
$$

$$
\begin{aligned}
\mathbf{r}_1' &= (-1.808, & -1.992, && 0)\\
\mathbf{r}_2' &= (0.036432, & -0.216352, && 0)\\
\mathbf{r}_3' &= (0.0146250 & -0.0110620, && 0)\\
\mathbf{r}_4' &= (0.0013365, & 0.0001266, && 0)\\
\mathbf{r}_5' &= (0.0000539, & 0.0000796, && 0)\\
\mathbf{r}_6' &= (-0.0000274, & 0.0000067, && 0)\\
\mathbf{r}_7' &= (-0.0000017, & -0.0000010, && 0)
\end{aligned}
$$

The convergence of the process is monitored either by computing $\|\mathbf{r}_n\|$ or $\|\mathbf{x}_n - \mathbf{x}_{n-1}\|$. Using the simply computed $\|\mathbf{v}\|_\infty$ we obtain:

$$
\begin{aligned}
\|\mathbf{r}_1\|_\infty &= 1.992 & \|\mathbf{x}_1 - \mathbf{x}_0\|_\infty &= 0.664\\
\|\mathbf{r}_2\| &= 0.216352 & \|\mathbf{x}_2 - \mathbf{x}_1\| &= 0.1812\\
\|\mathbf{r}_3\| &= 0.014625 & \|\mathbf{x}_3 - \mathbf{x}_2\| &= 0.0219995\\
\|\mathbf{r}_4\| &= 0.0013365 & \|\mathbf{x}_4 - \mathbf{x}_3\| &= 0.0014625\\
\|\mathbf{r}_5\| &= 0.0000796 & \|\mathbf{x}_5 - \mathbf{x}_4\| &= 0.0001337\\
\|\mathbf{r}_6\| &= 0.0000274 & \|\mathbf{x}_6 - \mathbf{x}_5\| &= 0.0000080\\
\|\mathbf{r}_7\| &= 0.0000017 & \|\mathbf{x}_7 - \mathbf{x}_6\| &= 0.0000028
\end{aligned}
$$

The original equations were well conditioned and at each iteration the norms we are evaluating are of the same order of magnitude. Whether $\|\mathbf{r}_n\|$ or $\|\mathbf{x}_n - \mathbf{x}_{n-1}\|$ is being monitored, we shall conclude that the process is converging and reach the same decision about when to terminate the process for any given required accuracy. For example, if 3 decimal place accuracy is required, the process can be terminated after 5 iterations to give $\mathbf{x}' = (0.024, -0.276, 0.740)$.

4.3.2 Matrix Norms

In Section 3.4, the concept of vector norms was introduced together with some of the norms which are used in practice. It is possible [Stewart, 1973] to define in a similar way a generalised matrix norm for any $m \times n$ matrix. For our purposes, matrix norms are required to analyse the errors occurring in the solution of linear equations. We shall confine ourselves to the rather more special case of norms of $n \times n$ matrices which are related to the previously introduced vector norms.

Definition

Let $\|\mathbf{x}\|$ be any norm on the n-dimensional vector space R^n. For any real $n \times n$ matrix A we define the **subordinate matrix norm** of A as:

$$\|A\| = \text{maximum} \frac{\|A\mathbf{x}\|}{\|\mathbf{x}\|}, \tag{4.26}$$

where the maximum is taken for all vectors $\mathbf{x}$ in R^n.

Properties

Because for any vector $\mathbf{x}$ in R_n, $A\mathbf{x}$ is also a vector, $\|A\|$ as defined by (4.26) is clearly a non-negative real number. From this definition, and the properties of the vector norm, we can deduce the following properties:

$MN1$; $\|\alpha A\| = |\alpha| \cdot \|A\|$ for any real scalar α,
$MN2$; $\|A\| \geqslant 0$, and $\|A\| = 0$ only if $A = 0$,
$MN3$; $\|A + B\| \leqslant \|A\| + \|B\|$,
$MN4$; $\|AB\| \leqslant \|A\| \cdot \|B\|$.

$MN1$ follows immediately from the definition and from $N1$ of Section 3.4.1. $MN2$ is a consequence of the fact that unless A is the zero matrix there will always be some vector $\mathbf{x}$ in R^n with $A\mathbf{x} \neq 0$.
$MN3$ is a consequence of $N3$ because:

$$\|(A + B)\mathbf{x}\| = \|A\mathbf{x} + B\mathbf{x}\| < \|A\mathbf{x}\| + \|B\mathbf{x}\| \text{ by } N3.$$

The result now follows after dividing by $\|\mathbf{x}\|$ and applying definition (4.26). $MN4$ is proved as follows:

$$\|AB\| = \max(\text{all } \mathbf{x}) \frac{\|AB\mathbf{x}\|}{\|\mathbf{x}\|}$$

$$= \max(\text{all } \mathbf{x}) \frac{\|AB\mathbf{x}\| \cdot \|B\mathbf{x}\|}{\|\mathbf{x}\| \; \|B\mathbf{x}\|}, \text{ if } B\mathbf{x} \neq 0,$$

$$= \max(\text{all } \mathbf{x}) \frac{\|A(B\mathbf{x})\|}{\|B\mathbf{x}\|} \cdot \frac{\|B\mathbf{x}\|}{\|\mathbf{x}\|}$$

But for any $\mathbf{x}$, $B\mathbf{x}$ is in R^n, hence $\dfrac{\|A(B\mathbf{x})\|}{\|B\mathbf{x}\|} \leqslant \|A\|$ and also by definition (4.26) $\dfrac{\|B\mathbf{x}\|}{\|\mathbf{x}\|} \leqslant \|B\|$. Hence $\|AB\| < \|A\| \cdot \|B\|$.

Evaluation of Particular Norms

Definition (4.26) can be rephrased to define $\|A\|$ as maximum $\|A\mathbf{x}\|$ for all $\mathbf{x}$ in R^n with $\|\mathbf{x}\| = 1$. This revised definition simplifies the computation of the particular norms, $\|A\|_1$, $\|A\|_\infty$ and $\|A\|_2$.

Considering $\|A\|_1$, let $\mathbf{x}$ be any vector with $\|\mathbf{x}\|_1 = 1$, that is with $\sum_{i=1}^{n} |x_i| = 1$. Let $\mathbf{v}_1, \mathbf{v}_2, \ldots, \mathbf{v}_n$ be the column vectors of A, then:

$$\begin{aligned} \|A\mathbf{x}\|_1 &= \|x_1\mathbf{v}_1 + x_2\mathbf{v}_2 + \ldots, x_n\mathbf{v}_n\|_1 \qquad (4.27)\\ &\leqslant |x_1|\ \|\mathbf{v}_1\|_1 + |x_2|\ \|\mathbf{v}_2\|_1 + \ldots\ |x_n|\ \|\mathbf{v}_n\|_1 \\ &\leqslant (|x_1| + |x_2| + \ldots + |x_n|) \max_{i=1\ldots n} \|\mathbf{v}_i\|_1 \\ &= \max_{i=1\ldots n} \|\mathbf{v}_i\|_1 \end{aligned}$$

Hence, because this is true for any $\mathbf{x}$ with $\|\mathbf{x}\|_1 = 1$, we obtain the result $\|A\|_1 \leqslant \max_{i=1\ldots n} \|\mathbf{v}_i\|_1$. That is to say, the norm is less than or equal to the greatest sum of column moduli in the matrix. To show that the norm has precisely this value, we must show that by a suitable choice of $\mathbf{x}$ we have $\|A\mathbf{x}\| = \max_{i=1\ldots n} \|\mathbf{v}_i\|$. Let the mth column of A have the greatest modular sum. Choose $\mathbf{x}$ so that $x_m = 1$, $x_i = 0$ for $i \neq m$. then $\max_{i=1..n} \|\mathbf{v}_i\|_1 = \|\mathbf{v}_m\|$ and, from (4.27), $\|A\mathbf{x}\| = \|x_m\mathbf{v}_m\|_1 = \|\mathbf{v}_m\|_1$. Hence $\|A\|_1$ is precisely the maximum of the sums of moduli in the columns of A. It is left as an exercise for the reader (Problem 4.11) to show in a similar way that $\|A\|_\infty$ is the maximum of the sums of moduli in the rows of A.

The above results show that $\|A\|_1$ and $\|A\|_\infty$ are particularly simple to calculate for any matrix A. (As an aid to memory, note that the same method can be used to compute $\|\mathbf{x}\|_1$ and $\|\mathbf{x}\|_\infty$ for the column vector $\mathbf{x}$. The largest 'sum' of row moduli in this case is the modulus of the largest element $= \|\mathbf{x}\|_\infty$, and the largest sum of the column moduli is precisely the sum of moduli of the elements of $\mathbf{x} = \|\mathbf{x}\|_1$). For a matrix A, $\|A\|_2$ is less easy to compute. As will be shown in Chapter 5, it depends upon the eigenvalues of $A'A$.

Example 4.4

$$A = \begin{pmatrix} 2 & 2 & -1 \\ 3 & 1 & -2 \\ -3 & 4 & -1 \end{pmatrix}, \qquad B = \begin{pmatrix} 1 & 0 & 2 \\ -1 & 2 & 3 \\ 1 & 3 & -2 \end{pmatrix}.$$

Find, for both the 1 norm and the ∞ norm, $\|A\|$, $\|B\|$, $\|AB\|$. Verify in each case that $\|AB\| \leqslant \|A\| \cdot \|B\|$.

Solution

$\|A\|_1 = 8$, the modular sum of column 1,
$\|B\|_1 = 7$, the modular sum of column 3,
$\|A\|_\infty = 8$, the modular sum of row 3,
$\|B\|_\infty = 6$, the modular sum of row 2 or row 3.

$$AB = \begin{pmatrix} -1 & 1 & 12 \\ 0 & -4 & 13 \\ -8 & 5 & 8 \end{pmatrix}. \quad \text{Thus } \|AB\|_1 = 33, \quad \|AB\|_\infty = 21.$$

For each of these norms: $\|AB\| \leqslant \|A\| \cdot \|B\|$.

4.3.3 Errors in Linear Equations – Condition Numbers

When solving the system of linear equations $A\mathbf{x} = \mathbf{b}$, it is frequently found that quite small errors in the constant vector $\mathbf{b}$, or in the coefficient matrix A, can lead to large errors in the solution $\mathbf{x}$. Such a system is said to be **ill-conditioned**. The original errors may be experimental errors in the original data or, if a computer is being used for the solution, may be rounding errors introduced by the computer. It is obviously convenient to have some method of detecting ill-conditioned systems and the **condition number** introduced in the following paragraphs provides precisely this.

In the first instance, we assume that the only error occurs on the right-hand-side of the equations. Rather than solving the exact equations $A\mathbf{x} = \mathbf{b}$, we are solving the erroneous equations $A(\mathbf{x} + \delta\mathbf{x}) = \mathbf{b} + \delta\mathbf{b}$ where $\delta\mathbf{b}$ is a small vector of error terms. If the problem is ill-conditioned we expect $\|\delta\mathbf{x}\|$ to be large for small values of $\|\delta\mathbf{b}\|$. The properties of the matrix norms enable us to estimate the largest value of $\|\delta\mathbf{x}\|$ which might occur.

Assuming A to be non-singular with exact inverse A^{-1} we have:

$$A\mathbf{x} = \mathbf{b}. \tag{4.28}$$

$$A(\mathbf{x} + \delta\mathbf{x}) = \mathbf{b} + \delta\mathbf{b}\,. \tag{4.29}$$

Hence,

$$A\,\delta\mathbf{x} = \delta\mathbf{b},$$

$$\text{or } \delta\mathbf{x} = A^{-1}\delta\mathbf{b}.$$

Using the defining property of the matrix norm:

$$\|\delta\mathbf{x}\| \leqslant \|A^{-1}\| \cdot \|\delta\mathbf{b}\|. \tag{4.30}$$

This shows that if A^{-1} has a large norm then, on occasions, large errors could occur when $\mathbf{b}$ is slightly perturbed.

It is more usual to consider the relative error in the solution, that is the value of $\dfrac{\|\delta\mathbf{x}\|}{\|\mathbf{x}\|}$. From (4.28) we obtain $\|\mathbf{b}\| \leqslant \|A\| \cdot \|\mathbf{x}\|$ or since $\|A\| > 0$,

$\|\mathbf{x}\| \geqslant \dfrac{\|\mathbf{b}\|}{\|A\|}$. (4.31).

Combining (4.30) and (4.31) gives the required result:

$$\frac{\|\delta\mathbf{x}\|}{\|\mathbf{x}\|} \leqslant \|A^{-1}\| \cdot \|A\| \cdot \frac{\|\delta\mathbf{b}\|}{\|\mathbf{b}\|}. \tag{4.32}$$

(4.32) is an inequality which compares the relative error in the solution to the relative error in the data. The critical number in this inequality is $\|A^{-1}\| \cdot \|A\|$, which is usually denoted $\chi(A)$ and referred to as the **condition number** of A. Since, for each matrix norm $1 = \|I\| = \|A^{-1}A\| \leqslant \|A^{-1}\| \cdot \|A\|$, $\chi(A)$ is always $\geqslant 1$.

The condition number occurs once more if we analyse the effect on the solution of errors in the coefficient matrix A.

Suppose:
$$A\mathbf{x} = \mathbf{b} \tag{4.33}$$

and
$$(A + \delta A)(\mathbf{x} + \delta\mathbf{x}) = \mathbf{b}. \tag{4.34}$$

From (4.34) we obtain $A\mathbf{x} + A\delta\mathbf{x} + \delta A\mathbf{x} + \delta A\delta\mathbf{x} = \mathbf{b}$. If we assume that δA and $\delta\mathbf{x}$ are both small, their product is a second order term which we neglect to obtain the approximation:

$$A\mathbf{x} + A\delta\mathbf{x} + \delta A\mathbf{x} \cong \mathbf{b}.$$

After substituting from (4.33) and re-arranging we obtain:

$$A\delta\mathbf{x} \cong -\delta A\mathbf{x}$$

Thus
$$\delta\mathbf{x} \cong -A^{-1}\delta A\mathbf{x}$$

and
$$\|\delta\mathbf{x}\| \leqslant \|A^{-1}\| \cdot \|\delta A\| \cdot \|\mathbf{x}\|.$$

Hence the relative error is given by:

$$\frac{\|\delta\mathbf{x}\|}{\|\mathbf{x}\|} \leqslant \|A^{-1}\| \, \|A\| \, \frac{\|\delta A\|}{\|A\|}.$$

Note that the simple error analysis above shows how in each case the condition number of the matrix provides an upper bound for the relative error which can occur in the solution. By no means all errors in the data or the matrix will lead to such large relative errors, but there will be some combination of vector **b** and data errors for which this bound is approached. A much more detailed error analysis can be found in [Wilkinson, 1964].

4.4 MINIMISATION OF FUNCTIONS   *might look at this later*

In this Section, we shall consider the problem of computing the minimum values of a continuous function $f(x_1, x_2, \ldots, x_n)$ of n independent real variables $x_1, \ldots, x_n$. The problem of computing maximum values is exactly similar because each maximum of f will coincide with a minimum of the function $-f$. The author's aim is not to give a comprehensive treatment of all aspects of function minimisation (see for instance, [Dixon, 1972]) but to show how frequently the ideas of linear algebra impinge upon the optimisation problem.

4.4.1 Definitions and Preliminary Analysis

The real function $f(x_1, x_2, \ldots, x_n) = f(\mathbf{x})$ has a **global minimum** at $\mathbf{x} = \mathbf{x}_0$ if $f(\mathbf{x}) > f(\mathbf{x}_0)$ for all $\mathbf{x} \neq \mathbf{x}_0$. $f(\mathbf{x})$ is said to have a **local minimum** at $\mathbf{x}_0$ if $f(\mathbf{x}) > f(\mathbf{x}_0)$ for all points $\mathbf{x}$ near to $\mathbf{x}_0$ that is for all $\mathbf{x}$ with $\|\mathbf{x} - \mathbf{x}_0\| < k$ for some $k > 0$.

In this and the following Sections, we shall be concerned with the properties and location of local minima of real functions of several real variables.

If $f(\mathbf{x})$ is continuous differentiable function of the independent variables $(x_1, x_2, \ldots, x_n)$ and has well behaved partial derivatives, we can apply **Taylor's Theorem** to establish a close link between the minima of $f(\mathbf{x})$ and the partial derivatives. From Taylor's Theorem, we have:

$$f(x_1 + h_1, x_2 + h_2, \ldots, x_n + h_n) = f(x_1, x_2, \ldots, x_n)$$

$$+ h_1 \frac{\partial f}{\partial x_1} + h_2 \frac{\partial f}{\partial x_2} + h_n \frac{\partial f}{\partial x_n} \qquad \leftarrow = 0 \text{ for stationary point}$$

$$+ \frac{1}{2}\left[h_1^2 \frac{\partial^2 f}{\partial x_1^2} + 2h_1 h_2 \frac{\partial^2 f}{\partial x_1 \partial x_2} + \ldots + 2h_{n-1}h_n \frac{\partial^2 f}{\partial x_{n-1}\partial x_n} + h_n^2 \frac{\partial^2 f}{\partial x_n^2} \right] + O(h^3).$$

$$(4.35)$$

The term $O(h^3)$ in Equation (4.35) refers to terms containing third or higher powers of the quantities $h_1, h_2, \ldots, h_n$, Provided $\|\mathbf{h}\|$ is small these third order terms will be negligible by comparison with the other terms in (4.35).

Using vector notation (4.35) can be re-arranged to give:

$$f(\mathbf{x} + \mathbf{h}) - f(\mathbf{x}) = \mathbf{h} \cdot \mathbf{g} + \tfrac{1}{2}\mathbf{h}'H\mathbf{h} + O(h^3) \qquad (4.36)$$

$f(x_1 + h_1, x_2 + h_2, \ldots, x_n + h_n) - f(x_1, x_2, \ldots x_n)$

is +ve for a minimum

where $\mathbf{g} = \left(\frac{\partial f}{\partial x_1}, \frac{\partial f}{\partial x_2}, \ldots, \frac{\partial f}{\partial x_n}\right)'$, the gradient of f,

and $H = \begin{pmatrix} \frac{\partial^2 f}{\partial x_1^2}, & \frac{\partial^2 f}{\partial x_1 \partial x_2} & \cdots & \frac{\partial^2 f}{\partial x_1 \partial x_n} \\ \frac{\partial^2 f}{\partial x_1 \partial x_2} & & & \\ \vdots & & & \\ \frac{\partial^2 f}{\partial x_1 \partial x_n} & & & \frac{\partial^2 f}{\partial x_n^2} \end{pmatrix}$, the symmetric Hessian matrix.

If f is to have a minimum at the point $\mathbf{x}$, the left-hand side, and consequently the right-hand side, of (4.36) must be positive for all $\mathbf{h}$ with $\mathbf{h}$ small. If $\mathbf{g} \neq \mathbf{0}$, the dominant term on the right-hand side when $\mathbf{h}$ is very small is $\mathbf{h} \cdot \mathbf{g}$. This term will change sign as $\mathbf{h}$ changes to $-\mathbf{h}$ hence a minimum is impossible unless $\mathbf{g} = \mathbf{0}$. Assuming $\mathbf{g} = \mathbf{0}$ we then have:

$$f(\mathbf{x} + \mathbf{h}) - f(\mathbf{x}) \cong \tfrac{1}{2}\mathbf{h}'H\mathbf{h}, \text{ for small } \mathbf{h}.$$

This is a quadratic form in the variables $(h_1, \ldots, h_n)$ and is clearly only positive for all small $\mathbf{h}$ if the matrix H is positive definite. Thus conditions for $f(\mathbf{x})$ to have a minimum at point $\mathbf{x}$ are:

$$\mathbf{g} = \mathbf{0} \tag{4.37}$$

and H is positive definite. (4.38)

These conditions can be compared to the conditions for a real function $\phi(t)$ to have a minimum at the point t_0, namely:

$$\phi'(t_0) = 0,$$

$$\phi''(t_0) > 0.$$

In theory, the minima of $f(\mathbf{x})$ can be located by solving the equations $\mathbf{g} = \mathbf{0}$ and verifying at the appropriate points that H is a positive definite matrix. In practice, it is usually difficult to obtain explicit solutions of (4.37) and some method of searching for the minimum is preferred. These search techniques have the advantage that they can be used even when the partial derivatives of the function $f(\mathbf{x})$ are not available.

4.4.2 Searching Methods

Won't look at rest of chapter from here it's NA

Many algorithms for locating local minima of $f(\mathbf{x})$ reduce the problem to that of minimizing a function of a single real variable by searching for the minimum in one direction at a time. The various algorithms differ in the method chosen for these searches and the way in which the search directions are chosen. If the search direction is in the direction of the vector $\mathbf{d}$ the immediate problem is reduced to that of finding the value of the single real variable θ for which $F(\theta) = f(\mathbf{x} + \theta\mathbf{d})$ is minimised. A simple technique for conducting this linear search is as follows:

(i) evaluate $f(\mathbf{x})$,

(ii) after deciding upon a suitable step length s, evaluate $f(\mathbf{x} + s\mathbf{d})$.

If $f(\mathbf{x} + s\mathbf{d}) \leqslant f(\mathbf{x})$ the step is called a success, otherwise it is called a failure. After a successful step the search continues from the new point $f(\mathbf{x} + \theta\mathbf{d}) = f(\mathbf{x} + s\mathbf{d})$ with doubled step length. After an unsuccessful step, the search continues from the new point but with the step length halved and reversed in direction. This first stage of the search then terminates when a successful step has been followed by a failure and the half-step back. A typical result is illustrated in Figure 4.5.

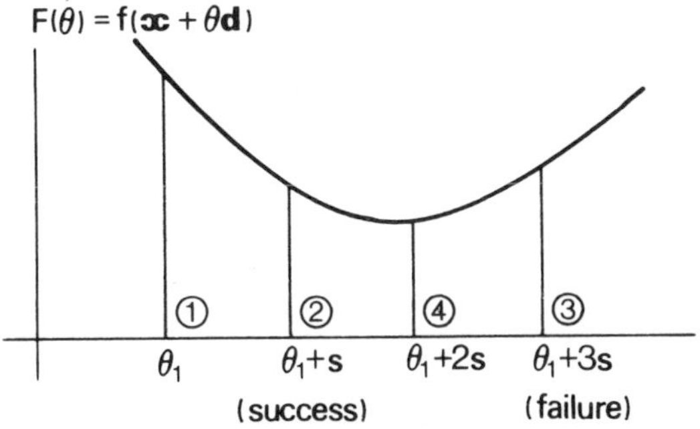

Fig. 4.5

The numbers in this Figure refer to the order in which the steps were taken.

Using this method, the final result is bound to be a set of four equally spaced points which between them contain the minimum of $F(\theta) = f(\mathbf{x} + \theta\mathbf{d})$. Rosenbrock's algorithm [Rosenbrock, 1960] accepts whichever of these four points gives the least value of $F(\theta)$ as an approximate minimum in this direction and then proceeds to the next search direction. The algorithm of Davies, Swann and Campey chooses whichever three of these four points will contain the minimum by rejecting either the point θ_1, or the point $\theta_1 + 3s$, depending upon which is furthest from the minimum of $f(\theta_1+s)$ and $f(\theta_1+2s)$. (In Fig. 4.5 the the point θ_1 would be rejected.) If the chosen points are denoted $\theta_1, \theta_2, \theta_3$ with $F_1 = F(\theta_1)$, $F_2 = F(\theta_2)$, $F_3 = F(\theta_3)$, then the minimum of the interpolating quadratic curve passing through (θ_1, F_1), (θ_2, F_2), (θ_3, F_3) occurs at the point

(θ_m, F_m) where $\theta_m = \theta_2 + s'$ and:

$$s' = \frac{s(F_1 - F_3)}{2(F_1 - 2F_2 + F_3)}$$

The value $\mathbf{x} + \theta_m \mathbf{d}$ is taken as the approximate location of the minimum of $f(\mathbf{x})$ in the direction $\mathbf{d}$. This algorithm, like that of Rosenbrock, then proceeds to the next search direction.

In both the Rosenbrock and the Davies, Swann and Campey algorithms, the linear search is carried out in n linearly independent directions before continuing with the next stage of the process. Usually the directions chosen initially are parallel to the coordinate axes, but these directions are modified, using information gained about the behaviour of the function, at each stage of the process. At the completion of each stage of the algorithm, the direction of progress is computed by adding together the n steps taken in different directions. A new set of search directions is then generated by using the Gram-Schmidt method and using the direction or progress just calculated as the first of the new set of orthogonal search directions. In this way, the search directions are varied, adapting themselves to the contours of the function and so making the algorithms more efficient.

Example 4.5

Use four iterations of the Davies, Swann and Campey algorithm to locate approximately a minimum of the function:

$$f(x_1, x_2) = 3x_1^3 + 2x_2^2 - 2x_1x_2 - x_1^2 - 4x_2.$$

For the first iteration the searches are in the axis directions. Let $\phi(\theta) = f(\theta, 0) = 3\theta^3 - \theta^2$. Starting with $\theta_0 = 0$, $s = 0.1$ and following the method described above we obtain:

$\phi(0) = 0,$
$\phi(0.1) = -0.007$ (success) – double step length,
$\phi(0.3) = -0.009$ (success) – double step length,
$\phi(0.7) = 0.539$ (failure) – halve step and reverse:
$\phi(0.5) = 0.125.$

The interpolation is now carried out on the three points $\theta_1 = 0.1$, $\phi_1 = 0.007$; $\theta_2 = 0.3$, $\phi_2 = -0.009$; $\theta_3 = 0.5$, $\phi_3 = 0.125$; $s = 0.2$. Using formula $s' = \dfrac{s(\phi_1 - \phi_3)}{2(\phi_1 - 2\phi_2 + \phi_3)}$ gives $s' = -0.09$. Thus $\theta = \theta_2 + s' = 0.21$ terminates the search in the first direction. The search in the second direction starts from the point (0.21,0) and is in the direction of the second axis. Defining $\phi(\theta) = f(0.21,\theta)$ and following the above method gives:

$$\begin{aligned}
\phi(0) &= -0.0163,\\
\phi(0.1) &= -0.4383 \text{ (success)},\\
\phi(0.3) &= -1.1623 \text{ (success)},\\
\phi(0.7) &= -2.1303 \text{ (success)},\\
\phi(1.5) &= -2.1463 \text{ (success)},\\
\phi(3.1) &= 5.5017 \text{ (Failure) -- halve step and reverse:}\\
\phi(2.3) &= 0.3977.
\end{aligned}$$

Interpolating on the points $\theta_1 = 0.7$, $\theta_2 = 1.5$, $\theta_3 = 2.3$ terminates this search at the point (0.21, 1.11).

This completes the first iteration of the algorithm. The direction of progress for the first iteration is $\mathbf{d} = (0.21,1.11)'$. The orthogonal unit vectors used for the searches in the next iteration are thus $\mathbf{v}_1 = (0.19,0.98)$ in the direction of $\mathbf{d}$ and $\mathbf{v}_2 = (0.98,-0.19)$. Searching from (0.21,1.11) in the direction of $\mathbf{v}_1$ we seek to minimise $\phi(\theta) = f(0.21 + 0.19\theta,\ 1.11 + 0.98\theta)$. Using the method described above, this search terminates at the point (0.218, 1.151).

The second search of this iteration is from (0.218,1.151) in the direction $\mathbf{v}_2 = (0.98,-0.19)$ and terminates, after interpolation, at the point (0.590, 1.079). The direction of progress for the second iteration is then

$$\mathbf{d} = (0.590, 1.079)' - (0.21,1.11)' = (0.38,-0.031).$$

For the third iteration, the starting point is (0.590,1.079) and the search directions are $\mathbf{v}_1 = (0.997,-0.081)'$ (parallel to $\mathbf{d}$) and $\mathbf{v}_2 = (0.081,0.997)$. These searches lead to the points (0.601,1.078) and (0.621,1,318) respectively. The direction of progress for the third iteration is

$$\mathbf{d} = (0.621,1,318)' - (0.590,1.079)' = (0.031,0.239)'.$$

The fourth iteration starts from (0.621,1.318) and searches in the directions $\mathbf{v}_1 = (0.129,0.992)'$, $\mathbf{v}_2 = (0.99,-0.129)$. The points reached are (0.621, 1.318) and (0.662,1.313) respectively.

Note that the example above is included merely as an illustration of the method. In practice, the algorithm is intended for minimising functions of many variables using a computer for the arithmetic computations. For the simple function $f(x_1, x_2)$ it is a trivial matter to solve explicitly the equations $\dfrac{\partial f}{\partial x_1} = 0$ and $\dfrac{\partial f}{\partial x_2} = 0$ to obtain the exact location $(\frac{2}{3}, \frac{4}{3})$ of the minimum.

4.4.3 Conjugate Directions

The previous Section gave details of methods of searching for the minimum of $f(\mathbf{x})$ in which the search directions are modified as the search progresses. The ideal search directions would, of course, be those which lead directly to the minimum in one iteration. In general, this ideal cannot be obtained but, as we shall show below, for quadratic functions a set of conjugate directions provides an ideal set of search direction. $f(\mathbf{x})$ is said to be a quadratic function if $f(\mathbf{x})$ contains only terms of the first order (x_i) or second order (x_ix_j or x_i^2) in the variables (x_1, x_2, . . ., x_n). Such a function can be expressed in the form: $f(\mathbf{x}) = \mathbf{x}'A\ \mathbf{x} + \mathbf{c}'\mathbf{x}$, where $\mathbf{c}$ is a constant vector and A is an $n \times n$ symmetric matrix.

Suppose the directions $\mathbf{v}_1$, $\mathbf{v}_2$, . . ., $\mathbf{v}_n$ are conjugate with respect to the symmetric matrix A, that is, for $i \neq j$ $\mathbf{v}_i'A\ \mathbf{v}_j = 0$.

If we start from the point $\mathbf{x}_0$ and seek a minimum of $f(\mathbf{x})$, we wish to find $\theta_1, \theta_2, \ldots, \theta_n$ which will minimise $\phi(\theta_1, \theta_2, \ldots, \theta_n) = f(\mathbf{x}_0 + \sum_{i=1}^{n} \theta_i\mathbf{v}_i)$.

$$\phi(\theta_1, \theta_2, \ldots, \theta_n) = (\mathbf{x}_0 + \sum_{i=1}^{n} \theta_i\mathbf{v}_i)'A(\mathbf{x}_0 + \sum_{j=1}^{n} \theta_j\mathbf{v}_j) + \mathbf{c}'(\mathbf{x}_0 + \sum_{i=1}^{n} \theta_i\mathbf{v}_i).$$

Using the symmetry of A and the conjugate property of the directions $\mathbf{v}_1$, $\mathbf{v}_2$, . . ., $\mathbf{v}_n$, this expression becomes:

$$\mathbf{x}_0'A\ \mathbf{x}_0 + \sum_{i=1}^{n} \theta_i^2\mathbf{v}_i'A\mathbf{v}_i + 2\sum_{i=1}^{n} \theta_i\mathbf{v}_i'A\mathbf{x}_0 + \mathbf{c}'\mathbf{x}_0 + \mathbf{c}'\sum_{i=1}^{n} \theta_i\mathbf{v}_i$$

$$= \mathbf{x}_0'A\mathbf{x}_0 + \mathbf{c}'\mathbf{x}_0 + \sum_{i=1}^{n} \phi_i(\theta_i),$$

where $\phi_i(\theta_i) = \theta_i^2\mathbf{v}_i'A\mathbf{v}_i + 2\theta_i\mathbf{v}_i'A\mathbf{x}_0 + \mathbf{c}'\theta_i\mathbf{v}_i$, for $i = 1, \ldots n$.

This shows that, unlike the variables (x_1, x_2, . . ., x_n), the variables (θ_1, θ_2, . . ., θ_n) are independent and uncoupled and the function $\phi(\theta_1, \theta_2, \ldots, \theta_n)$ can be minimised by finding the values of the θ_i which minimise the functions $\phi_i(\theta_i)$. The sum of these minima will give the minimum of $\phi(\theta_1, \ldots, \theta_n)$. The appropriate values of θ_i can be found by searching from $\mathbf{x}_0$ in the direction of $\mathbf{v}_i$ for the minimum of $f(x)$ since:

$$f(\mathbf{x}_0 + \theta_i\mathbf{v}_i) = \mathbf{x}_0'A\mathbf{x}_0 + \theta_i^2\mathbf{v}_i'A\mathbf{v}_i + 2\theta_i\mathbf{v}_i'A\mathbf{x}_0 + \mathbf{c}'\theta_i\mathbf{v}_i + \mathbf{c}'\mathbf{x}_0$$

$$= \phi_i(\theta_i) + \mathbf{x}_0'A\mathbf{x}_0 + \mathbf{c}'\mathbf{x}_0.$$

This differs from $\phi_i(\theta_i)$ only by a constant. The above argument shows that for a quadratic function, conjugate directions provide a set of ideal search directions. This is because if we start from any point and search in these directions, we shall reach the minimum in precisely n steps, the equivalent of one complete iteration of the D.S.C. algorithm.

Example 4.6

Show that the directions $\mathbf{v}_1 = (1,0,0)'$, $\mathbf{v}_2 = (-1,2,0)'$ and $\mathbf{v}_3 = (1,-2,3)$ are conjugate with respect to the matrix $A = \begin{pmatrix} 2 & 1 & 0 \\ 1 & 2 & 1 \\ 0 & 1 & 2 \end{pmatrix}$.

By carrying out linear searches in these directions, find the minimum of $f(x_1, x_2, x_3) = 2x_1^2 + 2x_2^2 + 2x_3^2 + 2x_1x_2 + 2x_2x_3 - 4x_1 - 2x_2 - x_3$.

Solution

$\mathbf{v}_1{}'A\mathbf{v}_2 = \mathbf{v}_2'A\mathbf{v}_3 = \mathbf{v}_3'A\mathbf{v}_1 = 0$, hence directions are conjugate. The above theory shows that the success of the conjugate searches is independent of the starting point, hence for simplicity we shall start from $\mathbf{x}_0 = \mathbf{0}$. Searching in the direction $\mathbf{v}_1$ we require a θ_1 which minimises $f(\theta_1, 0, 0) = 2\theta_1^2 - 4\theta_1$. The solution is $\theta_1 = 1$. Searching in direction $\mathbf{v}_2$ we require θ_2 to minimise $f(-\theta_2, 2\theta_2, 0)$ or $\phi_2(\theta_2) = 6\theta_2^2$. The solution is $\theta_2 = 0$. Finally, searching in direction $\mathbf{v}_3$, θ_3 is required to minimise $\phi_3(\theta_3) = f(\theta_3, -2\theta_3, 3\theta_3) = 12\theta_3^2 - 3\theta_3$. The minimum is given by $\theta_3 = \frac{1}{8}$. The minimum of $f(x)$ occurs at $\mathbf{x} = \theta_1\mathbf{v}_1 + \theta_2\mathbf{v}_2 + \theta_3\mathbf{v}_3 = (\frac{9}{8}, -\frac{1}{4}, \frac{3}{8})'$.

Note that in the above solution, we made use of the fact that the conjugate search directions are uncoupled and started all the searches from $\mathbf{x}_0 = \mathbf{0}$, rather than starting each search from the previous finishing point.

The above example shows that the problem of minimising a quadratic function can be considerably simplified by searching along a set of conjugate directions. For a function which is not quadratic there is no simple method of finding such an ideal set of search directions. However Fletcher and Reeves' algorithm [Fletcher and Reeves, 1964] is one among a number aiming to generate a set of search directions which will be conjugate for the quadratic function approximating to the function being minimised.

PROBLEMS

4.1 Find the polynomial of degree 3 which approximates to $f(x) = \sin x$ over the range $-1 \leqslant x \leqslant 1$.

(a) by the method of least squares, obtaining a solution of the normal equations;

(b) by using Legendre polynomials.

4.2 The least squares criteria for fitting a polynomial $y = \sum_{i=0}^{n} a_i x^i$ to the numerical data (x_i, y_i) $i = 1, \ldots, m$ requires the constants $a_0, a_1, \ldots, a_n$ to be chosen so that $\sum_{j=1}^{m} (y_j - \sum_{i=1}^{n} a_i x_j^{\,i})^2$ is minimised. Show that the values of these constants are determined by the normal equations:

$$\sum_{i=0}^{n} a_i \left(\sum_{j=1}^{m} x_j^{\,i+k}\right) = \sum_{j=1}^{m} y_j x_j^{\,k}, \quad \text{for } k = 0,1,\ldots,n.$$

Find and solve the normal equations for fitting the approximating quadratic curve $y = a_0 + a_1 x + a_2 x^2$ to the data points in the table below.

x_i	–1	0	1	2	3
y_i	2	1	5	7	9

4.3 Find the normal equations for approximating a quadratic curve to the function $y = e^x$ over the range $0 < x < 2$. Using the ℓ_∞ norm, find the condition number of the coefficient matrix of these equations.

4.4 A function $f(x)$ is defined by the equations:

$$f(x) = 1 - x \quad \text{for } x \geqslant 0,$$

$$f(x) = 1 + x \quad \text{for } x \leqslant 0.$$

Find the second order Legendre and Chebyshev polynomial series approximating to $f(x)$ over the range $-1 \leqslant x \leqslant 1$.

Evaluate these approximating polynomials at the points $x = 0$ and $x = 0.9$.

4.5 The Legendre polynomials can be defined as the polynomial solutions of a family of 2nd order differential equations. For $P_n(x)$ the differential equation is:

$$(1 - x^2)\frac{d^2p}{dx^2} - 2x\frac{dp}{dx} + n(n+1)p = 0.$$

Confirm this result by directly substituting the expressions for $P_0(x)$, $P_1(x)$, $P_2(x)$ into the appropriate differential equations.

Find the relative values of the coefficients of $P_3(x)$ by trying $p(x) = a_0 + a_1 x + a_2 x^2 + a_3 x^3$ as a solution of the differential equation with $n = 3$.

4.6 A periodic function of period 2π is defined by the equations:

$$f(x) = 1 - x \qquad 0 < x \leqslant \pi$$

$$f(x) = 1 \qquad -\pi < x \leqslant 0.$$

Sketch the function over the range $-2\pi < x < 2\pi$ and find the Fourier series expansion of $f(x)$.

4.7 V is the space of all continuous integrable functions over the range $a \leqslant x \leqslant b$. An inner product on V is defined as $(f(x), g(x)) = \int_a^b f(x)g(x)dx$. $P_0, P_1(x), \ldots, P_n(x)$ are orthogonal polynomials in $V, P_r(x)$ being a polynomial of degree r. Prove that $P_n(x)$ is orthogonal to every polynomial of degree less then n.

4.8 Find the Fourier series which represents the fully rectified sine wave:

$$f(x) = \sin x, \qquad 0 \leqslant x \leqslant \pi$$

$$f(x) = -\sin x. \quad -\pi \leqslant x \leqslant 0$$

Use your result to deduce the series which represents the half-rectified sine wave.

4.9 Find the Fourier series which represents the function defined in Problem 4.4 over the range $-\pi < x < \pi$. Use the first three terms of the series to estimate $f(\pi/4)$. Compare this answer to the result obtained by substituting $x = \pi/4$ in the Chebyshev polynomial series obtained in Problem 4.4.

4.10 A function $f(x)$ has Fourier series $\frac{1}{2}a_0 + \sum_{n=1}^{\infty} (a_n \cos nx + b_n \sin nx)$. Give the Fourier series which will represent the following functions (you may assume that all the series are convergent):

$$f_1(x) = f(-x),$$
$$f_2(x) = \tfrac{1}{2}(f(x) + f(-x)),$$
$$f_3(x) = f(2x),$$
$$f_4(x) = f(x - \pi/2),$$
$$f_5(x) = f'(x).$$

4.11 Using $\|A\|_\infty$, find the condition number of the matrix $A = \begin{pmatrix} 1.1 & -1 \\ -1 & 1 \end{pmatrix}$.

For this matrix A and $\mathbf{b}$ and $\delta\mathbf{b}$ such that, with the notation of Section 4.3.3, $\|\delta\mathbf{x}\|/\|\mathbf{x}\| = \text{cond}(A). \|\delta\mathbf{b}\|/\|\mathbf{b}\|$.

4.12 Use the Gauss-Seidel iterative method to find a solution correct to three decimal places of the equations:

$$\begin{aligned} 10x_1 + x_2 - x_3 &= 4, \\ x_1 + 5x_2 - x_3 &= 3, \\ 2x_1 + x_2 - 10x_3 &= 5. \end{aligned}$$

Show that the iterative process used can be expressed in matrix form as $\mathbf{x}_{N+1} = \mathbf{c} + M\mathbf{x}_N$, where M is a square matrix, and find $\|M\|_\infty$ for this example.

4.13 $\mathbf{x}_E$ denotes the exact solution of the linear equations $A\mathbf{x} = \mathbf{b}$. If the equations are being solved iteratively, the error at the Nth iteration is defined as $\mathbf{e}_N = \mathbf{x}_N - \mathbf{x}_E$. Show that for the iterative process defined by the equation $\mathbf{x}_{N+1} = \mathbf{c} + M\mathbf{x}_N$ the errors are related by the equation $\mathbf{e}_{N+1} = M\mathbf{e}_N$. Prove that the process will converge if $\|M\|_\infty < 1$. Deduce that the Gauss-Seidel process is convergent if the coefficient matrix A is diagonally dominant.

4.14 If A is an $n \times n$ matrix, prove that $\|A\|_\infty = \max_i \sum_{j=1}^{n} |a_{ij}|$.

If $A = \begin{pmatrix} 1 & 3 & -2 \\ 2 & -2 & 3 \\ 1 & 2 & 1 \end{pmatrix}$ find $\|A\|_\infty$ and a vector $\mathbf{x}$ such that $\|A\mathbf{x}\|_\infty = \|A\|_\infty \|\mathbf{x}\|_\infty$.

4.15 The $n \times n$ Hilbert matrix H_n is defined by the equations $h_{ij} = 1/(i+j-1)$. Find the approximate values of the condition numbers of H_n for $n = 2, 3$ and 4.

4.16 Use two iterations of the algorithm of Davies, Swann and Campey to find the approximate location of the minimum of the function:

$$g(x) = 3x_1^3 + 2x_2^2 - 2x_1x_2 - x_1^2 - 4x_2$$

4.17 State a sufficient set of conditions for a differentiable function $f(x) = f(x_1,x_2,x_3)$ to have a local maximum at the point (a_1,a_2,a_3). Find the maximum value of $f(x) = -6x_1^2 - 9x_2^2 + 2x_3^3 + 4x_1x_2 + 6x_1 + 12x_2 - 6x_3$ by finding points at which the gradient of f is zero.

4.18 Use two iterations of Rosenbrock's algorithm to find the approximate location of the maximum of the function $f(x)$ of Problem 4.17. Start with $\mathbf{x}_0 = 0$ and $s = 0.1$.

4.19 Use an algorithm, in which linear searches from $\mathbf{x}_0$ are conducted in directions which are conjugate with respect to the Hessian matrix H evaluated at $\mathbf{x}_0$ to find the approximate locations of the minimum of $f(\mathbf{x}) = x_1^3 + 2x_1^2 + 3x_2^2 + 2x_1x_2 - 3x_1$. Start with $\mathbf{x}_0 = (1,1)'$ and initial direction $\mathbf{v}_1 = (1,0)'$, and perform two complete iterations.

4.20 $A = \begin{pmatrix} 2 & 1 & 0 \\ 1 & 4 & 1 \\ 0 & 1 & 2 \end{pmatrix}, \quad \mathbf{v}_1 = \begin{pmatrix} 1 \\ 0 \\ 0 \end{pmatrix}.$

Find vectors $\mathbf{v}_2$, $\mathbf{v}_3$ such that $[\mathbf{v}_1,\mathbf{v}_2,\mathbf{v}_3]$ form a set of mutually conjugate directions with respect to the symmetric matrix A. By using (0,0,0) as a starting point and carrying out linear searches in the directions of $\mathbf{v}_1$, $\mathbf{v}_2$, $\mathbf{v}_3$, respectively, find the minimum of the function:

$$f(x_1,x_2,x_3) = 2x_1^2 + 4x_2^2 + 2x_3^2 + 2x_1x_2 + 2x_2x_3 - 4x_1 - 2x_2 - x_3 .$$

Chapter 5

Linear Transformations

INTRODUCTION

This Chapter is devoted to the theory of linear transformations. These are mappings of one vector space into another which preserve linear properties of the spaces as described in Chapter 1. The theory of linear transformations can be applied both to infinite dimensional vector spaces and to spaces of finite dimension. In the latter case, the transformations can be represented by matrices and a number of useful results in matrix algebra can be obtained from their properties. Linear transformations of a vector space into itself have many important practical applications. Both the theory of these transformations, and the corresponding properties of square matrices, are given in Section 5.3 of this Chapter.

5.1 GENERAL LINEAR TRANSFORMATIONS

5.1.1 Definitions

Let V and W be real vector spaces. A mapping ϕ of V into W is called a **linear transformation** if it has the following properties.

$LT1$; for each vector $\mathbf{v}$ in V, there is an unambiguously defined vector $\mathbf{w} = \phi(\mathbf{v})$ contained in W,

$LT2$; for all vectors $\mathbf{v}_1, \mathbf{v}_2$ in V, $\phi(\mathbf{v}_1 + \mathbf{v}_2) = \phi(\mathbf{v}_1) + \phi(\mathbf{v}_2)$,

$LT3$; for all vectors $\mathbf{v}$ in V and for all real constants α, $\phi(\alpha\mathbf{v}) = \alpha\phi(\mathbf{v})$.

The first of the above axioms, $LT1$, ensures that ϕ is a well defined mapping of V into W such that for each vector $\mathbf{v}$ we can find a corresponding image vector $\phi(\mathbf{v})$ in the space W. The definition carefully excludes the possibility of any vector $\mathbf{v}$ having more than one image, but it is quite permissible for one vector in W to correspond to several vectors in V. The last two axioms ensure that the transformation preserves the linear properties of vectors in V when transforming them into vectors in W. In particular, $LT3$ with $\alpha = 0$ ensures that the zero vector $\mathbf{O}$ in V is transformed into the zero vector in W.

Theorem 5.1

Let $\mathbf{v}_1, \mathbf{v}_2, \ldots, \mathbf{v}_n$ be a set of linearly dependent vectors in V, then their images $\phi(v_1), \ldots, \phi(v_n)$ will also be linearly dependent vectors.

$\phi_1 \ldots \phi_n$ are L.I. (i.e converse is not true)

Proof

Since $[v_1, v_2, \ldots, v_n]$ is a linearly dependent set, we can find $\alpha_1, \alpha_2, \ldots, \alpha_n$, not all zero, such that $\alpha_1 v_1 + \alpha_2 v_2 + \ldots + \alpha_n v_n = \mathbf{O}$.

The repreated application of axiom *LT*2 shows that:

$$\mathbf{O} = \phi(\mathbf{O}) = \phi(\alpha_1 v_1 + \alpha_2 v_2 + \ldots + \alpha_n v_n) = \phi(\alpha_1 v_1) + \ldots + \phi(\alpha_n v_n).$$

Using *LT*3 gives the result:

$$\mathbf{O} = \alpha_1 \phi(v_1) + \alpha_2 \phi(v_2) + \ldots + \alpha_n \phi(v_n),$$

which establishes the linear dependence of the vectors in the set $[\phi(v_1), \phi(v_2), \ldots, \phi(v_n)]$.

Associated with each linear transformation ϕ of V into W are two particular subspaces called the kernel of ϕ and the image space of ϕ. **The kernel of ϕ** is a subspace of V consisting of all vectors **v** in V such that $\phi(v) = \mathbf{O}$. The **image space of ϕ** is a subspace of W and consists of all the vectors in W which are images of some vector **v** in V, that is for which we can find a **v** in V such that $\phi(v) = w$.

The kernel and the image space as defined above are clearly subsets of V and W respectively. It remains to be proved that they are indeed subspaces.

Kernel   *image space*

Theorem 5.2

If ϕ is a linear transformation of V into W, the kernel of ϕ is a subspace of V and the image space is a subspace of W.

Proof

Let K be the kernel of ϕ.

Then K is a subset of V.

If $\mathbf{k}_1$ and $\mathbf{k}_2$ are vectors in K then, from the definition of the kernel, $\phi(\mathbf{k}_1) = \phi(\mathbf{k}_2) = \mathbf{O}$.

Using *LT*2 and *LT*3 we obtain:

$$\phi(\mathbf{k}_1 + \mathbf{k}_2) = \phi(\mathbf{k}_1) + \phi(\mathbf{k}_2) = \mathbf{O} + \mathbf{O} = \mathbf{O} \Rightarrow \mathbf{k}_1 + \mathbf{k}_2 \in K,$$

and $$\phi(\alpha \mathbf{k}_1) = \alpha \phi(\mathbf{k}_1) = \alpha \mathbf{O} = \mathbf{O} \text{ for all real } \alpha \Rightarrow \alpha \mathbf{k}_1 \in K.$$

Hence K is a subspace of V. (See Section 1.3.2).

Similarly, if I denotes the image space of ϕ, then for all w_1 and w_2 in I we have:

$$\mathbf{w}_1 = \phi(\mathbf{v}_1) \text{ and } \mathbf{w}_2 = \phi(\mathbf{v}_2) \text{ for some } \mathbf{v}_1, \mathbf{v}_2 \text{ in } V.$$

$$\phi(\mathbf{v}_1 + \mathbf{v}_2) = \phi(\mathbf{v}_1) + \phi(\mathbf{v}_2) = \mathbf{w}_1 + \mathbf{w}_2 \Rightarrow \mathbf{w}_1 + \mathbf{w}_2 \in I$$

and $$\phi(\alpha\mathbf{v}_1) = \alpha\phi(\mathbf{v}_1) = \alpha\mathbf{w}_1 \Rightarrow \alpha\mathbf{w}_1 \in I \text{ for all real } \alpha.$$

Hence I is a subspace of W.

The relationship between the spaces V and W and the subspaces, kernel of ϕ, or Ker ϕ, and the image space, or $\phi(V)$, is illustrated diagrammatically in Figure 5.1 below.

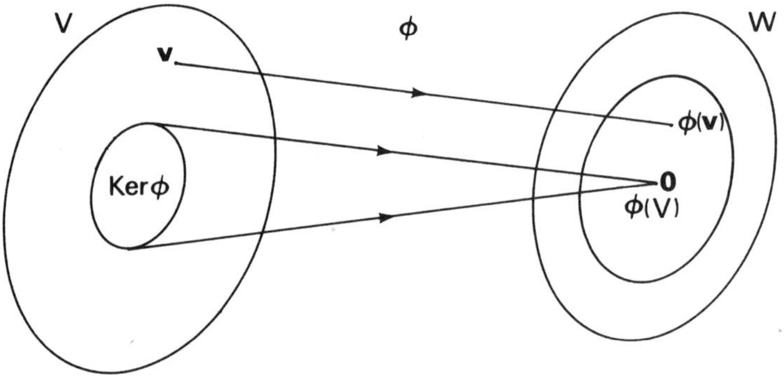

Figure 5.1

5.1.2 Examples of Linear Transformations

The definition given in the previous Section can be illustrated by a few simple examples to show the various forms which linear transformations can take.

Example 5.1

Let V be the space of all real differentiable functions and ϕ be the transformation $\phi(f(x)) = f'(x)$ of V into the space of all real functions. ϕ is a linear transformation because differentiation has the linear properties:

$$\frac{d}{dx}(f(x) + g(x)) = f'(x) + g'(x)$$

and $$\frac{d}{dx}(\alpha f(x)) = \alpha f'(x) \text{ for all real constants } \alpha.$$

Both V and the image space are of infinite dimension, but the kernel of ϕ contains only real constants and is of dimension 1.

Example 5.2

Let V be the space of real integrable functions and define $\phi(f(x)) = \int_a^b f(x)\,dx$, where a and b are fixed real constants. ϕ maps V into the one dimensional space R^1. ϕ is a linear transformation because:

$$\int_a^b (f(x) + g(x))dx = \int_a^b f(x)dx + \int_a^b g(x)dx$$

and $$\int_a^b \alpha f(x)dx = \alpha \int_a^b f(x)dx, \text{ for all real } \alpha.$$

The image space of ϕ is clearly one dimensional, but the kernel of ϕ is of infinite dimensions and contains all real functions $k(x)$ such that $\int_a^b k(x)dx = 0$.

Example 5.3

Let V be the space of all real **Laplace transformable functions.** From the linear properties of integration we can show that the Laplace transformation:

$$\mathcal{L}(f(t)) = \int_0^\infty e^{-st}\, f(t)\, dt = F(s)$$

is, for real s, a linear transformation of V into the space of all real functions.

The kernel of $\mathcal{L}$ is of particular significance and it has been proved that it contains only functions which are zero at almost every positive value of t. From this it is possible to deduce that the Laplace transform is essentially unique and that if two functions have the same Laplace transform they must take the same values at all but a finite number of points in the range $0 \leqslant t < \infty$. (See Theorem 5.3).

Example 5.4

Let V be the space R^3; define ϕ by the equations:

$$\phi(\mathbf{x}) = \begin{pmatrix} x_1 + x_2 - x_3 \\ 2x_1 + 2x_2 - 2x_3 \end{pmatrix}$$

ϕ is then a transformation of R^3 into R^2.

ϕ is a linear transformation because, from the above definition:

$$\phi(\mathbf{x} + \mathbf{y}) = \begin{pmatrix} (x_1 + y_1) + (x_2 + y_2) - (x_3 + y_3) \\ 2(x_1 + y_1) + 2(x_2 + y_2) - 2(x_3 + y_3) \end{pmatrix}$$

$$= \begin{pmatrix} x_1 + x_2 - x_3 \\ 2x_1 + 2x_2 - 2x_3 \end{pmatrix} + \begin{pmatrix} y_1 + y_2 - y_3 \\ 2y_1 + 2y_2 - 2y_3 \end{pmatrix}$$

$$= \phi(\mathbf{x}) + \phi(\mathbf{y})$$

and

$$\phi(\alpha\mathbf{x}) = \begin{pmatrix} \alpha x_1 + \alpha x_2 - \alpha x_3 \\ 2\alpha x_1 + 2\alpha x_2 - 2\alpha x_3 \end{pmatrix} = \alpha \begin{pmatrix} x_1 + x_2 - x_3 \\ 2x_1 + 2x_2 - 2x_3 \end{pmatrix} = \alpha\phi(\mathbf{x}).$$

From the definition we can deduce that any vector in the image space of ϕ must be of the form $\mathbf{y} = \begin{pmatrix} y_1 \\ 2y_1 \end{pmatrix}$, Hence the image space is one-dimensional with basis $(1,2)'$.

By solving the equation $\phi(\mathbf{x}) = \mathbf{O}$ we can find vectors in the kernel. A basis of Ker ϕ is $[(1,-1,0)', (0,1,1)']$.

5.1.3 Further Properties of Linear Transformations

Theorem 5.3

If ϕ is a linear transformation of a real vector space V into W, the most general solution of the equation $\phi(\mathbf{v}) = \mathbf{w}_0$ is $\mathbf{v} = \mathbf{v}_0 + \mathbf{k}$ where $\mathbf{v}_0$ is a particular solution and $\mathbf{k}$ is an arbitrary vector in Ker ϕ.

Proof

If $\mathbf{w}_0$ is not in the image space of ϕ, the equation $\phi(\mathbf{v}) = \mathbf{w}_0$ is, by definition, insoluble.

Assume $\mathbf{w}_0 \in \phi(V)$. There is then some vector $\mathbf{v}_0 \in V$ with $\phi(\mathbf{v}_0) = \mathbf{w}_0$. Let $\mathbf{k}$ be any vector in Ker ϕ.

$$\phi(\mathbf{v}_0 + \mathbf{k}) = \phi(\mathbf{v}_0) + \phi(\mathbf{k}) = \mathbf{w}_0 + \mathbf{O} = \mathbf{w}_0.$$

Hence $\mathbf{v}_0 + \mathbf{k}$ is also a solution of the equation. To show that this is the most general solution, it is necessary to show that every solution can be expressed in this form.

Suppose $\mathbf{v}_1$ is some other solution of $\phi(\mathbf{v}) = \mathbf{w}_0$. Then $\phi(\mathbf{v}_1) = \mathbf{w}_0$ and $\phi(\mathbf{v}_1 - \mathbf{v}_0) = \phi(\mathbf{v}_1) - \phi(\mathbf{v}_0) = \mathbf{w}_0 - \mathbf{w}_0 = \mathbf{0}$. Hence $(\mathbf{v}_1 - \mathbf{v}_0) \in$ Ker ϕ, and thus $\mathbf{v}_1 - \mathbf{v}_0 = \mathbf{k}$, for some $\mathbf{k} \in$ Ker ϕ.

We have now shown that $\mathbf{v}_1$ is also expressible as $\mathbf{v}_1 = \mathbf{v}_0 + \mathbf{k}$.

This Theorem has a number of important consequences which will be exploited in the next Chapter. It shows that the solution of $\phi(\mathbf{v}) = \mathbf{w}_0$ can only be unique in cases where the kernel of ϕ consists of the zero vector alone. Moreover, in cases where the kernel is of finite dimension, it provides a method of generating all the solutions once a particular solution has been found.

Theorem 5.4

If V and W are real vector spaces, the set of all linear transformations of V into W is also a real vector space when addition and multiplication by real scalars are suitably defined.

Proof

Let S be the set of all linear transformations of V into W.

If $\theta \in S$ and $\theta \in S$, define $\theta + \phi$ by the equation:

$$(\theta + \phi)(\mathbf{v}) = \theta(\mathbf{v}) + \phi(\mathbf{v}).$$

Define, for all real scalars α, $\alpha\theta$ by the equation:

$$\alpha\theta(\mathbf{v}) = \alpha(\theta(\mathbf{v})).$$

$\theta + \phi$ and $\alpha\theta$ are clearly transformations of V into W. They are linear transformations because:

$$\begin{aligned}(\theta + \phi)(\mathbf{v}_1 + \mathbf{v}_2) &= \theta(\mathbf{v}_1 + \mathbf{v}_2) + \phi(\mathbf{v}_1 + \mathbf{v}_2)\\ &= \theta(\mathbf{v}_1) + \theta(\mathbf{v}_2) + \phi(\mathbf{v}_1) + \phi(\mathbf{v}_2)\\ &= \theta(\mathbf{v}_1) + \phi(\mathbf{v}_1) + \theta(\mathbf{v}_2) + \phi(\mathbf{v}_2)\\ &= (\theta + \phi)(\mathbf{v}_1) + (\theta + \phi)(\mathbf{v}_2), \text{ for all } \mathbf{v}_1,\mathbf{v}_2 \in V.\end{aligned}$$

In addition, $(\theta + \phi)(\beta\mathbf{v}_1) = \theta(\beta\mathbf{v}_1) + \phi(\beta\mathbf{v}_1)$

$$\begin{aligned}&= \beta\theta(\mathbf{v}_1) + \beta\phi(\mathbf{v}_1)\\ &= \beta(\theta + \phi)(\mathbf{v}_1), \text{ for all real } \beta,\end{aligned}$$

and $\alpha\theta(\mathbf{v}_1 + \mathbf{v}_2) = \alpha(\theta(\mathbf{v}_1 + \mathbf{v}_2)) = \alpha(\theta(\mathbf{v}_1) + \alpha(\theta(\mathbf{v}_2))$

$$= \alpha\theta(\mathbf{v}_1) + \alpha\theta(\mathbf{v}_2), \text{ for all } \mathbf{v}_1, \mathbf{v}_2 \in V,$$

also $\alpha\theta(\beta\mathbf{v}_1) = \alpha(\theta(\beta\mathbf{v}_1)) = \alpha\beta(\theta(\mathbf{v}_1))$

$$= \beta\alpha(\theta(\mathbf{v}_1) = \beta(\alpha\theta(\mathbf{v}_1)), \text{ for all real } \beta.$$

These equations establish the closure of the set S under the operations of addition and multiplication by a scalar. It is left as an exercise for the reader to verify that the remaining axioms of a vector space are also valid in this case (see Section 1.2.1). The zero element in this space of linear transformations is the transformation 0(V), which maps every $\mathbf{v}$ in V onto the zero vector $\mathbf{O}$ in W. For this transformation Ker $0 = V$.

A particularly important example of the space of real linear transformations arises when W is the one-dimensional space R^1. In this case, the set of linear transformations of V into R^1 is called the set of linear functionals on V. Their further study is the subject matter of Functional Analysis.

Theorem 5.5

If U, V and W are real vector spaces and if ϕ is a linear transformation of U into V and θ is a linear transformation of V into W, then these transformations can be combined to define a linear transformation $\theta\phi$ of U into W.

Proof

Define $\theta\phi(\mathbf{u})$ by the equation $\theta\phi(\mathbf{u}) = \theta(\phi(\mathbf{u}))$. For all vectors $\mathbf{u} \in U$ this will define a unique vector $\mathbf{w} \in W$ such that $\mathbf{w} = \theta\phi(\mathbf{u})$. $\theta\phi$ is thus a transformation of U into W.

The linearity of $\theta\phi$ is established by showing that:

$$\begin{aligned}\theta\phi(\mathbf{u}_1 + \mathbf{u}_2) &= \theta(\phi(\mathbf{u}_1 + \mathbf{u}_2))\\ &= \theta(\phi(\mathbf{u}_1) + \phi(\mathbf{u}_2))\\ &= \theta(\phi(\mathbf{u}_1)) + \theta(\phi(\mathbf{u}_2))\\ &= \theta\phi(\mathbf{u}_1) + \theta\phi(\mathbf{u}_2), \text{ for all } \mathbf{u}_1,\mathbf{u}_2 \in U;\end{aligned}$$

and for all scalars α,

$$\begin{aligned}\theta\phi(\alpha\mathbf{u}) &= \theta(\phi(\alpha\mathbf{u}))\\ &= \theta(\alpha\phi(\mathbf{u})) = \alpha\theta(\phi(\mathbf{u})) = \alpha(\theta\phi(\mathbf{u})).\end{aligned}$$

It will be shown in Section 5.2.4 that when all the spaces concerned are of finite dimension, the definition of the product of transformations given here is consistent with the definition of matrix products. The properties of the product of linear transformations can be used to deduce properties of matrix ranks.

5.2 TRANSFORMATIONS OF FINITE DIMENSIONAL VECTOR SPACES

5.2.1 Matrix Representation

If V and W are finite dimensional vector spaces and if ϕ is a linear transformation of V into W, the linear properties of ϕ ensure that the value of $\phi(\mathbf{v})$ for any vector in V can be calculated if the transformation of each basis vector $\mathbf{v}_i$ of V is known. Let $[\mathbf{v}_1,\mathbf{v}_2, \ldots,\mathbf{v}_n]$ be a basis of V, then for any $\mathbf{v} \in V$ we have a unique expression $\mathbf{v} = \sum_{j=1}^{n} x_j\mathbf{v}_j$.

$$\begin{aligned}\phi(\mathbf{v}) &= \phi(\sum_{j=1}^{n} x_j(\mathbf{v}_j)) \qquad (5.1)\\ &= \sum_{j=1}^{n} x_j\phi(\mathbf{v}_j), \text{ using the linearity of } \phi.\end{aligned}$$

$\phi(\mathbf{v})$ is thus completely expressed in terms of the transformations of the basis vectors.

Using the fact that W is also finite dimensional, each of these transformed vectors $\phi(\mathbf{v}_i)$ will in turn be expressible in terms of the chosen basis $[\mathbf{w}_1,\mathbf{w}_2, \ldots, \mathbf{w}_m]$ of W. Suppose the expression is:

$$\phi(\mathbf{v}_j) = \sum_{i=1}^{m} a_{ij}\mathbf{w}_i, \text{ for } j = 1,\ldots,n. \tag{5.2}$$

This defines a matrix A which represents the linear transformation wrt. the two given bases.

Substituting from (5.2) into (5.1) for $\phi(\mathbf{v}_j)$ gives:

to find how any vector in the basis transforms

$$\phi(\mathbf{v}) = \sum_{j=1}^{n} \sum_{i=1}^{m} a_{ij}x_j\mathbf{w}_i$$

shows how we may now use this matrix

$$= \sum_{i=1}^{m} \sum_{j=1}^{n} a_{ij}x_j\mathbf{w}_i,$$

interchanging the order of summations.

$\phi(v) = \sum_{j=1}^{n} x_j \phi(v_j)$ this does not say that these are a basis for the codomain

If $y_i = \sum\limits_{j=1}^{n} a_{ij}x_j$, the expression for $\phi(\mathbf{v})$ simplifies to give $\phi(\mathbf{v}) = \sum\limits_{i=1}^{m} y_i\mathbf{w}_i = \mathbf{w}$.

Relative to the chosen bases $[\mathbf{v}_1,\mathbf{v}_2,\ldots,\mathbf{v}_n]$ of V and $[\mathbf{w}_1,\mathbf{w}_2,\ldots,\mathbf{w}_n]$ of W, $\mathbf{v}$ is represented by the column vector $\mathbf{x} = (x_1x_2,\ldots,x_n)'$ and $\mathbf{w} = \phi(\mathbf{v})$ is represented by $\mathbf{y} = (y_1,y_2,\ldots,y_m)'$. The relationship between $\mathbf{x}$ and $\mathbf{y}$ is given by the equation $\mathbf{y} = A\mathbf{x}$, where A is the $m \times n$ matrix defined by Equations (5.2). This matrix A is said to represent the linear transformation ϕ relative to the chosen bases. Equations (5.2) are equivalent to the statement that the jth column of A gives the components of the image of $\mathbf{v}_j$ in terms of the chosen basis of W.

what I said.

> two matrices that represent the same transformation but wrt to different bases

5.2.2 Change of Basis and Equivalent Matrices

We have shown how a linear transformation ϕ can be represented by a matrix A once the bases of V and W have been chosen. It was shown in Chapter 1 that any set of linearly independent vectors can be taken as a basis of a vector space, and it is reasonable to expect any change in basis of either V or W will lead to a change in the matrix A representing the linear transformation ϕ. The detailed effect of these changes can be analysed by substituting for $\mathbf{x}$ and $\mathbf{y}$ in terms of the new basis vectors.

Suppose the new basis of V is $[\mathbf{v}_1{}^*,\mathbf{v}_2{}^*,\ldots,\mathbf{v}_n{}^*]$ and the new basis of W is $[\mathbf{w}_1{}^*,\mathbf{w}_2{}^*,\ldots,\mathbf{w}_m{}^*]$. Relative to these bases, $\mathbf{v}$ is represented by $\mathbf{x}^*$ and $\mathbf{w} = \phi(\mathbf{v})$ by $\mathbf{y}^*$. It was shown in Section 1.7.2 that there will be a non-singular $n \times n$ matrix P such that $\mathbf{x}^* = P\mathbf{x}$ and a non-singular $m \times m$ matrix Q such that $\mathbf{y}^* = Q\mathbf{y}$.

In terms of the original bases, ϕ is represented by the vector and matrix equation:

$$\mathbf{y} = A\mathbf{x}. \tag{5.3}$$

However $\mathbf{x} = P^{-1}\mathbf{x}^*$ and $\mathbf{y} = Q^{-1}\mathbf{y}^*$; substituting into (5.3) gives:

$$Q^{-1}\mathbf{y}^* = AP^{-1}\mathbf{x}^*.$$

Pre-multiplying by Q gives:

$$\mathbf{y}^* = QAP^{-1}\mathbf{x}^* \tag{5.4}$$

Equation 5.4 expresses ϕ in terms of the new bases, showing that ϕ is now represented by the matrix $B = QAP^{-1}$.

Since any non-singular matrix can represent a change of basis in a vector space, it follows that if $B = QAP^{-1}$ where P and Q are any non-singular matrices, then for some appropriate choice of bases, B represents the same linear transformation as the matrix A. The matrices A and B are said to be **equivalent**. The question which now arises is, what is the simplest form of matrix equivalent to A? In terms of the linear transformation ϕ the question becomes, can ϕ be represented by a matrix of simple form if appropriate basis vectors are chosen? The answer to this question is provided in Theorem 5.6.

Theorem 5.6

If ϕ is a linear transformation of a finite dimensional vector space V into a finite dimensional vector space W, with at least one choice of basis vectors, ϕ is represented by a matrix $B = \left(\begin{array}{c|c} I_r & 0 \\ \hline 0 & 0 \end{array}\right)$, where I_r is an $r \times r$ identity matrix. If A is any $m \times n$ matrix, there are non-singular matrices P and Q such that $QAP^{-1} = B$.

Proof

This Theorem is established by showing how to choose the basis vectors in order to obtain a simple matrix representation of the linear transformation. The kernel of ϕ is a subspace of V; suppose it has dimension k.

Let $[\mathbf{v}_{n-k+1}, \ldots, \mathbf{v}_n]$ by any basis of Ker ϕ. $n-k$ linearly independent vectors can be added to this set to give a basis $[\mathbf{v}_1, \mathbf{v}_2, \ldots, \mathbf{v}_n]$ of V. Any vector in the image space of ϕ is of the form:

$$\mathbf{w} = \phi(\mathbf{v}) = \phi\left(\sum_{i=1}^{n} x_i\mathbf{v}_i\right) = \sum_{i=1}^{n} x_i\phi(\mathbf{v}_i) \tag{5.5}$$

Equation (5.5) shows that the vectors $[\phi(\mathbf{v}_1), \phi(\mathbf{v}_2), \ldots, \phi(\mathbf{v}_n)]$ generate $\phi(V)$.

Amongst these vectors $\phi(\mathbf{v}_{n-k+1}) = \phi(\mathbf{v}_{n-k+2}) = \ldots = \phi(\mathbf{v}_n) = \mathbf{0}$, from the defining property of the kernel. Hence the subset $[\phi(\mathbf{v}_1), \ldots, \phi(\mathbf{v}_{n-k})]$ is also a generating set for $\phi(V)$. To show that this set is in fact a basis of $\phi(V)$, we must show that it is also a linearly independent set.

Suppose, if possible, we can find $(y_1, y_2, \ldots, y_{n-k})$ such that $\sum_{i=1}^{n-k} y_i\phi(\mathbf{v}_i) = \mathbf{0}$. Then, using the linear properties of ϕ,

$$\phi\left(\sum_{i=1}^{n-k} y_i\mathbf{v}_i\right) = \mathbf{0}.$$

Hence the vector $\mathbf{v}_0 = \sum_{i=1}^{n-k} y_i\mathbf{v}_i$ is in Ker ϕ. $\mathbf{v}_0$ is thus linearly dependent upon the basis $[\mathbf{v}_{n-k+1}, \ldots, \mathbf{v}_n]$ of Ker ϕ.

Unless $\mathbf{v}_0 = \mathbf{0}$ this contradicts the linear independence of the basis $[\mathbf{v}_1, \mathbf{v}_2, \ldots, \mathbf{v}_n]$ of V. Thus $\mathbf{v}_0 = \sum_{i=1}^{n-k} y_i\mathbf{v}_i = \mathbf{0}$.

Because $[\mathbf{v}_1, \mathbf{v}_2, \ldots, \mathbf{v}_{n-k}]$ are linearly independent vectors, this is only possible if $y_i = 0$, for $i = 1, \ldots, n-k$. Thus the set $[\phi(\mathbf{v}_1), \ldots, \phi(\mathbf{v}_{n-k})]$ is a set of linearly independent vectors which must form a basis of $\phi(V)$.

Let $\mathbf{w}_i = \phi(\mathbf{v}_i)$ for $i = 1, \ldots, n-k$. A basis $[\mathbf{w}_1, \mathbf{w}_2, \ldots, \mathbf{w}_{n-k}, \ldots, \mathbf{w}_m]$ of W is obtained by adding linearly independent vectors to the set $[\mathbf{w}_1, \ldots, \mathbf{w}_{n-k}]$. Relative to the basis $[\mathbf{v}_1, \ldots, \mathbf{v}_n]$ of V and the basis $[\mathbf{w}_1, \ldots, \mathbf{w}_m]$ of W, ϕ is represented by the matrix:

$$B = \left(\begin{array}{c|c} I_r & 0 \\ \hline 0 & 0 \end{array}\right)$$

where $r = n-k$. (In the matrix representation, each column vector of the matrix represents the image of one basis vector of V in terms of the chosen basis of W.)

If A is any $m \times n$ matrix, it can be used to define a linear transformation ϕ of R^n into R^m relative to a basis $[\mathbf{e}_1, \mathbf{e}_2, \ldots, \mathbf{e}_n]$ of R^n and $[\mathbf{e}_1, \mathbf{e}_2, \ldots, \mathbf{e}_m]$ of R^m. The application of the above result then shows that A is equivalent to a matrix of the form $\left(\begin{array}{c|c} I_r & 0 \\ \hline 0 & 0 \end{array}\right) = QAP^{-1}$.

The non-singular matrices P and Q represent the changes of basis to those specially related to the transformation.

The simple form of matrix equivalent to A is frequently referred to as a **canonical form** of A. The non-singular matrices P and Q which reduce A to its canonical form are not generally uniquely determined. In the proof of Theorem 5.6, any basis of Ker ϕ can be chosen and each such basis will correspond to a different matrix P. Further flexibility is allowed when extending the basis of Ker ϕ to a basis of V and when extending the basis of $\phi(V)$ to a basis of W.

Associate normal form

Rather than considering the related linear transformation, a given matrix A can be reduced to its canonical form by a sequence of elementary row and column operations. All the elementary row operations correspond to pre-multiplying A by Q and all the column operations will correspond to the post-multiplication by P^{-1} (see Section 1.10 and Example 5.6).

Example 5.5

Show that the transformation $\phi(f(x)) = xf'(x) - f(x)$ is a linear transformation of the space P^2 of real polynomials of degree at most 2 into the space P^3 of real polynomials of degree at most 3. Find a matrix A which represents ϕ relative to the bases $[1,x,x^2]$ of P^2 and $[1,x,x^2,x^3]$ of P^3. Find bases such that ϕ is represented by a matrix of canonical form.

Solution

For all $f(x), g(x)$ in P^2,

$$\begin{aligned}\phi(f(x) + g(x)) &= xf'(x) + xg'(x) - (f(x) + g(x))\\ &= (xf'(x) - f(x)) + xg'(x) - g(x)\\ &= \phi(f(x)) + \phi(g(x)).\end{aligned}$$

Also
$$\begin{aligned}\phi(\alpha f(x)) &= x\alpha f'(x) - \alpha f(x) = \alpha(xf'(x) - f(x))\\ &= \alpha\phi(f)\ .\end{aligned}$$

Thus ϕ is a linear transformation which clearly transforms P^2 into P^3.

To find the matrix representing ϕ it is sufficient to consider the effect of ϕ on each of the basis vectors of P^2.

$$\begin{aligned}\phi(1) &= -1,\\ \phi(x) &= x.1 - x = 0,\\ \phi(x^2) &= x.2x - x^2 = x^2.\end{aligned}$$

Expressing each of these in terms of the chosen basis $[1,x,x^2,x^3]$ of P^3 gives the columns of the matrix A which represents ϕ.

$$A = \begin{pmatrix} -1 & 0 & 0\\ 0 & 0 & 0\\ 0 & 0 & 1\\ 0 & 0 & 0\end{pmatrix}.$$

The kernel of ϕ is given by solving the equation:

$$\phi(f(x)) = xf'(x) - f(x) = 0.$$

Ker ϕ is thus of one dimension with basis $[x]$.

Following the method of Theorem 5.6, we extend this set to form a basis of P^2. One such basis is $[x^2,1,x]$.

The first two elements in the chosen basis of P^3 must now be $\phi(x^2) = x^2$ and $\phi(1) = -1$; and linearly independent polynomials can be added to give a basis of P^3. One such basis is $[x^2,-1,x,x^3]$. Relative to these newly chosen bases ϕ is represented by

$$B = \begin{pmatrix} 1 & 0 & 0 \\ 0 & 1 & 0 \\ 0 & 0 & 0 \\ 0 & 0 & 0 \end{pmatrix}.$$

Example 5.6

$A = \begin{pmatrix} 1 & 3 & 4 \\ 2 & 1 & 5 \end{pmatrix}$. Reduce A to its equivalent canonical form by a sequence of elementary row and column operations. Hence find matrices Q and P^{-1} such that QAP^{-1} is in canonical form.

Solution

The reduction can be carried out in two stages, first reducing A to echelon form by a sequence of row operations and then applying column operations to obtain the final canonical form.

$$A = \begin{pmatrix} 1 & 3 & 4 \\ 2 & 1 & 5 \end{pmatrix},$$

$$R_2-2R_1 \quad \begin{pmatrix} 1 & 3 & 4 \\ 0 & -5 & -3 \end{pmatrix}$$

$$\begin{matrix} & C_2-3C_1 & C_3-4C_1 \end{matrix}$$
$$\begin{pmatrix} 1 & 0 & 0 \\ 0 & -5 & -3 \end{pmatrix}$$

$$\begin{matrix} & -1/5\ C_2 & C_3-3/5\ C_2 \end{matrix}$$
$$\begin{pmatrix} 1 & 0 & 0 \\ 0 & 1 & 0 \end{pmatrix} = B.$$

Applying the same sequence of row and column operations in the same order to the matrices I_2 and I_3 respectively gives:

$$Q = \begin{pmatrix} 1 & 0 \\ -2 & 1 \end{pmatrix} \quad \text{and} \quad P^{-1} = \begin{pmatrix} 1 & 3/5 & -11/5 \\ 0 & -1/5 & -3/5 \\ 0 & 0 & 1 \end{pmatrix}.$$

A check shows that $QAP^{-1} = B$.

5.2.3 The Rank of a Linear Transformation

Definitions

If ϕ is a linear transformation of a finite dimensional vector space V into a vector space W, the **rank of** ϕ is the dimension of the image space $\phi(V)$.

The **nullity of** ϕ is defined to be the dimension of the kernel, Ker ϕ.

Theorem 5.7

If ϕ is a linear transformation of an n-dimensional vector space V into an m-dimensional vector space W, then

$$\begin{aligned} &\text{rank } \phi \leqslant \text{minimum } (m,n), \\ &\text{rank } \phi + \text{nullity } \phi = n. \end{aligned}$$

Proof

Let $[\mathbf{v}_1,\mathbf{v}_2, \ldots,\mathbf{v}_n]$ be any basis of V. Rank $\phi =$ dimension $\phi(V)$, but $\phi(V)$ is generated by the set $[\phi(\mathbf{v}_1),\phi(\mathbf{v}_2), \ldots,\phi(\mathbf{v}_n)]$, hence rank $\phi \leqslant n$. But $\phi(V)$ is a subspace of W, hence rank $\phi \leqslant$ dimension $W = m$. In proving Theorem 5.6 it was shown that if dimension (Ker ϕ) $= k$, then a basis of $\phi(V)$ contains precisely $n-k$ vectors. Hence if $r =$ rank ϕ we have $r = n-k$ or $r+k = n$.

If ϕ is represented by a matrix A, the rank r of ϕ is identical to the dimension r of the matrix I_r which forms part of the canonical form of A. We shall now show that the rank of ϕ is the same as the column rank of the matrix A. In Chapter 1, the column rank of a matrix was defined to be the dimension of the subspace generated by the column vectors of A. If A represents ϕ relative to a basis $[\mathbf{v}_1,\mathbf{v}_2, \ldots,\mathbf{v}_n]$ of V, then the column vectors of A correspond to $[\phi(\mathbf{v}_1), \phi(\mathbf{v}_2), \ldots,\phi(\mathbf{v}_n)]$. However, these vectors are precisely the generators of $\phi(V)$. Hence the column space of A and the image space of ϕ must have the same dimension, or rank $\phi =$ column rank A.

5.2.4 Products of Transformations and of Matrices

The product of two linear transformations was defined in Section 5.1.3. If all spaces concerned are of finite dimension, it is worthwhile considering the consequences of this definition in more detail. We shall show that the product of transformations corresponds to the product of the matrices representing them.

Suppose U, V and W are real vector spaces of dimension ℓ, m and n respectively. Let ϕ be a linear transformation of U into V and θ be a linear transformation of V into W. Then, as shown in Theorem 5.5, $\theta\phi$ is a linear transformation of U into W.

Let the chosen bases be $[\mathbf{u}_1,\mathbf{u}_2,\ldots,\mathbf{u}_\ell]$, $[\mathbf{v}_1,\mathbf{v}_2,\ldots,\mathbf{v}_m]$ and $[\mathbf{w}_1,\mathbf{w}_2,\ldots,\mathbf{w}_n]$ respectively and suppose that relative to these bases ϕ is represented by a matrix B, θ by a matrix A and $\theta\phi$ by a matrix C. From Section 5.2.1, the elements of these matrices are such that:

$$\phi(\mathbf{u}_j) = \sum_{k=1}^{m} b_{kj}\mathbf{v}_k, \tag{5.6}$$

$$\theta(\mathbf{v}_k) = \sum_{i=1}^{n} a_{ik}\mathbf{w}_i \tag{5.7}$$

and

$$\theta\phi(\mathbf{u}_j) = \sum_{i=1}^{n} c_{ij}\mathbf{w}_i. \tag{5.8}$$

However

$$\begin{aligned}\theta\phi(\mathbf{u}_j) &= \theta(\phi(\mathbf{u}_j))\\ &= \theta(\sum_{k=1}^{m} b_{kj}\mathbf{v}_k), \text{ using 5.6,}\\ &= \sum_{k=1}^{m} b_{kj}\theta(\mathbf{v}_k)\\ &= \sum_{k=1}^{m}\sum_{i=1}^{n} b_{kj}a_{ik}\mathbf{w}_i.\end{aligned}$$

Re-arranging and changing the order of the summation gives:

$$\theta\phi(\mathbf{u}_j) = \sum_{i=1}^{n}\sum_{k=1}^{m} a_{ik}b_{kj}\mathbf{w}_i. \tag{5.9}$$

Equations (5.8) and (5.9) are both expressions for $\theta\phi(\mathbf{u}_j)$ in terms of the basis $[\mathbf{w}_1,\mathbf{w}_2,\ldots,\mathbf{w}_\ell]$. Because such an expression is unique we can equate coefficients to obtain:

$$c_{ij} = \sum_{k=1}^{m} a_{ik}b_{kj}, \tag{5.10}$$

for $i = 1,\ldots,n; j = 1,\ldots,n$. If Equation (5.10) is compared with the usual definition of a matrix product, it will be seen that $\theta\phi$ is represented by the $n \times l$ matrix $C = AB$.

Theorem 5.8

If θ is a linear transformation of an m dimensional vector space V into W and if ϕ is a linear transformation of a real vector space U of dimension ℓ into V, then rank $(\theta\phi) \leqslant$ minimum (rank θ, rank ϕ).

Proof

Rank $(\theta\phi)$ = dimension of image space of $\theta\phi$. Suppose $\mathbf{w} \in \theta\phi(U)$, then $\mathbf{w} = \theta(\phi(\mathbf{u}))$ for some $\mathbf{u} \in U$. However $\phi(\mathbf{u}) = \mathbf{v} \in V$, thus $\mathbf{w} = \theta(\mathbf{v})$. Hence $\mathbf{w} \in \theta(V)$, showing that $\theta\phi(U)$ is a subspace of $\theta(V)$ and hence rank $\theta\phi \leqslant$ rank θ.

Also the equation $\mathbf{w} = \theta(\phi(U))$ shows that each vector in $\theta\phi(U)$ is the image under θ of some vector in the image space of ϕ. If we now consider θ as a linear transformation of the image space $\phi(U)$ into the image space of $\theta\phi(U)$, the application of Theorem 5.7 shows that rank $\theta\phi \leqslant$ rank ϕ = dimension of image space of ϕ. Figure 5.2 illustrates the proof of this Theorem by showing the relationships between the image spaces.

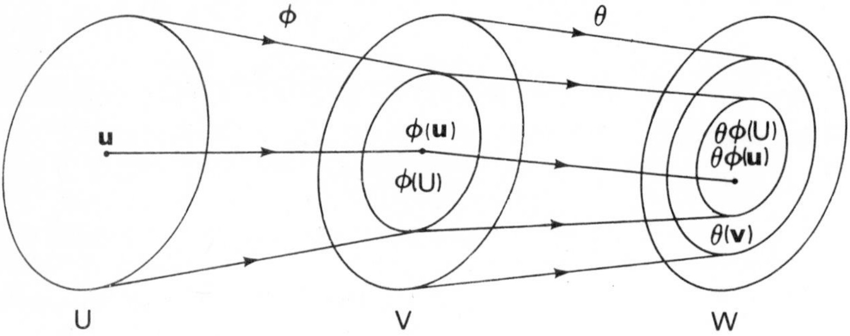

Fig. 5.2

Corollary 1

If A is an $n \times m$ matrix and if B is an $m \times l$ matrix then:

$$\text{column rank }(AB) \leqslant \min(\text{column rank } A, \text{column rank } B).$$

Proof

If, in Theorem 5.8, θ is represented by matrix A and ϕ is represented by matrix B, since for each of these matrices the column rank is equal to the rank of the corresponding linear transformation, the simple restatement of the result of this Theorem gives immediately:

$$\text{column rank }(AB) \leqslant \min(\text{column rank } A, \text{column rank } B).$$

Corollary 2

The column rank of a matrix is unaltered by pre- or post-multiplying by a non-singular matrix.

Proof

Suppose A is an $m \times n$ matrix, P a non-singular $m \times m$ matrix and Q a non-singular $n \times n$ matrix. Since $A = (P^{-1}P)A = P^{-1}(PA)$, the application of Corollary 1 shows that:

$$\text{column rank } A \leqslant \text{column rank } (PA).$$

However, column rank $PA \leqslant$ column rank A, by direct application of Corollary 1. Thus column rank $A \leqslant$ column rank $PA \leqslant$ column rank A, showing that column rank $PA =$ column rank A.

Similarly, since $A = AI = (AQ)Q^{-1}$, column rank $A =$ column rank AQ.

Corollary 3

Row rank $A =$ column rank A, for any $m \times n$ matrix A.

Proof

Using the result of Theorem 5.6, there are non-singular matrices P and Q such that $B = QAP^{-1}$ is in canonical form, $B = \left(\begin{array}{c|c} I_r & 0 \\ \hline 0 & 0 \end{array}\right)$.

From Corollary 2, B has the same column rank as A, and this rank is clearly r.

Transposing the above equation gives $B' = P^{-1'} A'Q'$, and by the same argument B' and A' will have the same column rank. However column rank A' $=$ row rank A, and clearly B has precisely r linearly independent rows and r linearly independent columns. Thus finally,

$$\text{row rank } A = \text{row rank } B = \text{column rank } B = \text{column rank } A.$$

It has already been shown that the column rank of matrix A is equal to the rank of the corresponding linear transformation ϕ. Hence we can refer unambiguously to the rank of a matrix in spite of the different definitions or row rank, column rank and rank of a linear transformation.

Theorem 5.8. gives an upper bound for the rank of a product of linear transformations by considering the image space of the combined transformation. A similar argument can be applied to the kernels of the various transformation in order to define a lower bound for the rank of a product of transformations (see Problem 5.21).

5.3 LINEAR TRANSFORMATIONS OF A VECTOR SPACE INTO ITSELF

A class of linear transformations of particular practical significance are those in which the vector space V is transformed into itself rather than into some other space. If V is a space of finite dimension, transformations of this type are represented by square matrices. Much of the earlier theory is still applicable to transformations of this type but because only one change of basis is permissible, the simplest canonical form will rarely be as simple as that obtained in Section 5.2.2.

5.3.1 Eigenvalues and Eigenvectors

If ϕ is a linear transformation of V into itself, it is possible to compare any vector $\mathbf{v}$ with its image $\phi(\mathbf{v})$. Generally there will be no obvious similarity between $\mathbf{v}$ and $\phi(\mathbf{v})$ but for some special values of $\mathbf{v}$ it may be unaltered by the transformation ϕ or, at worst, transformed into a simple multiple of itself.

Definition

If ϕ is a linear transformation of a vector space V into itself and if $\mathbf{v}$ is a non-zero vector such that $\phi(\mathbf{v}) = \lambda\mathbf{v}$ for some scalar constant λ, then $\mathbf{v}$ is called a proper **eigenvector** of ϕ and λ is called the **eigenvalue** associated with ϕ.

As a simple example, if ϕ is the linear transformation $\phi(f(x)) = f'(x)$ of the space of real differentiable functions into itself, then $e^{\alpha x}$ is an eigenvector of ϕ with associated eigenvalue α. This example shows that eigenvalues and eigenvectors can occur in infinite dimensional vector spaces although many of the common applications of the theory are found only in finite dimensional vector spaces and are associated with the properties of square matrices. Before considering the important finite dimensional case in more detail, a number of general properties of eigenvalues and eigenvectors can be established.

Theorem 5.9

If ϕ is a linear transformation of V into itself and if λ is a particular eigenvalue of ϕ, the set of all vectors $\mathbf{v}$ such that $\phi(\mathbf{v}) = \lambda\mathbf{v}$ is a subspace of V.

Proof

The definition given made the distinction between proper eigenvectors which are always non-zero, and the vector $\mathbf{O}$, which is in a sense an eigenvector for every value of λ because $\phi(\mathbf{O}) = \mathbf{O} = \lambda\mathbf{O}$. For the purposes of this theorem, $\mathbf{O}$, is regarded as an eigenvector because every subspace must contain the zero vector.

Let S denote the set of all $\mathbf{v}$ in V such that $\phi(\mathbf{v}) = \lambda\mathbf{v}$. If $\mathbf{v}_1 \in S$ and $\mathbf{v}_2 \in S$ then,

$$\phi(\mathbf{v}_1 + \mathbf{v}_2) = \phi(\mathbf{v}_1) + \phi(\mathbf{v}_2) = \lambda\mathbf{v}_1 + \lambda\mathbf{v}_2 = \lambda(\mathbf{v}_1 + \mathbf{v}_2)$$

Hence $\mathbf{v}_1 + \mathbf{v}_2 \in S$.

Also, for any constant k,

$$\phi(k\mathbf{v}_1) = k\phi(\mathbf{v}_1) = k\lambda\mathbf{v}_1 = \lambda(k\mathbf{v}_1),$$

showing that $k\mathbf{v}_1 \in S$.

S is thus seen to be a subspace of V because it satisfies the axioms.

In many cases the subspaces associated with a particular eigenvalue are one dimensional and are generated by a single eigenvector $\mathbf{v}$, all eigenvectors being multiples of $\mathbf{v}$. However there are cases in which an eigenvalue is associated with a multi-dimensional subspace.

Theorem 5.10

If ϕ is a linear transformation of a vector space V into itself and $\lambda_1, \lambda_2, \ldots, \lambda_n$ are distinct eigenvalues of ϕ, then the corresponding proper eigenvectors $\mathbf{v}_1, \mathbf{v}_2, \ldots, \mathbf{v}_n$ are linearly independent.

Proof

Suppose, if possible, that $[\mathbf{v}_1, \mathbf{v}_2, \ldots, \mathbf{v}_n]$ is a linearly dependent set. Let k, $1 \leqslant k \leqslant n$, be the least integer such that $[\mathbf{v}_1, \mathbf{v}_2, \ldots, \mathbf{v}_k]$ is a linearly dependent set. Then, for some $\alpha_1, \alpha_2, \ldots, \alpha_k$, with $\alpha_k \neq 0$, we have:

$$\sum_{i=1}^{k} \alpha_i \mathbf{v}_i = \mathbf{0}.$$

Hence
$$\mathbf{v}_k = - \sum_{i=1}^{k-1} \frac{\alpha_i}{\alpha_k} \mathbf{v}_i. \qquad (5.11)$$

Transforming Equation 5.11 gives
$$= -\frac{1}{\alpha_k}\left(\alpha_1 \mathbf{v}_1 \ldots \alpha_{k-1} \mathbf{v}_{k-1}\right)$$

$$\phi(\mathbf{v}_k) = - \sum_{i=1}^{k-1} \frac{\alpha_i}{\alpha_k} \phi(\mathbf{v}_i). \qquad = \lambda_i \mathbf{v}_i$$

Hence
$$\lambda_k \mathbf{v}_k = - \sum_{i=1}^{k-1} \frac{\alpha_i}{\alpha_k} \lambda_i \mathbf{v}_i. \qquad (5.12)$$

Multiplying Equation (5.11) by λ_k gives:

$$\lambda_k \mathbf{v}_k = - \sum_{i=1}^{k-1} \frac{\alpha_i}{\alpha_k} \lambda_k \mathbf{v}_i. \qquad (5.13)$$

The subtraction of Equation (5.12) from (5.13) gives:

$$\sum_{i=1}^{k-1} \frac{\alpha_i}{\alpha_k} (\lambda_i - \lambda_k)\mathbf{v}_i = \mathbf{O}. \tag{5.14}$$

Equation (5.14) contradicts the assumption that $[\mathbf{v}_1, \mathbf{v}_2, \ldots, \mathbf{v}_{k-1}]$ are linearly independent vectors because $\lambda_i - \lambda_k \neq 0$ for any value of i, and at least one of the values of α_i is also non-zero.

This contradiction shows that the initial assumption about the linear dependence of $[\mathbf{v}_1, \ldots, \mathbf{v}_n]$ was false. Hence the eigenvectors corresponding to distinct eigenvalues form a linearly independent set.

Corollary

If V is a vector space of dimension n, then any linear transformation ϕ of V into itself has at most n distinct eigenvalues.

Proof

This corollary follows immediately by combining the result of the Theorem with the fact that in a space of dimension n, no set of linearly independent vectors can contain more than n vectors. In the next Section an alternative proof of this result will be given together with a method of finding the eigenvalues of a linear transformation of a finite dimensional vector space into itself.

5.3.2 The Matrix Eigenvalue Problem

If ϕ is a linear transformation of an n-dimensional vector space V into itself, then after choosing a basis of V, ϕ is represented by an $n \times n$ matrix A such that if $\mathbf{v}$ is represented by a column vector $\mathbf{x}$ relative to the chosen basis, $\phi(\mathbf{v})$ is represented by $\phi(\mathbf{v}) = A\mathbf{x}$. With this representation, the defining equation for eigenvalues and eigenvectors, $\phi(\mathbf{v}) = \lambda\mathbf{v}$ becomes:

$$A\mathbf{x} = \lambda\mathbf{x}. \tag{5.15}$$

Equation (5.15) is called the matrix eigenvalue equation; it can be re-written as:

$$A\mathbf{x} = \lambda I\mathbf{x},$$

where I is the $n \times n$ identity matrix, or

$$(A - \lambda I)\mathbf{x} = \mathbf{O}. \tag{5.16}$$

Since $\mathbf{x}$ must be non-zero to be a proper eigenvector of the matrix A, Equation (5.16) shows clearly that for λ to be an eigenvalue of A, the matrix $(A - \lambda I)$

must be singular. A sufficient condition for this is

$$|(A - \lambda I)| = 0. \tag{5.17}$$

The determinantal Equation (5.17) is called the **Characteristic Equation** of A. When this is expanded it is a polynomial equation of degree n in λ. If A is a real matrix, the characteristic equation will have real coefficients and in general it will have precisely n roots but, as with all real polynomials, these roots need not all be distinct and some may be complex. In principle the characteristic equation can be solved to determine the eigenvalues $\lambda_1, \lambda_2, \ldots, \lambda_n$ of A, and for each of these eigenvalues Equation (5.16) can then be solved to determine the corresponding eigenvector. The philosophical difficulty with complex eigenvectors is overcome by considering A as a matrix representing a linear transformation of a complex vector space C^n into itself, the eigenvector corresponding to a complex eigenvalue will have some complex components.

A basic property of real polynomials is that any complex roots will appear in complex conjugate pairs. Hence if A has a complex eigenvalue λ it will also have an eigenvalue $\bar{\lambda}$. If $\mathbf{v} = \mathbf{u} + i\mathbf{v}$, where $\mathbf{u}$ and $\mathbf{v}$ are real vectors, is the eigenvector corresponding to λ, then:

$$A(\mathbf{u} + i\mathbf{v}) = \lambda(\mathbf{u} + i\mathbf{v}).$$

Taking the conjugate of this equation, because A is real, we obtain:

$$A(\mathbf{u} - i\mathbf{v}) = \bar{\lambda}(\mathbf{u} - i\mathbf{v}).$$

From this it is seen that an eigenvector corresponding to $\bar{\lambda}$ is the conjugate of the eigenvector corresponding to λ.

The coefficients of the characteristic equation are all expressible in terms of the individual elements of A. If n is large, some of these expressions are extremely cumbersome, but it can be quickly seen that the coefficient of λ^n is $(-1)^n$, and the coefficient of $\lambda^{(n-1)}$ is $(-1)^{n-1}(a_{11} + a_{22} + \ldots + a_{nn})$. Also the substitution of $\lambda = 0$ into (5.17) shows that the constant term in the characteristic polynomial is $|A|$. The coefficients of any polynomial can be simply related to the roots (see, for example, [Goult *et al*, *Applicable Mathematics,* Chapter 6]); using these relationships if A has eigenvalues $\lambda_1, \lambda_2, \ldots, \lambda_n$ then:

$$\lambda_1 + \lambda_2 + \ldots + \lambda_n = a_{11} + a_{22} + \ldots + a_{nn} = \text{trace } A$$

and

$$\lambda_1\lambda_2 \ldots \lambda_n = |A|.$$

Other, more complicated, relations can be obtained but the first of these results provides a simple check on the eigenvalues when they have all been evaluated.

Example 5.6

Find the eigenvalues and corresponding eigenvectors of the following matrices.

$$A = \begin{pmatrix} 1 & -3 \\ 1 & -2 \end{pmatrix}, \quad B = \begin{pmatrix} 1 & 1 & -2 \\ -1 & 2 & 1 \\ 0 & 1 & -1 \end{pmatrix}.$$

Solution

The characteristic equation of A is:

$$\begin{vmatrix} 1-\lambda & -3 \\ 1 & -2-\lambda \end{vmatrix} = 0.$$

Expanding this directly gives

$$\lambda^2 + \lambda + 1 = 0.$$

The roots of this quadratic equation are

$$\lambda_1 = -\tfrac{1}{2} + i\sqrt{3}/2 \text{ and } \lambda_2 = -\tfrac{1}{2} - i\sqrt{3}/2.$$

The eigenvector $\mathbf{v}_1$ corresponding to λ_1 is given by solving the equation $(A - \lambda_1 I)\mathbf{v}_1 = \mathbf{0}$. The equation is:

$$\begin{pmatrix} 3/2 - i\sqrt{3}/2, & -3 \\ 1 & , -3/2 - i\sqrt{3}/2 \end{pmatrix} \mathbf{v}_1 = \mathbf{0}.$$

One solution of this equation is $\mathbf{v}_1 = (3/2 + i\sqrt{3}/2, 1)'$. Using the conjugate property, one value of $\mathbf{v}_2$ is $\mathbf{v}_2 = (3/2 - i\sqrt{3}/2, 1)'$.

Because any scalar multiple of an eigenvector is also an eigenvector there is no necessity for $\mathbf{v}_1$ and $\mathbf{v}_2$ to be conjugate since either of them could be multiplied by an arbitrary complex number to invalidate this property.

The characteristic polynomial of B is:

$$\begin{vmatrix} 1-\lambda & 1 & -2 \\ -1 & 2-\lambda & 1 \\ 0 & 1 & -1-\lambda \end{vmatrix} = 0.$$

Before expanding this determinant it is worthwhile using the properties of a determinant to obtain one of the factors. Subtracting row 3 from row 1 gives:

$$\begin{vmatrix} 1-\lambda & 0 & -1+\lambda \\ -1 & 2-\lambda & 1 \\ 0 & 1 & -1-\lambda \end{vmatrix} = 0$$

$$= (1-\lambda)\begin{vmatrix} 1 & 0 & -1 \\ -1 & 2-\lambda & 1 \\ 0 & 1 & -1-\lambda \end{vmatrix}.$$

Adding column 1 to column 3 and expanding the determinant by the first row gives, finally,

$$(1-\lambda)(2-\lambda)(-1-\lambda) = 0.$$

The eigenvalues are thus $\lambda_1 = 1$, $\lambda_2 = 2$, $\lambda_3 = -1$. A check shows that $\lambda_1 + \lambda_2 + \lambda_3 = \text{trace } B$. In fact in this case the eigenvalues coincide with the diagonal elements of the matrix, which is not usually the case. The eigenvectors are obtained by solving directly the equation $(A - \lambda_i I)\mathbf{v}_i = \mathbf{O}$.

$\mathbf{v}_1$ is obtained from $\begin{pmatrix} 0 & 1 & -2 \\ -1 & 1 & 1 \\ 0 & 1 & -2 \end{pmatrix} \mathbf{v}_1 = \mathbf{O}$.

In this case the coefficient matrix is obviously singular. From the first two rows of this matrix a simple solution is $\mathbf{v}_1 = (3,2,1)'$. $\mathbf{v}_2$ and $\mathbf{v}_3$ can be obtained in a similar way. Solutions are $\mathbf{v}_2 = (1,3,1)'$, $\mathbf{v}_3 = (1,0,1)'$.

In Example 5.6 the matrices involved were comparatively small and consequently it was not difficult to find an explicit expression for the characteristic polynomial and then to find the eigenvalues exactly. In the case of larger matrices, the evaluation of the coefficients of the characteristic polynomial is difficult and even after achieving this the problem of evaluating the roots of a polynomial of high degree is far from easy. The polynomials of degree greater than four, the exact determination of the roots is not generally possible and some method of numerical approximation has to be used. After finding the approximate eigenvalues, the eigenvector determination is complicated by the fact that the coefficient matrix $A - \lambda I$ will not be singular if λ is only an approximation to an eigenvalue. Because of the practical importance of the problem, a number of efficient methods have been developed for the computation of approximate eigenvalues and eigenvectors of matrices but these methods never rely on the direct evaluation of the characteristic polynomial. [See Wilkinson 1965 or Goult, Hoskins, Milner, Pratt 1974].

Theorem 5.11

If A is any $n \times n$ matrix and if P is any non-singular $n \times n$ matrix, then the matrices A and $B = PAP^{-1}$ have the same eigenvalues. If $\mathbf{x}$ is an eigenvector of A corresponding to λ then $P\mathbf{x}$ is an eigenvector of B.

Proof

The characteristic polynomial of B is $|B - \lambda I| = 0$ or $|PAP^{-1} - \lambda PIP^{-1}| = 0$. Hence $|P|\,|A - \lambda I|\,|P^{-1}| = 0$.

However $|P^{-1}| = |P|^{-1}$, thus $|A - \lambda I| = 0$, showing that A and B have the same characteristic polynomial and must therefore have the same eigenvalues.

If $\mathbf{x}$ is an eigenvector of A corresponding to λ then,

$$A\mathbf{x} = \lambda\mathbf{x}$$

Multiplying the vector $\mathbf{y} = P\mathbf{x}$ by B gives:

$$B\mathbf{y} = (PAP^{-1})P\mathbf{x} = PA\mathbf{x} = P(\lambda\mathbf{x}) = \lambda P\mathbf{x} = \lambda\mathbf{y}.$$

$P\mathbf{x}$ is thus seen to be an eigenvector of B corresponding to λ.

This Theorem has a simple interpretation in terms of the linear transformation ϕ represented by the matrix A relative to the chosen basis. If a new basis is chosen, such that any vector $\mathbf{v}$ represented by $\mathbf{x}$ relative to the original basis is represented by $\mathbf{y} = P\mathbf{x}$ relative to the new basis, then the analysis of Section 5.2.2 shows that ϕ is represented by PAP^{-1} relative to the new basis. This shows that the matrices A and B in Theorem 5.11 are simply two matrices representing the same linear transformation relative to different bases. The conclusions in the Theorem are then obvious.

The matrices A and PAP^{-1} are said to be **similar matrices**; Theorem 5.11 can then be replaced by the statement that similar matrices have the same eigenvalues and simply related eigenvectors. Many of the numerical algorithms for eigenvalue calculation replace A by a sequence of similar matrices with the ultimate aim of producing a matrix similar to A but of a simpler form from which the eigenvalues can be found. A question of more than theoretical significance is that of specifying for a given matrix A the simplest possible matrix similar to A. A partial answer to this question is given by Theorem 5.12.

Theorem 5.11 shows that similar matrices have the same eigenvalues. The converse of this result is not generally true because it will be shown in Section 5.3.3 that examples can be found of matrices with the same eigenvalues which are not similar.

Theorem 5.12

If A is an $n \times n$ matrix with n linearly independent eigenvectors $[\mathbf{v}_1,\mathbf{v}_2,\ldots,\mathbf{v}_n]$, then A is similar to a diagonal matrix whose elements are $\lambda_1,\lambda_2,\ldots,\lambda_n$.

Proof

This Theorem can be proved either by using the properties of a linear transformation, or by matrix algebra. Both proofs are given below because the former is simple, but the second proof provides a useful computational method of reducing a matrix to a similar diagonal form which can be applied elsewhere.

Suppose A represents a linear transformation σ of V into itself. Since the eigenvectors are linearly independent, they form a possible basis of the n-dimensional space V.

Referred to basis $(\mathbf{v}_1,\mathbf{v}_2,\ldots,\mathbf{v}_n)$, the matrix B which represents σ has as its ith column vector a vector corresponding to $\sigma(\mathbf{v}_i) = \lambda_i\mathbf{v}_i$.

B is thus the matrix

$$\begin{pmatrix} \lambda_1 & 0 & \ldots & \ldots 0 \\ 0 & \lambda_2 & 0 & \ldots 0 \\ \vdots & & & \\ 0 & \ldots\ldots & \ldots & \ldots\lambda_n \end{pmatrix} = \text{diag}\,(\lambda_1,\lambda_2,\ldots,\lambda_n).$$

A is thus similar to the diagonal matrix B because they represent the same linear transformation.

Alternatively, let P be the matrix whose ith column vector is $\mathbf{v}_i$, $P = (\mathbf{v}_1, \mathbf{v}_2, \ldots, \mathbf{v}_n)$. P is sometimes called the **modal matrix** of A. Because the eigenvectors are linearly independent, the matrix P is non-singular and has an inverse P^{-1}.

Let $B = P^{-1}AP$. Then,

$$\begin{aligned} B &= P^{-1}A(\mathbf{v}_1,\mathbf{v}_2,\ldots,\mathbf{v}_n) \\ &= P^{-1}(A\mathbf{v}_1,A\mathbf{v}_2,\ldots,A\mathbf{v}_n), \text{ from the definition of a matrix product,} \\ &= P^{-1}(\lambda_1\mathbf{v}_1,\lambda_2\mathbf{v}_2,\ldots,\lambda_n\mathbf{v}_n). \end{aligned}$$

But the matrix $(\lambda_1\mathbf{v}_1,\lambda_2\mathbf{v}_2,\ldots,\lambda_n\mathbf{v}_n)$ corresponds to the matrix obtained from P by performing the column operations of multiplying the ith column by λ_i for $i = 1,\ldots,n$.

Hence $B = P^{-1}(\mathbf{v}_1,\mathbf{v}_2,\ldots,\mathbf{v}_n)\text{diag}(\lambda_1,\lambda_2,\ldots,\lambda_n)$, since this diagonal matrix is the result of performing the same column operations on I.

Thus $B = P^{-1}P\text{diag}(\lambda_1, \ldots, \lambda_n) = \text{diag}(\lambda_1, \ldots, \lambda_n)$.

If Q is used to denote P^{-1} we finally obtain $\text{diag}(\lambda_1, \ldots, \lambda_n) = B = P^{-1}AP = QAQ^{-1}$, showing that A is similar to a diagonal matrix.

The assumptions necessary to prove this Theorem were that the matrix should possess a full set of linearly independent eigenvectors. It was not necessary to assume any particular properties of the eigenvalues. If, however, a matrix A has all its eigenvalues distinct. Theorems 5.10 and 5.12 can be combined to show that such a matrix is similar to a diagonal matrix.

5.3.3 Matrices with Multiple Eigenvalues

The fundamental theorem of algebra ensures that any polynomial of degree n has precisely n roots. Hence any $n \times n$ matrix will have precisely n eigenvalues. Unfortunately the fundamental theorem does not guarantee that all the eigenvalues will be distinct.

If λ_i is an eigenvalue of A then $(\lambda - \lambda_i)$ is a factor of the characteristic polynomial $|A - \lambda I|$. If $(\lambda - \lambda_i)^m$ is the greatest power of this factor which occurs in the characteristic polynomial, then λ_i is said to be an eigenvalue of A of algebraic multiplicity m. The number of linearly independent eigenvectors corresponding to λ_i is called the **geometric multiplicity** of λ_i. As will be seen in Example 5.7, this is not necessarily the same as the algebraic multiplicity. If the matrix $A - \lambda_i I$ has rank $n - \ell$, the geometric multiplicity of λ_i is ℓ.

Example 5.7

The matrices $A = \begin{pmatrix} 1 & -3 & 3 \\ 3 & -5 & 3 \\ 6 & -6 & 4 \end{pmatrix}$ and $B = \begin{pmatrix} -3 & 1 & -1 \\ -7 & 5 & -1 \\ -6 & 6 & -2 \end{pmatrix}$ both have eigenvalues $-2, -2, 4$. Find the corresponding eigenvectors.

similar matrices have the same eigenvalues but the converse is not necessarily true. In this case A & B are not similar

Solution

For $\lambda_1 = \lambda_2 = -2$ the eigenvectors of A are given by solving:

$$(A + 2I)\mathbf{x} = \begin{pmatrix} 3 & -3 & 3 \\ 3 & -3 & 3 \\ 6 & -6 & 6 \end{pmatrix} \mathbf{x} = \mathbf{0}.$$

The coefficient matrix has rank 1 showing that $\lambda = -2$ is a root of geometric multiplicity 2.

Two linearly independent eigenvectors are $\mathbf{v}_1 = (0,1,1)'$ and $\mathbf{v}_2 = (1,1,0)'$. Any vector in the two-dimensional subspace generated by $[\mathbf{v}_1, \mathbf{v}_2]$ is an eigenvector for $\lambda = -2$. For $\lambda_3 = 4$, the eigenvector is given by solving:

$$(A - 4I)\mathbf{v}_3 = \mathbf{0} = \begin{pmatrix} -3 & -3 & 3 \\ 3 & -9 & 3 \\ 6 & -6 & 0 \end{pmatrix} \mathbf{v}_3 .$$

One such eigenvector is $\mathbf{v}_3 = (1,1,2)'$.

For $\lambda_1 = \lambda_2 = -2$, the eigenvectors of B are given by:

$$(B + 2I)v = \begin{pmatrix} -1 & 1 & -1 \\ -7 & 7 & -1 \\ -6 & 6 & 0 \end{pmatrix} v = 0 \ .$$

This coefficient matrix has rank 2 showing that although $\lambda = -2$ has algebraic multiplicity 2, the geometric multiplicity is 1. A corresponding eigenvector is $v_1 = (1,1,0)'$. For $\lambda_3 = 4$, an eigenvector of B is $v_3 = (0,1,1)'$.

Example 5.7 provides a simple example of matrices which have the same eigenvalues but are not similar. A is clearly similar to the diagonal matrix diag$(-2,-2,4)$, but B cannot be reduced to this diagonal form because any such reduction would imply the existence of a second eigenvector corresponding to $\lambda = -2$.

proof they're not similar

— A is similar to diagonal matrix — B is not.

Theorem 5.13

If A is an $n \times n$ matrix with a multiple eigenvalue λ, the geometric multiplicity of λ can never exceed the algebraic multiplicity.

Proof

Suppose A represents a linear transformation of an n-dimensional vector space V into itself relative to a given basis.

If λ_1 has geometric multiplicity r then A has r linearly independent eigenvectors $v_1, v_2, \ldots, v_r$. This set of vectors can be extended to form a new basis $[v_1, v_2, \ldots v_r, v_{r+1}, \ldots, v_n]$ of V. Relative to this new basis ϕ is represented by a matrix B of the form $B = \begin{pmatrix} \lambda_1 & & & & & \\ 0 & \cdot & & & & \\ 0 & & \cdot & & D & \\ 0 & & & \cdot & & \\ 0 & & & & \lambda_r & \\ \hline & & 0 & & & C \end{pmatrix}$ where $\lambda_1 = \lambda_2 = \ldots = \lambda_r$ and C is

an $n - r \times n - r$ matrix.

Because A and B both represent the same linear transformation, they are similar matrices and, by Theorem 5.11, have the same characteristic polynomial. The characteristic polynomial of B is $|(B - \lambda I_n)| = (\lambda_1 - \lambda)^r |(C - \lambda I_{n-r})|$. $\lambda_1 - \lambda$ is thus seen to be a factor of the characteristic polynomial of A and B of multiplicity at least r. (The multiplicity exceeds this if $\lambda_1 - \lambda$ is also a factor of $|(C - \lambda I_{n-r})|$.)

This proves that the algebraic multiplicity of a multiple eigenvalue is always equal to, or greater than, the geometric multiplicity. Only those matrices for which, whenever a multiple eigenvalue occurs, the algebraic multiplicity is equal to the geometric multiplicity, are similar to diagonal matrices.

Matrices with multiple eigenvalues for which the geometric multiplicity is less than the algebraic multiplicity are not similar to a diagonal matrix. Such matrices are said to be **defective.** It can be shown that for such matrices the simplest form of similar matrix is a matrix in **Jordan canonical form.** The proof of this result is rather lengthy and is beyond the scope of this book [see Nering 1963]. A matrix in Jordan canonical form has zeroes everywhere except for the diagonal elements and a number of small non-zero sub-matrices lying along the diagonal. A typical Jordan sub-matrix of order r is

$$J_r(\lambda) = \begin{pmatrix} \lambda & 1 & 0 & . & & . & 0 \\ 0 & \lambda & 1 & & & & . \\ . & & \vdots & & & & \\ & & & . & & & \\ & & & & . & & . \\ . & & & & . & & 0 \\ 0 & & & & 0 & \lambda & 1 \\ 0 & . & & & . & 0 & \lambda \end{pmatrix}.$$

This sub-matrix $J_r(\lambda)$ has an eigenvalue λ of multiplicity r, but since rank $(J_r(\lambda) - \lambda I) = r - 1$, the geometric multiplicity is one.

5.4 EIGENVALUES AND EIGENVECTORS OF REAL SYMMETRIC MATRICES

Real symmetric matrices were introduced in Chapter 3 when it was shown that any real quadratic form can be associated with a symmetric matrix. In addition to this application, so many physical problems can be expressed in terms of symmetric matrices that a special study of the properties of the eigenvalues and eigenvectors of these matrices is well worthwhile. In a number of important respects the properties of the eigenvalues and eigenvectors of symmetric matrices are much simpler than those of real non-symmetric matrices and special techniques have been developed for their evaluation [Wilkinson 1965; Goult, Hoskins, Milner, Pratt, 1974].

Theorem 5.14

The eigenvalues of a real symmetric matrix A are all real.

Proof

It was established in Section 5.3.2 that any real $n \times n$ matrix will have n eigenvalues but it is possible that some, or all, of these will be complex.

Let $\lambda = \alpha + i\beta$ be an eigenvalue of A associated with an eigenvector $\mathbf{v} = \mathbf{u} + i\mathbf{w}$, where $\alpha, \beta, \mathbf{u}, \mathbf{w}$ are real. Then,

$$A(\mathbf{u} + i\mathbf{w}) = (\alpha + i\beta)(\mathbf{u} + i\mathbf{w}). \tag{5.18}$$

Pre-multiplying Equation (5.18) by the transpose of the complex conjugate of **v** gives:

$$\begin{aligned}(\mathbf{u}' - i\mathbf{w}')A(\mathbf{u} + i\mathbf{w}) &= (\alpha + i\beta)(\mathbf{u}' - i\mathbf{w}')(\mathbf{u} + i\mathbf{w}) \\ &= (\alpha + i\beta)(|\mathbf{u}|^2 + |\mathbf{w}|^2). \qquad (5.19)\end{aligned}$$

Taking the complex conjugate and transpose of Equation (5.19) gives:

$$(\mathbf{u}' - i\mathbf{w}')\bar{A}'(\mathbf{u} + i\mathbf{w}) = (\alpha - i\beta)(|\mathbf{u}|^2 + |\mathbf{w}|^2).$$

However, because A is a real symmetric matrix $\bar{A}' = A$, hence,

$$(\mathbf{u}' - i\mathbf{w}')A(\mathbf{u} + i\mathbf{w}) = (\alpha - i\beta)(|\mathbf{u}|^2 + |\mathbf{w}|^2). \qquad (5.20)$$

Subracting (5.20) from (5.19) gives:

$$2i\beta(|\mathbf{u}|^2 + |\mathbf{w}|^2) = 0.$$

Hence $\beta = 0$ because **u** and **w** cannot both be zero vectors.

This proof relied essentially on the fact that $\bar{A}' = A$. The same argument can be used to prove that for any matrix H with complex elements such that $\bar{H}' = H$, the eigenvalues will all be real. Matrices of this type are called **Hermitian matrices.**

Since the eigenvalues of a real symmetric matrix are all real, it can be safely assumed when considering the properties of the eigenvectors that these are real.

Theorem 5.15

The eigenvectors of a real symmetric matrix corresponding to distinct eigenvalues λ_i and λ_j are orthogonal.

Proof

Suppose the corresponding eigenvectors are $\mathbf{v}_i$ and $\mathbf{v}_j$, we must show that $\mathbf{v}_j.\mathbf{v}_i = \mathbf{v}_j'\mathbf{v}_i = 0$. From the defining property of the eigenvalues:

$$A\mathbf{v}_i = \lambda_i\mathbf{v}_i \text{ and } A\mathbf{v}_j = \lambda_j\mathbf{v}_j.$$

Pre-multiplying the first of these equations by $\mathbf{v}_j'$ gives:

$$\mathbf{v}_j'A\mathbf{v}_i = \lambda_i\mathbf{v}_j'\mathbf{v}_i. \qquad (5.21)$$

Transposing the second equation and post-multiplying by $\mathbf{v}_i$ gives:

$$\mathbf{v}_j'A\mathbf{v}_i = \lambda_j\mathbf{v}_j'\mathbf{v}_i. \qquad (5.22)$$

Subtracting Equation (5.22) from (5.21) gives

$$(\lambda_i - \lambda_j)\mathbf{v}_j'\mathbf{v}_i = 0.$$

Since $\lambda_i \neq \lambda_j$, we obtain the required result $\mathbf{v}_j'\mathbf{v}_i = \mathbf{v}_j.\mathbf{v}_i = 0$.

Theorem 5.16

If A is a real symmetric $n \times n$ matrix with a multiple eigenvalue, then the algebraic multiplicity of λ is equal to its geometric multiplicity.

Proof

Suppose λ has geometric multiplicity m, then rank $(A - \lambda I) = n - m$. The eigenvectors corresponding to λ will then form an m dimensional subspace of R^n. Let $[\mathbf{v}_1,\mathbf{v}_2,\ldots,\mathbf{v}_m]$ be an orthonormal basis of this subspace. This set can be extended to form an orthonormal basis:

$$[\mathbf{v}_1,\mathbf{v}_2,\ldots,\mathbf{v}_m,\mathbf{w}_{m+1},\ldots,\mathbf{w}_n] \text{ of } R^n.$$

Let P be the matrix whose column vectors are $(\mathbf{v}_1,\ldots,\mathbf{v}_m,\mathbf{w}_{m+1},\ldots,\mathbf{w}_n)$. Consider the matrix $P'AP$. Since A is symmetric $P'AP$ will be symmetric and:

$$P'AP = \begin{pmatrix} \mathbf{v}_1' \\ \cdot \\ \cdot \\ \mathbf{v}_m' \\ \hline \mathbf{w}_{m+1}' \\ \cdot \\ \cdot \\ \mathbf{w}_n' \end{pmatrix} A(\mathbf{v}_1,\mathbf{v}_2,\ldots,\mathbf{v}_m \,|\, \mathbf{w}_{m+1},\ldots,\mathbf{w}_n)$$

$$= \begin{pmatrix} \mathbf{v}_1' \\ \cdot \\ \cdot \\ \mathbf{v}_m' \\ \hline \mathbf{w}_{m+1}' \\ \cdot \\ \cdot \\ \mathbf{w}_n' \end{pmatrix} (\lambda\mathbf{v}_1,\lambda\mathbf{v}_2,\ldots,\lambda\mathbf{v}_m \,|\, A\mathbf{w}_{m+1},\ldots,A\mathbf{w}_n).$$

Because the vectors $[\mathbf{v}_1, \ldots, \mathbf{v}_m, \mathbf{w}_{m+1}, \ldots, \mathbf{w}_n]$ form an orthonormal set, this product matrix takes the simplified form:

$$\left(\begin{array}{c|c} \lambda I_m & V'AW \\ \hline 0 & W'AW \end{array}\right),$$

where $V = (\mathbf{v}_1, \ldots, \mathbf{v}_m)$ and $W = (\mathbf{w}_{m+1}, \ldots, \mathbf{w}_n)$. This matrix must also be symmetric; hence $V'AW = 0$. Let $B = P'AP - \lambda I$. Since P is non-singular, rank $B = \text{rank}\,(A - \lambda I) = n - m$.

$$B = P'AP - \lambda I = \left(\begin{array}{c|c} 0 & 0 \\ \hline 0 & W'AW - \lambda I_{n-m} \end{array}\right).$$

Because B is of rank $n - m$, $W'AW - \lambda I_{n-m}$ must be non-singular, showing that λ is an eigenvalue of $P'AP$, and hence of A, of algebraic multiplicity precisely m.

The preceding three Theorems establish the essential properties of the eigenvalues of a real symmetric matrix. They show that for such a matrix the eigenvalues are always real, the matrix can never be defective and the eigenvectors corresponding to distinct eigenvalues are mutually orthogonal. A symmetric matrix always has at least one orthonormal set of eigenvectors because, as in proving Theorem 5.16, it is always possible to select an orthogonal set of eigenvectors corresponding to a multiple eigenvalue and all the ~~eigenvalues~~ eigenvectors can be multiplied by appropriate scalars to ensure that they are of unit length. If P is the matrix whose column vectors are an orthonormal set of eigenvectors of a given symmetric matrix A, then P has the properties:

$$P'P = I \text{ and } P'AP = \text{diag}\,(\lambda_1, \ldots, \lambda_n).$$

A matrix P such that $P'P = I$ is called an **orthogonal matrix**. Orthogonal similarity transformations of the form $A \rightarrow P'AP$ have many applications because they preserve the symmetry of the matrix and are important in numerical analysis. This is because, unlike other similarity transformations, when they are used to simplify an eigenvalue problem they can never make the problem ill-conditioned [Wilkinson 1965].

Example 5.8

Find the eigenvalues and eigenvectors of the symmetric matrix:

$$A = \begin{pmatrix} 5 & 2 & -2 \\ 2 & 5 & -2 \\ -2 & -2 & 5 \end{pmatrix}.$$

Hence find an orthogonal matrix P such that $P'AP$ is a diagonal matrix.

Solution

The characteristic equation of A is:

$$|(A - \lambda I)| = \begin{vmatrix} 5-\lambda & 2 & -2 \\ 2 & 5-\lambda & -2 \\ -2 & -2 & 5-\lambda \end{vmatrix} = 0.$$

This determinant can be simplified by adding $R3$ to $R1$ to give:

$$\begin{vmatrix} 3-\lambda & 0 & 3-\lambda \\ 2 & 5-\lambda & -2 \\ -2 & -2 & 5-\lambda \end{vmatrix} = \begin{vmatrix} 3-\lambda & 0 & 0 \\ 2 & 5-\lambda & -4 \\ -2 & -2 & 7-\lambda \end{vmatrix} = 0.$$

This gives $(3-\lambda)(\lambda^2 - 12\lambda + 27) = 0, (3-\lambda)(3-\lambda)(9-\lambda) = 0$. The eigenvalues of A are 3, 3, 9.

Corresponding to the multiple eigenvalue 3, the eigenvectors are given by:

$$(A - 3I)\mathbf{x} = \begin{pmatrix} 2 & 2 & -2 \\ 2 & 2 & -2 \\ -2 & -2 & 2 \end{pmatrix} \mathbf{x} = \mathbf{0}.$$

The coefficient matrix is of rank 1. Two linearly independent eigenvectors are $\mathbf{v}_1 = (0,1,1)'$, $\mathbf{v}_2 = (1,0,1)'$. Corresponding to the eigenvalue $\lambda = 9$, the eigenvector is given by:

$$(A - 9I)\mathbf{x} = \begin{pmatrix} -4 & 2 & -2 \\ 2 & -4 & -2 \\ -2 & -2 & -4 \end{pmatrix} \mathbf{x} = \mathbf{0}.$$

An eigenvector is $\mathbf{v}_3 = (1,1,-1)'$.

The required diagonalising matrix P has columns which are an orthonormal set of eigenvectors for A. $[\mathbf{v}_1,\mathbf{v}_2,\mathbf{v}_3]$ is not an orthonormal set of vectors and must be modified accordingly.

The Gram-Schmidt process could be applied to $[\mathbf{v}_1,\mathbf{v}_2]$. Alternatively, in this simple case $\mathbf{v}_1 + \alpha\mathbf{v}_2 = (\alpha,1,1+\alpha) = \mathbf{w}_2$ and $\mathbf{v}_1.\mathbf{w}_2 = 2 + \alpha$, showing that $[\mathbf{v}_1,\mathbf{w}_2]$ are orthogonal if $\alpha = -2$. Hence mutually orthogonal eigenvectors for A are $(0,1,1)'$, $(-2,1,-1)'$. Dividing each of these vectors by its length gives an orthonormal set of eigenvectors. The corresponding orthogonal matrix P is:

$$P = \begin{pmatrix} 0 & -2/\sqrt{6} & 1/\sqrt{3} \\ 1/\sqrt{2} & 1/\sqrt{6} & 1/\sqrt{3} \\ 1/\sqrt{2} & -1/\sqrt{6} & -1/\sqrt{3} \end{pmatrix}.$$

The reader can easily verify that $P'AP = \text{diag}\,(3,3,9)$.

The fact that for every symmetric matrix A there is a diagonalising orthogonal matrix P, can be used to establish the link between positive definite matrices and their eigenvalues. Theorem 5.17 below shows that a positive definite matrix must have positive eigenvalues, so providing a simple practical test for positive definiteness.

Theorem 5.17

If A is a real symmetric $n \times n$ matrix, then A is positive definite if and only if all the eigenvalues of A are positive.

Proof

In Chapter 3 a positive definite matrix A was defined as one for which the associated quadratic form $Q(x_1,x_2,\ldots,x_n) = \mathbf{x}'A\mathbf{x}$ is greater than zero for all non-zero values of $\mathbf{x}$.

Suppose A has eigenvalues $\lambda_1, \lambda_2, \ldots, \lambda_n$ and let P be an orthogonal matrix whose columns are eigenvectors of A. Then,

$$P'AP = \text{diag}\,(\lambda_1,\lambda_2,\ldots,\lambda_n). \tag{5.23}$$

P can also be used to define a change of variables in the quadratic form $\mathbf{y} = P'\mathbf{x}$, $\mathbf{x} = P\mathbf{y}$. (Since P is orthogonal, $|\mathbf{x}| = |\mathbf{y}|$, showing that this particular transformation preserves the lengths of the vectors). Then,

$$Q(x_1,x_2,\ldots,x_n) = \mathbf{x}'A\mathbf{x} = \mathbf{y}'P'AP\mathbf{y}. \tag{5.24}$$

Using Equation (5.23), this quadratic form is simplified to:

$$Q(x_1,\ldots,x_n) = \sum_{i=1}^{n} \lambda_i y_i^2. \tag{5.25}$$

If $Q(x_1,\ldots,x_n) > 0$ for all non zero $\mathbf{x}$, and hence all $\mathbf{y}$, then $\sum_{i=1}^{n} \lambda_i y_i^2 > 0$ for all $\mathbf{y} \neq \mathbf{0} \Rightarrow \lambda_i > 0$ for $i = 1,\ldots,n$. Conversely, if $\lambda_i > 0$ for $i = 1,\ldots,n$, then, the right hand side of (5.25) is positive for all non-zero $\mathbf{y}$ showing that $(Q(x_1,\ldots,x_n)$ is positive definite.

PROBLEMS

5.1 Show that the transformation:

$$\phi(f(x,y)) = \int_{-1}^{1} f(x,y)\, dy$$

is a linear transformation from the space of homogeneous polynomials of the form $ax^3 + bx^2y + cxy^2 + dy^3$ into the space of real polynomials in x. Find suitable bases for the kernel and the image space of ϕ.

5.2 P_3 denotes the space of all real polynomials of degree 3 or less. Which of the following mappings are linear transformations of P_3 into itself?

(i) $\phi_1(f(x)) = \dfrac{df}{dx} - x,$

(ii) $\phi_2(f(x)) = x(\dfrac{df}{dx} - f(x)),$

(iii) $\phi_3(f(x)) = \int_0^1 f(x)\, dx,$

(iv) $\phi_4(f(x)) = (x \dfrac{df}{dx})^2.$

5.3 S denotes the set of all periodic functions of the real variable x which have period 2π. (That is $f(x + 2\pi) = f(x)$ for all real x). Show that S is a vector space and that the mapping $\phi(f(x)) = f(x) - \sin x\, f(x)$ is a linear transformation of S into itself.

5.4 ϕ is a linear transformation of a real vector space V into itself. Prove that ϕ^2 is also a linear transformation of V into itself. By considering the kernels of ϕ and ϕ^2 prove that if A is any real $n \times n$ matrix rank $A^2 \leqslant$ rank A.

5.5 P^n denotes the space of all real polynomials of degree n or less. Show that $\phi(f(x)) = \dfrac{d^2f}{dx^2} + x\dfrac{df}{dx} - 3f(x)$ is a linear transformation of P^3 into P^2.

Relative to bases $\mathbf{v}_1 = x^3, \mathbf{v}_2 = x^2, \mathbf{v}_3 = x, \mathbf{v}_4 = 1$ of P^3 and $\mathbf{u}_1 = x^2, \mathbf{u}_2 = x,$ $\mathbf{u}_3 = 1$ of P^2 find the matrix A which represents ϕ. Hence find the basis of the kernel of ϕ and the most general solution in P^3 of:

$$\frac{d^2f}{dx^2} + x\frac{df}{dx} - 3f = 6x.$$

5.6 An equivalence relation $\sim$ on a set S is a relation with the properties:

$a \sim a$ for all a in S (Reflexive property),

$a \sim b \Rightarrow b \sim a$ (Symmetric property),

and $a \sim b,\, b \sim c \Rightarrow a \sim c$ (Transitive property).

Prove that the equivalence of matrices ($A \sim B$ if $B = PAQ$ where P, Q are non-singular matrices) is an equivalence relation on the set of all $m \times n$ matrices. Find which, if any, of the following matrices are equivalent.

$$A = \begin{pmatrix} 1 & 2 & 3 & 4 \\ 5 & 6 & 7 & 8 \\ 9 & 10 & 11 & 12 \end{pmatrix}, \quad B = \begin{pmatrix} 1 & 0 & 1 & 0 \\ 0 & 1 & 0 & 1 \\ 1 & 2 & 1 & 3 \end{pmatrix},$$

$$C = \begin{pmatrix} 1 & 2 & 5 & 6 \\ 4 & 3 & 8 & 1 \\ 2 & -1 & 3 & 0 \end{pmatrix}, \quad D = \begin{pmatrix} 2 & 3 & 1 & 5 \\ 4 & 2 & 1 & 6 \\ 0 & 4 & 1 & 4 \end{pmatrix}.$$

5.7 Relative to bases $[\mathbf{v}_1,\mathbf{v}_2,\mathbf{v}_3]$ of V and $[\mathbf{w}_1,\mathbf{w}_2]$ of W, a linear transformation ϕ of V into W is represented by the matrix $A = \begin{pmatrix} 1 & 2 & 1 \\ 2 & 3 & 2 \end{pmatrix}$.

Find in terms of $\mathbf{v}_1, \mathbf{v}_2, \mathbf{v}_3$ and $\mathbf{w}_1, \mathbf{w}_2$ bases of V and W for which ϕ is represented by $B = \begin{pmatrix} 1 & 0 & 0 \\ 0 & 1 & 0 \end{pmatrix}$.

5.8 R^n denotes the real n-dimensional vector space. Prove that the set S of all linear transformations ϕ of R^3 into R^2 is also a real vector space. Show that for fixed bases of R^2 and R^3, each such linear transformation can be associated with a unique matrix. Hence find the dimension of S.

5.9 Find non-singular matrices P and Q such that PAQ is of the equivalent canonical form $\begin{pmatrix} I_r & 0 \\ 0 & 0 \end{pmatrix}$ if $A = \begin{pmatrix} 1 & 2 & 1 & 3 \\ 4 & 3 & -1 & 2 \\ 2 & -1 & -3 & -4 \end{pmatrix}$.

5.10 Show that the set S of all real 2×2 matrices is a vector space and find its dimension. A mapping ϕ of S into R (the set of real numbers) is defined by the equation $\phi(A) = \text{trace } A$.

Prove that ϕ is a linear transformation and find a basis of the kernel of ϕ.

5.11 Find the matrix Q which represents the change of basis in the space P^2 of real polynomials of degree $\leqslant 2$ from $[1,x,x^2]$ to $[1+x,1-x,x^2+1]$.

Find the matrices A and B which represent the linear transformation $\phi(f(x)) = 2f(x) - \dfrac{df}{dx}$ of P^2 into itself with respect to each of these bases. Verify the relationship between A, B and Q.

5.12 ϕ is a linear transformation of a real vector space V into itself. Prove that if λ is an eigenvalue of ϕ, the set of all corresponding eigenvectors $\mathbf{v}$ such that $\phi(\mathbf{v}) = \lambda\mathbf{v}$ is a subspace of V. If V is the set of all real differentiable functions $f(x)$ and ϕ is the linear transformation $\phi(f(x)) = \dfrac{d^2f}{dx^2}$, find a basis of the subspace of V associated with eigenvalue -1.

5.13 Find a real matrix A with eigenvalues $\lambda_1 = 1$, $\lambda_2 = 1 + i$ and $\lambda_3 = 1 - i$ and associated eigenvectors $\mathbf{v}_1 = (1,1,0)'$, $\mathbf{v}_2 = (0,1,i)$ and $\mathbf{v}_3 = (0,1,-i)$.

5.14 Find the eigenvalues and eigenvectors of the matrix:

$$A = \begin{pmatrix} 1 & 1 & -2 \\ -1 & 2 & 1 \\ 0 & 1 & -1 \end{pmatrix}.$$

Hence find a matrix P such that $P^{-1}AP$ is a diagonal matrix. Use this result to find A^5 and A^{-1}.

5.15 $f(x)$ is a real polynomial $f(x) = a_0 + a_1x + a_2x^2 + a_3x^3$. If A is an nXn matrix $f(A)$ is defined as:

$$f(A) = a_0I + a_1A + a_2A^2 + a_3A^3.$$

Find the characteristic polynomial $f(\lambda)$ of the matrix:

$$A = \begin{pmatrix} 1 & 2 & 1 \\ 2 & 3 & 1 \\ 3 & 5 & 3 \end{pmatrix}$$

and show that $f(A) = 0$.

Hence find an expression for A^5 in terms of I, A, A^2.

5.16 A is a non-defective nXn matrix with eigenvectors $\mathbf{v}_1, \mathbf{v}_2, \ldots, \mathbf{v}_n$. If the characteristic polynomial of A is $f(\lambda)$, prove, by considering the factorised form of the polynomial, that $f(A)\mathbf{v}_i = \mathbf{0}$ for $i = 1, \ldots, n$. Deduce that $f(A) = 0$.

* [This is a special case of the Cayley Hamilton Theorem that a matrix satisfies its own characteristic polynomial.] - an important thm. - true for any matrix - proof - see notes

5.17 Show that the matrices A, B, D below all have eigenvalues $-2, -2, 4$. Which of these matrices are similar under the similarity transformation $A \to P^{-1}AP$? Give reasons for your answer.

$$A = \begin{pmatrix} 0 & 2 & -1 \\ -8 & -10 & 7 \\ -12 & -12 & 10 \end{pmatrix}, \quad B = \begin{pmatrix} -2 & 0 & 0 \\ -6 & -8 & 6 \\ -12 & -12 & 10 \end{pmatrix}, \quad D = \begin{pmatrix} -2 & 0 & 0 \\ 0 & -2 & 0 \\ 0 & 0 & 4 \end{pmatrix}.$$

5.18 A is a non-defective $n \times n$ matrix with eigenvalues $\lambda_1, \lambda_2, \ldots, \lambda_n$ such that $|\lambda_1| > |\lambda_2| > |\lambda_3| > \ldots > |\lambda_n|$ and associated eigenvectors $\mathbf{v}_1, \mathbf{v}_2, \ldots, \mathbf{v}_n$. What are the eigenvalues and eigenvectors of A^m where m is a positive integer?

An iterative process is defined by the equations:

$$\mathbf{w}_{r+1} = A\mathbf{u}_r$$
$$\mathbf{u}_{r+1} = \frac{1}{|\mathbf{w}_{r+1}|}\mathbf{w}_{r+1}.$$

Show that from an arbitrary initial vector $\mathbf{u}_0$ the process will generally converge to give $\lim_{r\to\infty} \mathbf{u}_r = \mathbf{v}_1$ and $\lim_{r\to\infty} |\mathbf{w}_r| = |\lambda_1|$.

Use this process to estimate the eigenvalue of largest modulus of the matrix $A = \begin{pmatrix} 10 & 1 & -1 \\ 2 & -1 & 3 \\ 1 & 2 & 0 \end{pmatrix}$.

5.19 By considering $\bar{\mathbf{v}}'\mathbf{v}$ where $\mathbf{v}$ is an eigenvector and $\bar{}$ denotes the complex conjugate, prove that all the eigenvalues of a real orthogonal matrix P have modulus 1. Deduce that if P is an orthogonal matrix of order n when n is odd, then P has an eigenvalue of 1 or -1.

The orthogonal matrix $P = \begin{pmatrix} 1/\sqrt{2} & -1/\sqrt{6} & -1/\sqrt{3} \\ 0 & 2/\sqrt{6} & -1/\sqrt{3} \\ 1/\sqrt{2} & 1/\sqrt{6} & 1/\sqrt{3} \end{pmatrix}$ represents a rotation of coordinate axes in 3-dimensional space. Find the axis of rotation.

5.20 A is an $n \times n$ matrix with distinct eigenvalues $\lambda_1, \lambda_2, \ldots, \lambda_n$ and associated eigenvectors $\mathbf{v}_1, \mathbf{v}_2, \ldots, \mathbf{v}_n$. Prove that $n \times n$ matrix B will commute with A (that is $AB = BA$) if, and only if, the eigenvectors of B are also $\mathbf{v}_1, \mathbf{v}_2, \ldots, \mathbf{v}_n$.

If $A = \begin{pmatrix} 7 & -10 \\ 3 & -4 \end{pmatrix}$ and $B = \begin{pmatrix} -16 & 30 \\ -9 & 17 \end{pmatrix}$, verify that A and B commute and find the eigenvalues and eigenvectors of A, B, AB and $A - B$.

5.21 A is a real $m \times n$ matrix and B is a real $n \times p$ matrix. By considering the kernels of the corresponding linear transformations, prove that:

$$\text{rank}\,(AB) \geqslant \text{rank}\,A + \text{rank}\,B - n.$$

5.22 Show that the mapping $\phi(f) = \dfrac{\partial^2 f}{\partial x^2} + \dfrac{\partial^2 f}{\partial y^2} + \dfrac{\partial^2 f}{\partial z^2}$ is a linear transformation of the space S of all real homogeneous polynomials of degree 2 in x,y,z together with zero into R (the real numbers). Find the dimension of S and of the image space. Deduce that Ker ϕ has dimension 5 and find a basis of Ker ϕ.

5.23 Prove that two $n \times n$ matrices with the same eigenvalues and the same set of n linearly independent eigenvectors are equal. Give a simple counter example to show that this is not true for defective matrices.

5.24 Show that the matrices A and B below have the same eigenvalues. Find a matrix Q such that $A = Q^{-1}BQ$.

$$A = \begin{pmatrix} -1 & 2 & -2 \\ -2 & 3 & -1 \\ 2 & -2 & 4 \end{pmatrix} \qquad B = \begin{pmatrix} 1 & 0 & -1 \\ 1 & 2 & 1 \\ 2 & 2 & 3 \end{pmatrix}.$$

5.25 A symmetric matrix A has an orthonormal set of eigenvectors $[\mathbf{u}_1, \mathbf{u}_2, \ldots, \mathbf{u}_n]$ with associated eigenvalues $\lambda_1, \lambda_2, \ldots, \lambda_n$. Show that A can be expressed as the sum:

$$A = \lambda_1 \mathbf{u}_1 \mathbf{u}_1' + \lambda_2 \mathbf{u}_2 \mathbf{u}_2' + \ldots + \lambda_n \mathbf{u}_n \mathbf{u}_n'.$$

Find a symmetric matrix with eigenvalues 1, 2 and 3 and associated eigenvectors $(1,1,1)'$, $(1,-2,1)'$ and $(1,0,-1)'$.

5.26 By considering the diagonalisation of the symmetric matrix $A'A$, prove that for any real $n \times n$ matrix A, $\|A\|_2 = \sqrt{(\lambda_1)}$ where λ_1 is the largest eigenvalue of $A'A$.

Chapter 6

Applications of Linear Transformations

INTRODUCTION

The theory of linear transformations developed in the previous Chapter has many applications in science, engineering and other branches of mathematics. These applications are too numerous and too varied for the author to attempt to give even brief details of all of them, but it is hoped that the following Sections of this Chapter will give at least some idea of the variety of the potential applications. The general theory is used mainly to illuminate some of the underlying properties of the problem being solved and to show how apparently unrelated problems possess essentially the same mathematical structure. Eigenvalue theory can be used more explicitly as a practical aid to solving real problems, and this is particularly true if the theory is combined with a knowledge of modern numerical methods which can compute efficiently the eigenvalues and eigenvectors of quite large matrices. It is the author's experience that post-graduate workers solving problems in structural stability, dynamics or control theory all need to compute eigenvalues at some stage of their work.

6.1 APPLICATIONS OF GENERAL LINEAR TRANSFORMATIONS

In Chapter 5 it was proved that if ϕ is a linear transformation of a vector space V into a vector space W, then the equation $\phi(\mathbf{x}) = \mathrm{w}$ is only soluble if $\mathbf{w}$ is in the image space $\phi(V)$. In this case all the solutions are of the form $\mathbf{x} = \mathbf{x}_0 + \mathbf{k}$, where $\mathbf{x}_0$ is a particular solution of $\phi(\mathbf{x}) = \mathbf{w}$, and $\mathbf{k}$ is an arbitrary vector in the kernel Ker ϕ. The examples below illustrate the application of these principles to a variety of problems.

Example 6.1 – The Laplace Transformation

The Laplace transformation $\mathcal{L}(f(t)) = \displaystyle\int_0^\infty e^{-st} f(t)\mathrm{d}t = F(s)$ is a linear transformation of an infinite dimensional space of functions of t into the space of all functions of s. One of the simplest applications of Laplace transformations is in the solution of linear differential equations with constant coefficients. In this case the differential equation for $x(t)$ is transformed to produce an algebraic equation in s which can be readily solved for the transformed function $X(s)$. The final stage in the solution is the **inversion problem**, that is finding $x(t)$ when its Laplace transform $X(s)$ is known. An elementary method of solving this inversion problem is to express $X(s)$ as a linear combination of simple functions which can be recognised as Laplace transforms of known functions of t. [See Goult, Hoskins, Milner, Pratt 1973]. Inherent in this approach is the assumption that the inversion process is unique in the sense that given $X(s)$ there will only be one corresponding function $x(t)$. The theory of linear transformations shows that this assumption is valid only if there are no non-zero functions in the kernel of the Laplace transformation. In fact this is not strictly true, but the only functions $f(t)$ for which $\mathcal{L}(f(t)) = 0$ are identically zero for all $t > 0$ except at a few isolated points. From this we can deduce that for a given $X(s)$ there can be at most one corresponding continuous function $x(t)$ and if $\mathcal{L}(x_1(t)) = \mathcal{L}(x_2(t)) = X(s)$, then $x_1(t) = x_2(t)$ at all but a few points.

The theory of other integral transforms, such as Fourier transforms, can be developed in a similar way.

Example 6.2 – Linear Differential Equations

A differential equation of the form

$$\frac{d^n y}{dx^n} + f_1(x)\frac{d^{n-1}y}{dx^{n-1}} + f_2(x)\frac{d^{n-2}y}{dx^{n-2}} + \ldots\ldots + f_{n-1}(x)\frac{dy}{dx} + f_n(x)y = g(x), \tag{6.1}$$

where $f_1(x), f_2(x), \ldots, f_n(x), g(x)$ are given functions of x (or, in simple cases, constants) is called a **linear differential equation.** It is left as a simple exercise for the reader to show that the left hand side of Equation (6.1) defines a linear transformation of the space of real differentiable functions into the space of functions. It can also be proved that although this is a linear transformation between infinite dimensional vector spaces, the kernel is finite dimensional and in fact has dimension n. The theory of linear transformations can be used to show that the general solution of Equation (6.1) will be of the form $y(x) = y_0(x) + k(x)$, where $y_0(x)$ is a particular solution and $k(x)$ is an arbitrary function in the kernel of the transformation. It is usual in this application to call $y_0(x)$ the **particular integral** and $k(x)$ the **complementary function.** Because the dimension of the kernel is n, $k(x)$ is expressible as $k(x) = \alpha_1 k_1(x) + \alpha_2 k_2(x) + \ldots + \alpha_n k_n(x)$ where $\alpha_1, \alpha_2, \ldots, \alpha_n$ are arbitrary constants and $k_1(x), k_2(x), \ldots, k_n(x)$ are linearly independent functions forming a basis of the kernel. The numerical values of $\alpha_1, \alpha_2, \ldots, \alpha_n$ are generally determined from the boundary conditions of the actual problem being solved, and for Equation (6.1) n boundary conditions are necessary for a unique solution. As a simple example, consider the following problem:

Solve $\dfrac{d^2y}{dx^2} - 3\dfrac{dy}{dx} + 2y = \sin x$ with $y(0) = 1, y'(0) = 2$.

Solution

The corresponding linear transformation is:

$$\phi(y) = \frac{d^2y}{dx^2} - 3\frac{dy}{dx} + 2y.$$

Any function in Ker ϕ is such that $\dfrac{d^2y}{dx^2} - 3\dfrac{dy}{dx} + 2y = 0$. It is clear that any function satisfying this equation must be such that the function is closely related to its derivative. We therefore try as a solution $y = e^{\alpha x}$. Then,

$$\phi(y) = \frac{d^2y}{dx^2} - 3\frac{dy}{dx} + 2y = (\alpha^2 - 3\alpha + 2)e^{\alpha x} = (\alpha - 2)(\alpha - 1)e^{\alpha x}.$$

Two functions in the kernel are thus e^x and e^{2x} and these functions provide a basis of Ker ϕ. The complementary function is $k(x) = \alpha_1 e^x + \alpha_2 e^{2x}$. We now require a particular solution of $\phi(y) = \sin x$.

Elementary substitution gives:

$$\phi(\sin x) = \sin x - 3\cos x, \tag{6.2}$$

$$\phi(\cos x) = \cos x - 3\sin x. \tag{6.3}$$

Using Equations (6.2) and (6.3) together with the linear properties of ϕ gives the required particular integral $\phi(-\frac{1}{8}\sin x - \frac{3}{8}\cos x) = \sin x$. (In effect Equations (6.2) and (6.3) show that ϕ is also a linear transformation of the subspace with basis $[\sin x, \cos x]$ into itself.)

The general solution $y_0(x) + k(x)$ is given by:

$$y(x) = -\frac{1}{8}\sin x - \frac{3}{8}\cos x + \alpha_1 e^x + \alpha_2 e^{2x}. \tag{6.4}$$

The boundary condition $y(0) = 1$ gives the equation:

$$1 = -\frac{3}{8} + \alpha_1 + \alpha_2. \tag{6.5}$$

Differentiating Equation 6.4 and using the second boundary condition $y'(0) = 2$ gives:

$$2 = -\frac{1}{8} + \alpha_1 + 2\alpha_2. \tag{6.6}$$

Equations (6.5) and (6.6) are simple linear equations which can be solved for α_1 and α_2. The solution is $\alpha_1 = 5/8$, $\alpha_2 = 3/4$. The solution of the differential equation is thus:

$$y = \frac{1}{8}(5e^x + 3e^{2x} - \sin x - 3\cos x).$$

Example 6.3 – The Theory of Linear Equations.

The theory of linear equations originally developed in Chapter 2 can also be interpreted in terms of the properties of linear transformations. Equations (2.1), expressible in matrix form as $A\mathbf{x} = \mathbf{c}$, are closely related to a linear transformation ϕ of R^n into R^m. Relative to the elementaty bases $[\mathbf{e}_1,\mathbf{e}_2,\ldots,\mathbf{e}_n]$ of R^n, and $[\mathbf{e}_1,\mathbf{e}_2,\ldots,\mathbf{e}_m]$ of R^m, ϕ is represented by the $m\times n$ matrix A. A solution $(x_1,x_2,\ldots,x_n)$ of the equations can be identified with a vector $\mathbf{x}$ satisfying the transformation equation:

$$\phi(\mathbf{x}) = \mathbf{c}. \tag{6.7}$$

Using the theory of linear transformations, any solution of Equation (6.7) is of the form $\mathbf{x} = \mathbf{x}_0 + \mathbf{k}$, where $\mathbf{k}$ is an arbitrary vector in the kernel of ϕ and $\mathbf{x}_0$ is a particular solution.

From this we can deduce that the equations are only soluble if $\mathbf{c}$ is in the image space of ϕ. A condition for this is that rank $(A,\mathbf{c}) =$ rank (A) as shown in Theorem 2.1. The solution will be unique if dimension Ker $\phi = 0$; this will be the case if rank $A = n$. The equation is soluble for all values of $\mathbf{c}$ if the image space of ϕ coincides with R^m; this occurs when rank $A = m$. The equations are always soluble and have a unique solution if A is an $n\times n$ matrix of rank n. In this case ϕ^{-1} is a well defined linear transformation of R^n into R^n and is represented by the matrix A^{-1}. In the more general case, if rank $A = r < n$ the kernel of ϕ will have dimension $n - r$. The general solution of (6.7) (and hence of 2.1), if it exists, will then contain precisely $n - r$ arbitrary constants.

6.1.1 Linear Transformations and Geometry

Euclidean geometry can be considered as a study of the properties of objects in space which are independent of their actual position in space. One of the most important concepts in Euclidean geometry is the distance between two points and the only allowable geometric transformations are those which leave this distance invariant. In geometric terms, the permissible transformations in 3-dimensions are **translation** (that is moving the entire object parallel to a given line), **rotation about a given axis** and **reflection in a given plane**. These transformations can all be described algebraically if we represent a point $P(x_1,x_2,x_3)$ in 3-dimensional Euclidean space by the vector $\mathbf{x} = (x_1,x_2,x_3)'$.

A translation is given by:

$$T(\mathbf{x}) = \mathbf{x} + \mathbf{t}, \tag{6.8}$$

where $\mathbf{t}$ is a fixed vector defining the direction and magnitude of the translation. Both rotations and reflections can be described in matrix terms as:

$$\phi(x) = P\mathbf{x}, \tag{6.9}$$

where P is some 3X3 matrix.

For example, a rotation through an angle θ about the axis $0x_3$ is represented by the matrix:

$$P = \begin{pmatrix} \cos\theta & -\sin\theta & 0 \\ \sin\theta & \cos\theta & 0 \\ 0 & 0 & 1 \end{pmatrix}.$$

A reflection in the plane of x_1 and x_2 is given by $P = \text{diag}(1,1,-1)$. A translation, as described by Equation (6.8), is not a linear transformation because $T(\alpha\mathbf{x}) = \alpha\mathbf{x} + \mathbf{t} \neq \alpha T(\mathbf{x})$. However Equation (6.9) clearly corresponds to a linear transformation of R^3 into itself.

It is now reasonable to ask which of the possible linear transformations of R^3 into itself leave the distance between any 2 points invariant and so correspond to geometric transformations.

Let ϕ be a linear transformation of R^3 into itself represented by a matrix A relative to the basis $[\mathbf{e}_1,\mathbf{e}_2,\mathbf{e}_3]$. If $\mathbf{x}_1$ and $\mathbf{x}_2$ correspond to the points P_1 and P_2, then (distance $P_1P_2)^2 = (\mathbf{x}_1 - \mathbf{x}_2)\cdot(\mathbf{x}_1 - \mathbf{x}_2) = (\mathbf{x}_1' - \mathbf{x}_2')(\mathbf{x}_1 - \mathbf{x}_2)$. After transformation P_1' is given by $\phi(\mathbf{x}_1) = A\mathbf{x}_1$ and P_2' corresponds to $\phi(\mathbf{x}_2) = A\mathbf{x}_2$.

$$(\text{distance } P_1'P_2')^2 = (A\mathbf{x}_1 - A\mathbf{x}_2)\cdot(A\mathbf{x}_1 - A\mathbf{x}_2) = (\mathbf{x}_1' - \mathbf{x}_2')A'A(\mathbf{x}_1 - \mathbf{x}_2).$$

A comparison of the expressions for the distances before and after transformation shows that the distances will be unaltered for all values of $\mathbf{x}_1$ and $\mathbf{x}_2$ if $A'A = I$, that is if A is an orthogonal matrix. When solving geometrical problems, translations and orthogonal transformations are widely employed as a computational tool to simplify the working. [Faux and Pratt, 1978].

A more general view of geometry is to consider it as the study of invariant properties under certain classes of transformation. For Euclidean geometry the allowable transformations are translations, reflections and orthogonal transformations, but extending the range of allowable transformations gives non-Euclidean geometries such as affine geometry and projective geometry. [Semple and Kneebone, 1952].

6.2 EIGENVALUE AND EIGENVECTOR APPLICATIONS

6.2.1 Stochastic Matrices

Stochastic matrices occur in probability theory [Gray, 1967] when systems with a finite number of states are being studied. At each **trial** or **experiment** there is assumed to be fixed probability of changing from one state to another. If n states are possible, the transition probability of changing from state S_j to state S_i in any trial is given by the element t_{ij} of the stochastic transition matrix T. The probabilities associated with the n states at any particular time can be described by a probability vector $\mathbf{p} = (p_1,p_2,\ldots,p_n)'$, p_i giving the probability of being in the state S_i. Since the elements of $\mathbf{p}$ and T are all probabilities, they have a number of special properties.

$0 \leqslant t_{ij} \leqslant 1$ and $0 \leqslant p_i \leqslant 1$, because probabilities are always measured on a scale from 0 (impossible) to 1 (absolutely certain). $p_1 + p_2 + \ldots + p_n = 1$, because the system must be in precisely one of the n possible states $S_1, S_2', \ldots, S_n$ Also, because t_{ij} represents the conditional probability that state S_j will change to state S_i at a trial and precisely one of the states $S_1, S_2, \ldots, S_n$ must follow S_j, $t_{1j} + t_{2j} + \ldots + t_{nj} = 1$.

A stochastic matrix is thus one in which all the elements are positive and less than or equal to 1 and in which all the column sums are precisely 1.

Consider as a simple example the various states of the weather. These states might be: S_1 = sunny, S_2 = cloudy, S_3 = rainy. In this example a 'trial' is the change from one day's weather to the next. The transition matrix T might then be:

$$T = \begin{pmatrix} 0.5 & 0.2 & 0.3 \\ 0.3 & 0.4 & 0.3 \\ 0.2 & 0.4 & 0.4 \end{pmatrix}.$$

In this example the element $t_{12} = 0.2$ describes the probability that if it is cloudy one day, it will be sunny the following day.

If in this example the probable weather state on one day is given by $\mathbf{p}$, then the probability vector for the following day is $T\mathbf{p}$ and after 2 days it is $T^2\mathbf{p}$. For instance, it might be raining on the first day giving $\mathbf{p} = (0,0,1)'$, the next day's probability vector is $T\mathbf{p} = (0.3,0.3,0.4)'$ and for the subsequent day $T^2\mathbf{p} = (0.33,0.33,0.34)$.

Because of the special nature of stochastic matrices, their eigenvalues have special properties and these have important consequences for the associated statistical model.

Theorem 6.1

If T is an $n \times n$ stochastic matrix, T has an eigenvalue $\lambda_1 = 1$. All the eigenvalues of T satisfy the condition $|\lambda| \leqslant 1$.

Proof

Because T is a stochastic matrix $0 \leqslant t_{ij} \leqslant 1$ for all i and j. Moreover, $\sum_{i=1}^{n} t_{ij} = 1$ for all j.

Consider the matrix $T - I = A$. Each column of A has a sum $-1 + \sum_{i=1}^{n} t_{ij} = 0$, hence the row vectors of A are linearly dependent $(\mathbf{r}_1 + \mathbf{r}_2 + \ldots + \mathbf{r}_n = \mathbf{0})$. Because A is singular, $\lambda = 1$ is an eigenvalue of T.

The second part of the Theorem is proved by considering the properties of the transposed matrix T'. Since $|(T - \lambda I)| = |(T - \lambda I)'| = |(T' - \lambda I)|$, T' has the same eigenvalues as T. If λ is an eigenvalue and $\mathbf{v}$ is the associated eigenvector of T' then,

$$T'\mathbf{v} = \lambda \mathbf{v}. \tag{6.10}$$

Suppose $\mathbf{v}$ has an element of largest modulus v_m such that $|v_m| \geqslant |v_i|$ for $i = 1, \ldots, n$ ($\mathbf{v}$ may be real or complex). The mth row of Equation 6.10 gives:

$$\lambda v_m = t_{1m}v_1 + t_{2m}v_2 + \ldots + t_{nm}v_m.$$

Thus

$$|\lambda|\,|v_m| \leqslant t_{1m}|v_m| + t_{2m}|v_m| + \ldots + t_{nm}|v_m|, \tag{6.11}$$

since $0 \leqslant t_{im}$ and $|v_i| \leqslant |v_m|$ for $i = 1, \ldots, n$.

Using the column sum property of the stochastic matrix gives finally:

$$|\lambda|\,|v_m| \leqslant |v_m| \quad \text{or} \quad |\lambda| \leqslant 1.$$

Note that the method used to prove this Theorem can be readily adapted to prove that for any matrix the eigenvalue of largest modulus can never exceed the sum of the moduli of the elements in any row, or in any column of the matrix. This provides easily calculated upper and lower bounds for the eigenvalues.

Theorem 6.1 does not exclude the possibility that a stochastic matrix may have more than one eigenvalue of modulus 1. If $\lambda_1 = 1$ is not a repeated root and if $|\lambda_i| < 1$ for all $i > 1$, then in a long series of trials, regardless of the starting point, the system will tend to a limiting steady state probability vector

$\mathbf{p}_0 = \mathbf{v}_1$. This is proved in the case of non-defective matrices T by the following argument.

Let $Q = (\mathbf{v}_1, \mathbf{v}_2, \ldots, \mathbf{v}_n)$ be the modal matrix of T. Then

$$Q^{-1}TQ = D = \text{diag}\,(\lambda_1, \lambda_2, \ldots, \lambda_n).$$

Also
$$Q^{-1}T = DQ^{-1}. \tag{6.12}$$

Transposing Equation (6.12) gives: $T'Q^{-1'} = Q^{-1'}D.$ (6.13)

If the row vectors of Q^{-1} are denoted $\mathbf{w}_1', \mathbf{w}_2', \ldots, \mathbf{w}_n'$, Equation (6.13) shows that $\mathbf{w}_i$ is an eigenvector of T' corresponding to λ_i. $\mathbf{w}_i'$ is sometimes referred to as a left-hand eigenvector or eigenrow of T. In particular $\mathbf{w}_1$ is the eigenvector of T' corresponding to λ_1; the column sum property of T shows that $\mathbf{w}_1$, is proportional to $(1,1,\ldots,1)$. Also, because $Q^{-1}Q = I$, considering the first element of the first row of this product gives $\mathbf{w}_1'\mathbf{v}_1 = 1$. However, $\mathbf{v}_1 = \mathbf{p}_0$, a probability vector whose elements have sum $= 1$. Hence $\mathbf{w}_1 = (1,1,\ldots,1)$.

From Equation (6.12) $T = QDQ^{-1}$, hence, for any positive integer n,

$$T^n = QD^nQ^{-1}. \tag{6.14}$$

In the limit as $n \to \infty$, $\lambda_1{}^n = 1$ and $\lambda_i^n \to 0$ for $i > 1$. As n increases indefinitely, $D^n \to \text{diag}\,(1,0,\ldots,0)$. Thus, from (6.14), $T^n \to Q\,\text{diag}\,(1,0,\ldots,0)Q^{-1}$.

This product is expressible in terms of the eigenvectors and eigenrows as:

$$(\mathbf{v}_1, \mathbf{v}_2, \ldots, \mathbf{v}_n)\begin{pmatrix} 1 & 0 & . & . & . & 0 \\ 0 & 0 & 0 & . & . & 0 \\ & & & & & . \\ & & & & & . \\ 0 & . & . & . & 0 & 0 \end{pmatrix}\begin{pmatrix} \mathbf{w}_1' \\ \mathbf{w}_2' \\ . \\ . \\ \mathbf{w}_n' \end{pmatrix}$$

$$= (\mathbf{v}_1, \mathbf{v}_2, \ldots, \mathbf{v}_n)\begin{pmatrix} 1 & 1 & . & . & . & 1 \\ 0 & 0 & . & . & . & 0 \\ & & & & & . \\ & & & & & . \\ 0 & . & . & \ldots & . & 0 \end{pmatrix}, \text{ since } \mathbf{w}_1' = (1,1,\ldots,1),$$

$$= (\mathbf{v}_1, \mathbf{v}_1, \ldots, \mathbf{v}_1) = \lim_{n\to\infty} T^n.$$

If $\mathbf{p}$ is any probability vector with $\sum_{i=1}^{n} p_i = 1$, then:

$$\lim_{n\to\infty} T^n\mathbf{p} = \mathbf{v}_1 = \mathbf{p}_0. \tag{6.15}$$

Equation (6.15) shows that regardless of the initial probability vector **p**, after a sufficient number of repetitions of the experiment the probability vector approaches the steady state $\mathbf{p}_0$.

6.2.2 Systems of Linear Differential Equations

The system of linear differential equations:

$$\begin{aligned} \dot{y}_1 &= a_{11}y_1 + a_{12}y_2 + \ldots. + a_{1n}y_n \\ \dot{y}_2 &= a_{21}y_1 + a_{22}y_2 + \ldots. + a_{2n}y_n \\ &\vdots \\ \dot{y}_n &= a_{n1}y \;+ a_{n2}y \;\; + \ldots. + a_{nn}y_n,, \end{aligned} \tag{6.16}$$

with boundary conditions $y_i(0) = c_i$ for $i = 1,\ldots,n$, is said to be a **coupled system of linear differential equations with constant coefficients.** These equations, as written, are not readily solved because each equation involves all the variables. If the coefficient matrix A is non-defective then after a change of variables A can be replaced by an equivalent diagonal matrix so giving a simple uncoupled system of linear equations.

Equations (6.16) can be written in matrix form as:

$$\frac{\mathrm{d}\mathbf{y}}{\mathrm{d}t} = \dot{\mathbf{y}} = A\mathbf{y}, \quad \mathbf{y}(0) = \mathbf{c}. \tag{6.17}$$

Let $Q = (\mathbf{v}_1,\mathbf{v}_2,\ldots,\mathbf{v}_n)$ be a modal matrix of A, then $Q^{-1}AQ = D = \mathrm{diag}(\lambda_1,\ldots,\lambda_n)$, where the eigenvalues of A are $\lambda_1,\ldots,\lambda_n$. Let $\mathbf{y} = Q\mathbf{z}$, then using the linear properties of differentiation, $\dot{\mathbf{y}} = Q\dot{\mathbf{z}}$. After making the appropriate substitutions, (6.17) becomes:

$$Q\dot{\mathbf{z}} = AQ\mathbf{z} \quad \text{or} \quad \dot{\mathbf{z}} = Q^{-1}AQ\mathbf{z}. \tag{6.18}$$

The ith row Equation (6.18) can be simply written as:

$$\dot{z}_i = \lambda_i z_i.$$

The general solution of this equation is $z_i = k_i e^{\lambda_i t}$, where k_i is an arbitrary constant.

The values of the constants $k_1,\ldots,k_n$ are determined by the boundary conditions; because $\mathbf{z}(0) = \mathbf{k}$, we can obtain directly $\mathbf{k} = Q^{-1}\mathbf{y}(0) = Q^{-1}\mathbf{c}$. This method has practical disadvantages because it involves the computation of the inverse of the modal matrix.

As an alternative method, since $\mathbf{y} = Q\mathbf{z}$, these constants can be determined by solving the linear equation $Q\mathbf{k} = \mathbf{c}$. The solution of the differential equations can then be expressed as

$$\mathbf{y} = Q\mathbf{z} = \sum_{i=1}^{n} k_i e^{\lambda_i t}\mathbf{v}_i. \tag{6.19}$$

Example 6.4

Solve the differential equations:

$$\begin{aligned} \dot{y}_1 &= -\ y_1 + 2y_2 - y_3 \qquad \text{with } y_1(0) = 1, \\ \dot{y}_2 &= -\ 6y_1 + 7y_2 - 4y_3 \qquad\qquad y_2(0) = 2, \\ \dot{y}_3 &= -\ 6y_1 + 6y_2 - 4y_3 \qquad\qquad y_3(0) = 3. \end{aligned}$$

Solution

The reader is invited to verify for himself that the coefficient matrix A of these differential equations has eigenvalues $\lambda_1 = 1$, $\lambda_2 = 2$, $\lambda_3 = -1$ and associated eigenvectors $\mathbf{v}_1 = (1,1,0)'$, $\mathbf{v}_2 = (1,2,1)'$, $\mathbf{v}_3 = (0,1,2)'$.

A modal matrix of A is thus $Q = (\mathbf{v}_1,\mathbf{v}_2,\mathbf{v}_3)$. The linear substitution $\mathbf{y} = Q\mathbf{z}$ will produce an uncoupled set of differential equations of the form $\dot{z}_i = \lambda_i z_i$, with solution $z_i = k_i e^{\lambda_i t}$. Substituting these values of z_i into the equation $\mathbf{y} = Q\mathbf{z}$ gives as solution:

$$\mathbf{y} = \sum_{i=1}^{n} k_i e^{\lambda_i t}\mathbf{v}_i \text{ or } \begin{pmatrix} y_1 \\ y_2 \\ y_3 \end{pmatrix} = k_1 e^{t}\begin{pmatrix} 1 \\ 1 \\ 0 \end{pmatrix} + k_2 e^{2t}\begin{pmatrix} 1 \\ 2 \\ 1 \end{pmatrix} + k_3 e^{-t}\begin{pmatrix} 0 \\ 1 \\ 2 \end{pmatrix}.$$

k_1, k_2, k_3 are then found by substituting the value $t = 0$. The equations to be solved are then:

$$\begin{aligned} k_1 + k_2 \qquad &= 1, \\ k_1 + 2k_2 + k_3 &= 2, \\ k_2 + 2k_3 &= 3. \end{aligned} \tag{6.20}$$

The augmented matrix corresponding to Equations (6.20) is:

$$\left(\begin{array}{ccc|c} 1 & 1 & 0 & 1 \\ 1 & 2 & 1 & 2 \\ 0 & 1 & 2 & 3 \end{array}\right).$$

The sequence of elementary row operations $R_2 - R_1; R_3 - R_2$ reduces this to the echelon form:

$$\left(\begin{array}{ccc|c} 1 & 1 & 0 & 1 \\ 0 & 1 & 1 & 1 \\ 0 & 0 & 1 & 2 \end{array}\right).$$

From this the solution $k_1 = 2, k_2 = -1, k_3 = 2$ is obtained to give the solution of the differential equations:

$$\begin{aligned} y_1 &= 2e^t - e^{2t} \\ y_2 &= 2e^t - 2e^{2t} + 2e^{-t} \\ y_3 &= -e^{2t} + 4e^{-t}. \end{aligned}$$

6.2.3 Undamped Vibrations of a Mechanical System

For a vibrating mechanical system with n degrees of freedom, the equations of motion, in the absence of damping, are of the form $M\ddot{\mathbf{x}} + K\mathbf{x} = 0$ [McCallion, 1973]. M is called the **mass matrix**, K is the **stiffness matrix** and both matrices are symmetric. M is always a positive definite matrix for real physical systems.

The vector $\mathbf{x}$ describes the displacement of the system and for such systems there will always be some solutions in which the motion is simple harmonic with all the displacements proportional to sin ωt (or cos ωt). $\mathbf{x}$ is then of the form $\mathbf{x} = \mathbf{v} \sin \omega t$, where $\mathbf{v}$ is a fixed vector. ω is then called a **natural frequency** of the system and $\mathbf{v}$ is the associated **normal mode**. As is demonstrated below, these normal modes and normal frequencies are closely related to the eigenvalues and eigenvectors of a particular matrix.

Suppose $\mathbf{x} = \mathbf{v} \sin \omega t$ defines a normal mode and frequency of the system whose equation is $M\ddot{\mathbf{x}} + K\mathbf{x} = 0$. Then, since $\ddot{\mathbf{x}} = -\mathbf{v}\,\omega^2 \sin \omega t$, $\mathbf{v}$ and ω must satisfy the equation

$$-\omega^2 M\mathbf{v} + K\mathbf{v} = 0. \tag{6.21}$$

Equation (6.21) is in the form of a generalised eigenvalue problem. It can be re-written in standard form as:

$$M^{-1}K\mathbf{v} = \omega^2\mathbf{v}. \tag{6.22}$$

$\mathbf{v}$ is now seen to be an eigenvector of the matrix $A = M^{-1}K$ with associated eigenvalue $\lambda = \omega^2$.

One disadvantage of this formulation is that although M and K are symmetric matrices. the product $M^{-1}K$ will not usually be symmetric. This suggests that some of the eigenvalues of A might be complex.

The symmetry of the problem may be maintained by using the **Cholesky**

factorisation [Goult *et al.* 1974] of the positive definite matrix M. In this factorisation $M = LL'$ where L is a real lower triangular matrix. Equation (6.21) can then be re-written as:

$$Kv = \omega^2 LL'v,$$

or

$$L^{-1}Kv = \omega^2 L'v.$$

The substitution $\mathbf{w} = L'\mathbf{v}$ simplifies this equation to:

$$L^{-1}K(L^{-1})'\mathbf{w} = \omega^2\mathbf{w}. \tag{6.23}$$

This is now formulated as a standard eigenvalue equation for the symmetric matrix $B = L^{-1}A(L^{-1})'$. If K is positive definite, all the eigenvalues of this matrix will be positive giving real natural frequencies $\omega_1, \omega_2, \ldots, \omega_n$. Since the eigenvectors of B are mutually orthogonal, we can deduce that, because $\mathbf{w}_i = L'\mathbf{v}_i$, the normal modes corresponding to distinct natural frequancies ω_i, ω_j will be such that:

$$0 = \mathbf{w}_i \,.\, \mathbf{w}_j = \mathbf{w}_i'\mathbf{w}_j = \mathbf{w}_i LL'\mathbf{v}_j = \mathbf{v}_i'M\mathbf{v}_j. \tag{6.24}$$

Equation (6.24) shows that these normal modes are in conjugate directions relative to the mass matrix M.

Once all the normal modes and normal frequencies have been determined, linearly independent solutions of $M\ddot{\mathbf{x}} + K\mathbf{x} = 0$ are $\mathbf{v}_1 \sin \omega_1 t, \mathbf{v}_1 \cos \omega_1 t, \ldots, \mathbf{v}_n \cos \omega_n t$. The general solution is then:

$$\mathbf{x} = \sum_{i=1}^{n} (s_i \sin \omega_i t + c_i \cos \omega_i t)\mathbf{v}_i.$$

The $2n$ coefficients **s** and **c** are determined from the boundary conditions as defined by the starting conditions of the problem.

Example 6.5

Figure 6.1 shows a simple spring mass system consisting of three masses of mass M_1, M_2, and M_3 respectively connected by springs of stiffness k_1, k_2, k_3, k_4. Find the normal modes and normal frequencies of the system if the numerical values of the system constants are $M_1 = 2$, $M_2 = M_3 = 1$; $k_1 = 4$, $k_2 = k_3 = 2$, $k_4 = 1$. (It is assumed that the system is constrained to move vertically.)

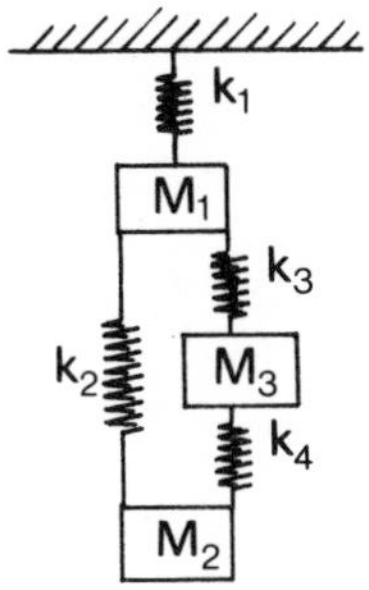

Figure 6.1

If x_1, x_2, x_3 respectively denote the displacements of M_1, M_2 and M_3 from their equilibrium position, the equations of motion are [see Burghes and Downs, 1975]:

$$\begin{aligned} M_1\ddot{x}_1 &= -k_1x_1 + k_2(x_2 - x_1) + k_3(x_3 - x_1), \\ M_2\ddot{x}_2 &= -k_2(x_2 - x_1) - k_4(x_2 - x_3), \\ M_3\ddot{x}_3 &= -k_3(x_3 - x_1) + k_4(x_2 - x_3). \end{aligned}$$

These can be rearranged as:

$$\begin{pmatrix} M_1 & 0 & 0 \\ 0 & M_2 & 0 \\ 0 & 0 & M_3 \end{pmatrix} \ddot{\mathbf{x}} + \begin{pmatrix} k_1 + k_2 + k_3, & -k_2 & -k_3 \\ -k_2 & k_2 + k_4, & -k_4 \\ -k_3 & -k_4 & k_3 + k_4 \end{pmatrix} \mathbf{x} = 0,$$

with symmetric mass matrix M and stiffness matrix K. For the given values of the system constants, these equations become:

$$\begin{pmatrix} 2 & 0 & 0 \\ 0 & 1 & 0 \\ 0 & 0 & 1 \end{pmatrix} \ddot{\mathbf{x}} + \begin{pmatrix} 8 & -2 & -2 \\ -2 & 3 & -1 \\ -2 & -1 & 3 \end{pmatrix} \mathbf{x} = 0.$$

The normal modes and the values of ω_i^2 are given by finding the eigenvectors and eigenvalues of $M^{-1}K$.

The characteristic polynomial of $M^{-1}K$ is:

$$\begin{vmatrix} (4-\lambda) & -1 & -1 \\ -2 & (3-\lambda) & -1 \\ -2 & -1 & (3-\lambda) \end{vmatrix} = 0.$$

This reduces to $(4-\lambda)(\lambda^2 - 6\lambda - 4) = 0$.

The normal frequencies are given by:

$$\omega_1^2 = 4, \omega_2^2 = 3 + \sqrt{5}, \omega_3^2 = 3 - \sqrt{5}.$$

The corresponding normal modes are given by solving:

$$\begin{pmatrix} 0 & -1 & -1 \\ -2 & -1 & -1 \\ -2 & -1 & -1 \end{pmatrix} \mathbf{v}_1 = \mathbf{0} \quad \text{and} \quad \begin{pmatrix} 1 \mp \sqrt{5}, & -1, & -1 \\ -2, & \mp\sqrt{5}, & -1 \\ -2, & -1, & \mp\sqrt{5} \end{pmatrix} \mathbf{v}_i = \mathbf{0},$$

for $i = 2,3$. The solutions are $\mathbf{v}_1 = (0,1,-1)'$, $\mathbf{v}_2 = (-\tfrac{1}{2} - \sqrt{5}/2,1,1)'$, $\mathbf{v}_3 = (-\tfrac{1}{2} + \sqrt{5}/2,1,1)'$.
In the first mode, M_1 is stationary and M_2 and M_3 are moving in opposite directions. In the second and third modes, M_2 and M_3 are vibrating together with M_1 either making large movements in the opposite direction (mode 2) or smaller movements in the same direction (mode 3).

6.2.4 Transfer Function Matrices

The use of Laplace transformations in linear system theory [Rosenbrock, 1970] gives a transfer function matrix which describes the response characteristics of the system. The transfer function matrix is of the form:

$$G(s) = C(sI - A)^{-1}B, \tag{6.25}$$

where s is the Laplace transform variable, A is an $n\times n$ matrix, B an $n\times p$ matrix and C an $m\times n$ matrix. In order to simplify the problem of finding the inverse Laplace transform, it is more convenient to have an expression for $G(s)$ as a sum of partial fractions in s. The method described below uses the eigenvalue properties of A in order to achieve this simplification.

If we assume that A is a non-defective matrix with eigenvalues $\lambda_1, \lambda_2, \ldots, \lambda_n$, then there is a modal matrix $P = (\mathbf{v}_1, \ldots, \mathbf{v}_n)$ such that $P^{-1}AP = D = \text{diag}(\lambda_1,\lambda_2,\ldots,\lambda_n)$. $sI - A$ can then be expressed in terms of D and P as:

$$(sI - A) = P(sI - D)P^{-1},$$

and hence

$$(sI - A)^{-1} = P(sI - D)^{-1}P^{-1}. \tag{6.26}$$

$(sI - D)$ is a diagonal matrix with elements $s - \lambda_i$; its inverse is therefore also a diagonal matrix with elements $(s - \lambda_i)^{-1}$. Substituting from Equation (6.26) into (6.25) gives:

$$G(s) = CP(\text{diag}((s - \lambda_1)^{-1}, \ldots, (s - \lambda_n)^{-1})P^{-1}B. \tag{6.27}$$

$G(s)$ will be expressed as a sum of simple fractions if the matrix coefficients of the individual terms $(s - \lambda_i)^{-1}$ in (6.27) can be identified.

Let $CP = E$ and $P^{-1}B = F$. If the column vectors of E are $\mathbf{u}_1, \ldots, \mathbf{u}_n$ and the row vectors of F are $\mathbf{w}_1', \ldots, \mathbf{w}_n'$, then Equation (6.27) can be rewritten as:

$$G(s) = (\mathbf{u}_1, \mathbf{u}_2, \ldots, \mathbf{u}_n) \begin{pmatrix} (s - \lambda_1)^{-1}\mathbf{w}_1' \\ (s - \lambda_2)^{-1}\mathbf{w}_2' \\ \cdot \\ \cdot \\ (s - \lambda_n)^{-1}\mathbf{w}_n' \end{pmatrix} .$$

Then
$$G(s) = \sum_{i=1}^{n} \frac{1}{s - \lambda_i} M^{(i)} \tag{6.28}$$

where the matrix $M^{(i)} = \mathbf{u}_i\mathbf{w}_i'$.

Equation (6.28) expresses $G(s)$ as a sum of partial fractions as required, but if some of the eigenvalues of A are complex, the terms in this expression cannot all be real. In this case it is possible, with a slight modification of method, to obtain an expression for $G(s)$ as a sum of real partial fractions with linear or quadratic denominators [Goult and Lipscombe, 1975].

Example 6.6

$$A = \begin{pmatrix} -1 & 2 & -1 \\ -6 & 7 & -4 \\ -6 & 6 & -4 \end{pmatrix} \quad C = \begin{pmatrix} 1 & 2 & 3 \\ 1 & 0 & 1 \end{pmatrix} \quad B = \begin{pmatrix} 1 & 2 \\ 0 & 1 \\ -1 & 1 \end{pmatrix} .$$

Find an expression for $G(s) = C(sI - A)^{-1}B$ in terms of partial fractions.

Solution

The matrix A in this example is identical to the coefficient matrix of Example 6.4. The eigenvalues of A are $\lambda_1 = 1, \lambda_2 = 2, \lambda_3 = -1$, and a modal matrix is $P = \begin{pmatrix} 1 & 1 & 0 \\ 1 & 2 & 1 \\ 0 & 1 & 2 \end{pmatrix}$ with inverse $P^{-1} = \begin{pmatrix} 3 & -2 & 1 \\ -2 & 2 & -1 \\ 1 & -1 & 1 \end{pmatrix}$.

Following the method described above:

$$E = CP = \begin{pmatrix} 1 & 2 & 3 \\ 1 & 0 & 1 \end{pmatrix} \begin{pmatrix} 1 & 1 & 0 \\ 1 & 2 & 1 \\ 0 & 1 & 2 \end{pmatrix} = \begin{pmatrix} 3 & 5 & 8 \\ 1 & 2 & 2 \end{pmatrix} = (\mathbf{u}_1, \mathbf{u}_2, \mathbf{u}_3)$$

and
$$F = P^{-1}B = \begin{pmatrix} 3 & -2 & 1 \\ -2 & 2 & -1 \\ 1 & -1 & 1 \end{pmatrix} \begin{pmatrix} 1 & 2 \\ 0 & 1 \\ -1 & 1 \end{pmatrix} = \begin{pmatrix} 2 & 5 \\ -1 & -3 \\ 0 & 2 \end{pmatrix} = \begin{pmatrix} \mathbf{w}_1' \\ \mathbf{w}_2' \\ \mathbf{w}_3' \end{pmatrix} .$$

Then $G(s) = C(sI - A)^{-1}B = E(sI - D)^{-1}F = \sum_{i=1}^{n} \frac{1}{s - \lambda_i} \mathbf{u}_i\mathbf{w}_i'$

$$= \frac{1}{s-1}\begin{pmatrix}6 & 15\\ 2 & 5\end{pmatrix} + \frac{1}{s-2}\begin{pmatrix}-5 & -15\\ -2 & -6\end{pmatrix} + \frac{1}{s+1}\begin{pmatrix}0 & 16\\ 0 & 4\end{pmatrix}.$$

6.3 SYMMETRIC MATRIX APPLICATIONS

In the previous Chapter it was shown that eigenvalues and eigenvectors of real symmetric matrices have particularly simple properties. Of these, the most important is that such a matrix is never defective even if it has multiple eigenvalues and is therefore always similar to a diagonal matrix. From the practical point of view it is useful to know that the eigenvalues are always real and therefore, unlike the general eigenvalue problem, there is no need to make provision for the possibility of complex eigenvectors occurring. Real symmetric matrices occur in a number of mathematical and physical problems and the application of their eigenvalue properties can lead to considerable simplification in these problems. Section 6.3.1 shows the relationship between quadric surfaces in 3-dimensional space and symmetric matrices. Section 6.3.2 is concerned with second order symmetric tensors which have applications in mechanics and elasticity.

6.3.1 Quadric Surfaces

In two-dimensional cartesian geometry, a general equation of degree two,

$$ax^2 + by^2 + 2cxy + 2dx + 2ey = 1, \tag{6.29}$$

represents a conic section. After a simple translation (change of origin) and rotation of the axes, Equation (6.29) is reduced to one of the simple standard forms:

$$\frac{Y^2}{A^2} + \frac{Y^2}{B^2} = 1, \qquad \text{(Ellipse)}$$

$$\frac{X^2}{A^2} - \frac{Y^2}{B^2} = 1, \qquad \text{(Hyperbola)}$$

or

$$Y^2 = 4AX \qquad \text{(Parabola).}$$

The particular form obtained will of course depend upon the coefficients in the original equation.

In three-dimensional geometry, an obvious generalisation of the above is to consider the surfaces represented by equations of the form:

$$ax^2 + by^2 + cz^2 + 2dyz + 2exz + 2fxy + 2gx + 2hy + 2kz = 1. \qquad (6.30)$$

Equation (6.30) defines a **quadratic surface.** In order to recognise the surface represented, the equation must be reduced to a simple standard form by using suitable geometric transformations.

The linear terms $2gx + 2hy + 2kz$ can be eliminated from (6.30) by the translation $x = X + \alpha$, $y = Y + \beta$, $z = Z + \gamma$ provided α,β,γ can be found to satisfy the equations:

$$\begin{aligned} a\alpha + f\beta + e\gamma &= -g, \\ f\alpha + b\beta + d\gamma &= -h, \\ e\alpha + d\beta + c\gamma &= -k. \end{aligned} \qquad (6.31)$$

If these equations are insoluble, the geometric interpretation is that the quadric has no finite centre and is called a **paraboloid.**

After solving Equations (6.31) and translating, Equation (6.30) becomes:

$$aX^2 + bY^2 + cZ^2 + 2dYZ + 2eXZ + 2fXY = K. \qquad (6.32)$$

Equation (6.32) is the general equation of a **central quadric**, that is it is the equation of a quadric surface with centre at the origin. If K is non-zero, it can be further simplified by dividing by K. The resulting equation is of the form:

$$a_{11}X^2 + a_{22}Y^2 + a_{33}Z^2 + 2a_{23}XZ + 2a_{13}XZ + 2a_{12}XY = 1. \qquad (6.33)$$

The left hand side of Equation (6.33) is a simple quadratic form. This suggests that the equation can be written in matrix form as:

$$\mathbf{x}'A\mathbf{x} = 1, \qquad (6.34)$$

where $\mathbf{x}' = (X,Y,Z)$ and A is a real symmetric 3X3 matrix.

Since A is a symmetric matrix, it will have three real eigenvalues associated with three mutually orthogonal eigenvectors. If the eigenvectors are divided by a scaling factor to give an orthonormal set of vectors, then the spectral matrix $P = (\mathbf{v}_1,\mathbf{v}_2,\mathbf{v}_3)$ will be orthogonal. The transformation $\mathbf{y} = P'\mathbf{x}$ corresponds to a rotation and after this rotation (6.34) is further simplified to:

$$\lambda_1 y_1{}^2 + \lambda_2 y_2{}^2 + \lambda_3 y_3{}^2 = 1. \qquad (6.35)$$

The eigenvectors of A are called the **Principal axes** of the quadric and (6.35) is the equation of a central quadric referred to its principal axes. From Equation (6.35) the geometric classification of the quadric is easily obtained.

If λ_1, λ_2, and λ_3 are all positive, the quadric is an **ellipsoid** with semi-axes $1/\sqrt{\lambda_1}$, $1/\sqrt{\lambda_2}$ and $1/\sqrt{\lambda_3}$. If the set $[\lambda_1,\lambda_2,\lambda_3]$ contains two positive terms and one negative term, the quadric is called a **hyperboloid of one sheet**. If we assume $\lambda_1 > 0$, $\lambda_2 > 0$ and $\lambda_3 < 0$, the cross-sections of the quadric by planes y_3 = constant are all ellipses, but the cross-sections by planes y_2 = constant or y_1 = constant are hyperbolae. If the set $[\lambda_1,\lambda_2,\lambda_3]$ contains two negative terms and only one positive term, the surface is a **hyperboloid of two sheets**. In this case the surface is in two distinct parts because if we assume $\lambda_1 < 0$, $\lambda_2 < 0$ and $\lambda_3 > 0$, the planes $y_3 = c$ will only intersect the surface if $|c| > 1/\sqrt{\lambda_3}$.

Finally, if λ_1, λ_2, λ_3 are all negative, there are no real points on the surface and (6.35) is then the equation of a **virtual quadric**.

Example 6.7

Find the directions of the principal axes of the central quadric:

$$x^2 + y^2 + z^2 + 2xy + 2xz - 2yz = 1.$$

Find the equation of this quadric when referred to its principal axes.

Solution

The equation can be written in matrix form as:

$$(x \quad y \quad z)\begin{pmatrix} 1 & 1 & 1 \\ 1 & 1 & -1 \\ 1 & -1 & 1 \end{pmatrix}\begin{pmatrix} x \\ y \\ z \end{pmatrix} = 1.$$

The principal axes are the eigenvectors of the coefficient matrix A. The eigenvalues of A are given by solving the characteristic equation:

$$|A - \lambda I| = \begin{vmatrix} 1-\lambda, & 1, & 1 \\ 1, & 1-\lambda, & -1 \\ 1, & -1, & 1-\lambda \end{vmatrix} = \begin{vmatrix} 2-\lambda, & 2-\lambda, & 0 \\ 1, & 1-\lambda, & -1 \\ 1, & -1, & 1-\lambda \end{vmatrix} = (2-\lambda)\begin{vmatrix} -\lambda & -1 \\ -2 & 1-\lambda \end{vmatrix}$$

The eigenvalues are thus $\lambda_1 = 2$, $\lambda_2 = 2$, $\lambda_3 = -1$.

Corresponding to $\lambda_3 = -1$, an eigenvector $\mathbf{v}_3$ is given by:

$$\begin{pmatrix} 2 & 1 & 1 \\ 1 & 2 & -1 \\ 1 & -1 & 2 \end{pmatrix}\mathbf{v}_3 = \mathbf{0}.$$

$\mathbf{v}_3$ is proportional to $(1,-1,-1)'$ and a vector in this direction of unit length is $\mathbf{u}_3 = (1/\sqrt{3},-1/\sqrt{3},-1/\sqrt{3})'$. Corresponding to $\lambda_1 = \lambda_2 = 2$ the eigenvectors are found by solving:

$$\begin{pmatrix} -1 & 1 & 1 \\ 1 & -1 & -1 \\ 1 & -1 & -1 \end{pmatrix} \mathbf{v} = \mathbf{0}.$$

In this case the coefficient matrix is of rank 1, showing that two linearly independent eigenvectors can be found here. A suitable pair of orthogonal vectors is $\mathbf{u}_1 = (1/\sqrt{2},0,1/\sqrt{2})'$ and $\mathbf{u}_2 = (-1/\sqrt{6},-2/\sqrt{6},1/\sqrt{6})'$.

An orthogonal spectral matrix for A is $P = (\mathbf{u}_1,\mathbf{u}_2,\mathbf{u}_3)$, and because $P'AP =$ diagonal $(2,2,-1)$, the equation of the quadric when referred to axes in the directions of $\mathbf{u}_1$, $\mathbf{u}_2$ and $\mathbf{u}_3$ respectively is:

$$2y_1^2 + 2y_2^2 - y_3^2 = 1.$$

This is the equation of a hyperboloid of one sheet.

Note that since $\lambda_1 = \lambda_2$, the directions of $\mathbf{u}_1$ and $\mathbf{u}_2$ are not uniquely determined and any two orthogonal directions in the plane normal to $\mathbf{u}_3$ could have been chosen as principal axes. In this special case, the cross-sections of the quadric by planes y_3 = constant are circles rather than ellipses. The surface could be generated by rotating the hyperbola $2y_2^2 - y_3^2 = 1$ about the axis $\mathbf{u}_3 = Oy_3$.

6.3.2 Cartesian Tensors

Cartesian tensors are physical quantities associated with 3-dimensional space which obey certain transformation laws when the coordinate axes are rotated.

A zero order tensor is a scalar and for this tensor the value is quite unaltered by any rotation of axes. Mass is a simple example of a tensor quantity of order zero.

A tensor of order 1 is a vector, and for this the transformation law is the same as that of the coordinates themselves. If the rotation from coordinate axes $Ox_1x_2x_3$ to $Ox_1{}^*x_2{}^*x_3{}^*$ is represented by the orthogonal matrix P, then a tensor of order 1 is any set of three quantities $\mathbf{v} = (v_1,v_2,v_3)'$ which transforms to the law:

$$\mathbf{v}^* = P\mathbf{v}. \tag{6.36}$$

The notation adopted here is that $\mathbf{v}$ gives the value of the tensor when referred to the original axes and $\mathbf{v}^*$ gives the corresponding values when referred to the new axes. Simple examples of vectors or first order tensors are the velocity and the acceleration of a particle.

A tensor of order 2 is a set of nine quantities, represented by the 3X3 matrix T, which transform according to the law:

$$T^* = PTP' \tag{6.37}$$

when referred to the new coordinate axes. In practice, second order tensors are often symmetric and contain only six distinct elements because $t_{12} = t_{21}$, $t_{13} = t_{31}$ and $t_{23} = t_{32}$. Equation (6.37) clearly shows that if T is symmetric when referred to one particular set of cartesian axes, it is symmetric for all possible rotations of the axes. Examples of second order symmetric tensors are the inertia tensor of a rigid body and stress and strain tensors. [S. C. Hunter, 1976]. In the following paragraphs, the properties of the inertia tensor are examined indetail, but all second order symmetric tensors have similar properties.

6.3.3 Inertia Tensors

The **inertia tensor** describes the distribution of mass in a rigid body and it is used in calculating the angular momentum and kinetic energy of the body when it is rotating. For a body consisting of a number of particles of masses m_k, $k = 1,2,\ldots,n$ and with position vectors $\mathbf{x}_k$, $k = 1,2,\ldots,n$, the inertia tensor H can be defined by the matrix equation:

$$H = (\Sigma m_k \mathbf{x}_k' \mathbf{x}_k)I - \Sigma m_k \mathbf{x}_k \mathbf{x}_k'. \tag{6.38}$$

In this equation the summation is all over particles of the body; for a continuous body this summation is replaced by integration. To show that H is a second order tensor, we must consider the effect on H of a rotation of the coordinate axes. Since this rotation does not affect the masses, relative to the new axes:

$$H^* = (\Sigma m_k \mathbf{x}_k^{*\prime} \mathbf{x}_k^*)I - \Sigma m_k \mathbf{x}_k^* \mathbf{x}_k^{*\prime}.$$

But for each particle $\mathbf{x}_k^* = P\mathbf{x}$. Hence we obtain:

$$H^* = (\Sigma m_k \mathbf{x}_k' P' P \mathbf{x}_k)I - \Sigma m_k P \mathbf{x}_k \mathbf{x}_k' P'. \tag{6.39}$$

Using the orthogonal properties of P, Equation (6.39) can be re-written as:

$$H^* = P[(\Sigma m_k \mathbf{x}_k' \mathbf{x}_k)I - \Sigma m_k \mathbf{x}_k \mathbf{x}_k']P' = PHP'.$$

This shows that H is indeed a second order tensor.

If $\mathbf{x} = (x,y,z)$, the individual elements of H are:

$$H = \begin{pmatrix} \Sigma m_k(y_k^2 + z_k^2), & -\Sigma m_k x_k y_k, & -\Sigma m_k x_k z_k, \\ -\Sigma m_k x_k y_k, & \Sigma m_k(x_k^2 + z_k^2), & -\Sigma m_k y_k z_k, \\ -\Sigma m_k x_k z_k, & -\Sigma m_k y_k z_k, & \Sigma m_k(x_k^2 + y_k^2) \end{pmatrix}.$$

The diagonal terms of this matrix are called **moments of inertia** and the off-diagonal terms, after changing signs, are called **products of inertia.**

Associated with any second order tensor are three **tensor invariants.** These tensor invariants are functions of the elements which are unaltered by any rotation of the axes. If the elements of H are denoted h_{ij}, the three invariants are:

$$I_1 = \text{trace}\, H = h_{11} + h_{22} + h_{33},$$

$$I_2 = \begin{vmatrix} h_{11} & h_{12} \\ h_{21} & h_{22} \end{vmatrix} + \begin{vmatrix} h_{11} & h_{13} \\ h_{31} & h_{33} \end{vmatrix} + \begin{vmatrix} h_{22} & h_{23} \\ h_{32} & h_{33} \end{vmatrix},$$

and

$$I_3 = |H|.$$

The invariance of these three expressions is deducible from the eigenvalue properties of H. Equation (6.37) shows that H and H^* are similar matrices, thus H and H^* must have the same characteristic polynomial. Expanding $|(H - \lambda I)|$ shows that I_1, I_2 and I_3 are respectively the coefficients of λ^2, $-\lambda$ and the constant term of the characteristic polynomial of H. The coefficients of the characteristic polynomial of H^* will have the same values, hence I_1, I_2 and I_3 are invariant under axis rotations.

Because H is a real symmetric 3X3 matrix, it will have three mutually orthogonal eigenvectors. If the coordinate axes are rotated to coincide with the directions of these vectors, H^* will have the simple form $H^* = PHP'$ $=$ diagonal $(\lambda_1, \lambda_2, \lambda_3)$. The eigenvalues λ_1, λ_2 and λ_3 are called the **principal moments of inertia** and their associated eigenvectors are called the **principal axes.** It is only when the principal axes are used as reference axes that all the products of inertia are zero. As in Example 6.7, the principal axes are not uniquely determined if two or more principal moments of inertia are equal.

λ_1, λ_2 and λ_3 represent the moments of inertia about the principal axes, for example $\lambda_1 = \Sigma m_k(y_k^{*2} + z_k^{*2})$. For a body of finite dimensions, these moments must all be positive. Hence $\lambda_1 > 0$, $\lambda_2 > 0$ and $\lambda_3 > 0$, showing that the inertia tensor is positive definite. This is a special property of the inertia tensor which it does not share with the stress and strain tensors because negative stresses and strains are physically possible. When a body with inertia tensor H is rotating about O with angular velocity $\boldsymbol{\omega}$, the angular momentum $\mathbf{h}$ is given by

$$\mathbf{h} = H\boldsymbol{\omega}. \tag{6.39}$$

In general **h** and $\boldsymbol{\omega}$ will not be in the same direction. Equation (6.39) shows clearly that **h** and $\boldsymbol{\omega}$ will only be parallel when $\boldsymbol{\omega}$ is an eigenvector of H, that is when the body is rotating about one of its principal axes.

Example 6.8

Referred to cartesian axes $Oxyz$, a body consists of a light framework with particles of mass m at points (1,0,0), (0,1,0), (0,1,1) and (1,0,1). Find the inertia tensor about O of the body, the directions of the principal axes and the principal moments of inertia.

Solution

The moments and products of inertia are:

$$\begin{aligned}
\Sigma m(y^2 + z^2) &= m.0 + m.1 + m.2 + m.1 = 4m,\\
\Sigma m(x^2 + z^2) &= m.1 + m.0 + m.1 + m.2 = 4m,\\
\Sigma m(x^2 + y^2) &= m.1 + m.1 + m.1 + m.1 = 4m,\\
\Sigma mxy &= m.0 + m.0 + m.0 + m.0 = 0,\\
\Sigma mxz &= m.0 + m.0 + m.0 + m.1 = m,\\
\text{and} \quad \Sigma myz &= m.0 + m.0 + m.1 + m.0 = m.
\end{aligned}$$

Referred to the original axes, the inertia tensor is:

$$H = m\begin{pmatrix} 4 & 0 & -1 \\ 0 & 4 & -1 \\ -1 & -1 & 4 \end{pmatrix}.$$

The eigenvalues of $1/m\, H$ are given by:

$$\begin{vmatrix} 4-\lambda & 0 & -1 \\ 0 & 4-\lambda & -1 \\ -1 & -1 & 4-\lambda \end{vmatrix} = \begin{vmatrix} 4-\lambda & 0 & -1 \\ \lambda-4 & 4-\lambda & -1 \\ 0 & -1 & 4-\lambda \end{vmatrix} = 0.$$

This reduces to $(4-\lambda)\begin{vmatrix} 4-\lambda & -2 \\ -1 & 4-\lambda \end{vmatrix} = 0$,

giving eigenvalues $\lambda_1 = 4$, $\lambda_2 = 4 + \sqrt{2}$, $\lambda_3 = 4 - \sqrt{2}$. The principal moments are thus $4m$, $(4+\sqrt{2})m$ and $(4-\sqrt{2})m$. The principal axes are given by solving:

$$\begin{pmatrix} 0 & 0 & 1 \\ 0 & 0 & -1 \\ -1 & -1 & 0 \end{pmatrix}\mathbf{v}_1 = \mathbf{0}, \quad \begin{pmatrix} -\sqrt{2} & 0 & -1 \\ 0 & -\sqrt{2} & -1 \\ -1 & -1 & -\sqrt{2} \end{pmatrix}\mathbf{v}_2 = \mathbf{0} \text{ and } \begin{pmatrix} \sqrt{2} & 0 & -1 \\ 0 & \sqrt{2} & -1 \\ -1 & -1 & \sqrt{2} \end{pmatrix}\mathbf{v}_3 = \mathbf{0}.$$

Unit vectors in the directions of the principal axes are thus $\mathbf{v}_1 = (1/\sqrt{2}, -1/\sqrt{2}, 0)'$, $\mathbf{v}_2 = (1/2, 1/2, -\sqrt{2}/2)'$ and $\mathbf{v}_3 = (1/2, 1/2, \sqrt{2}/2)'$.

The reader is invited to verify that if $P' = (\mathbf{v}_1,\mathbf{v}_2,\mathbf{v}_3)$ then $H^* = PHP'$ is a diagonal tensor.

6.3.4 Stress Tensors

The **stress tensor** S describes the internal forces acting in a continuous body. Stress is defined to be force per unit area and the components of the stress tensor are defined below.

Referred to cartesian axes $Oxyz$:

$$S = \begin{pmatrix} \sigma_{xx} & \sigma_{xy} & \sigma_{xz} \\ \sigma_{yx} & \sigma_{yy} & \sigma_{yz} \\ \sigma_{zx} & \sigma_{zy} & \sigma_{zz} \end{pmatrix} .$$

If a plane whose normal is in the direction Ox is drawn through a fixed internal point P of the body, there will generally be an internal stress acting across this plane at P. This stress can be resolved into three components parallel to the axes Ox, Oy and Oz respectively. These three components define the stress components σ_{xx}, σ_{yx} and σ_{zx} at P (see Figure 6.2).

$(\sigma_{xy},\sigma_{yy},\sigma_{zy})$ and $(\sigma_{xz},\sigma_{yz},\sigma_{zz})$ are similarly defined for planes through P with normals in the directions of Oy and Oz respectively.

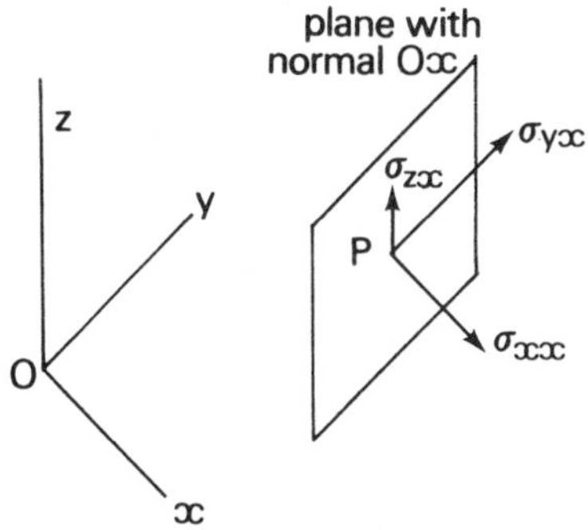

Figure 6.2

Note that, as shown in Figure 6.2, σ_{xx} is the force per unit area at P exerted by the part of the body to the right of the plane on the part to the left of this plane.

The under tensor S can be shown to be symmetric by considering the moments about P of the forces acting on an infinitesimal cube surrounding P with edges parallel to the coordinate axes. It can also be proved [S. C. Hunter, 1976] that S is a second order tensor.

Although the elements of S are related to the stresses across three particular planes through P, S provides a complete description of the stress at P. The stress s across a plane through P whose normal is in the direction of the unit vector **n** is given by the equation:

$$\mathbf{s} = S\mathbf{n}. \tag{6.40}$$

In this equation s_1, s_2 and s_3 are the resolved parts of the stress in the directions of Ox, Oy and Oz respectively. Equation (6.40) shows that the stress acting across a plane surface will not be normal to the plane unless **n** is an eigenvector of S. Since S is represented by a real symmetric matrix, it will have eigenvectors in three mutually orthogonal directions. These are called the directions of the principal axes and the corresponding eigenvalues are called the principal stresses.

PROBLEMS

6.1 Show that the mapping $\phi(f(x,y)) = \dfrac{\partial f}{\partial x}$ is a linear transformation of the space of differentiable fractions of two real variables into the space of functions of two real variables. Find the kernel of ϕ and hence find the general solution of $\dfrac{\partial f}{\partial x} = e^{xy}$.

6.2 Solve the differential equation:

$$\frac{d^2y}{dx^2} - 3\frac{dy}{dx} - 4y = e^{2x} \text{ with } y(0) = 0,\ y'(0). = 1.$$

6.3 Solve the differential equation:

$$\frac{d^2y}{dx^2} - \frac{dy}{dx} - 6y = x + 1 \text{ with } y(0) = y'(0) = 2.$$

6.4 $A = \begin{pmatrix} 1 & 2 & 1 & 0 \\ 2 & 1 & 3 & 1 \\ 5 & 4 & 7 & 2 \end{pmatrix}$.

Find rank(A) and the most general solution of the linear equations $A\mathbf{x} = (2,1,4)'$.

6.5 **x** and **y** are vectors in R^3 referred to rectangular cartesian axes. Show that the value of the scalar product **x**.**y** is invariant under any rotation of the axes. Is the value of **x**.**y** affected by translation?

6.6 Show that the matrix,

$$S = \begin{pmatrix} 0 & \frac{1}{2} & \frac{1}{4} & \frac{1}{4} \\ \frac{1}{2} & 0 & \frac{1}{4} & \frac{1}{2} \\ \frac{1}{4} & 0 & \frac{1}{4} & \frac{1}{4} \\ \frac{1}{4} & \frac{1}{2} & \frac{1}{4} & 0 \end{pmatrix}$$

Is stochastic and find its steady state vector.

6.7 Prove that if A and B are stochastic $n \times n$ matrices, the product AB is also a stochastic matrix. Deduce that A^n is stochastic for any positive integer n.

6.8 Prove that, for the stochastic matrix $A = \begin{pmatrix} 0 & \frac{1}{2} & 0 \\ 1 & 0 & 1 \\ 0 & \frac{1}{2} & 0 \end{pmatrix}$, $A^{2n+1} = A$ for any positive integer n. Show that there is a steady state vector $\mathbf{p}_0$ such that $A\mathbf{p}_0 = \mathbf{p}_0$ but deduce that the system will not approach this steady state from an arbitrary initial probability vector $\mathbf{p}$.

6.9 Solve the differential equations:

$$\begin{aligned} \dot{x}_1 &= 16x_1 - x_2 - 6x_3 \quad \text{with } x_1(0) = 0 \\ \dot{x}_2 &= 22x_1 - x_2 - 8x_3 \qquad\quad x_2(0) = 1 \\ \dot{x}_3 &= 38x_1 - 2x_2 - 15x_3 \qquad x_3(0) = -1. \end{aligned}$$

6.10 Solve the differential equations:

$$\frac{d^2x_1}{dt^2} = -14x_1 + 5x_2 \quad \text{with } x_1(0) = 1, \ \dot{x}_1(0) = 0,$$

$$\frac{d^2x_2}{dt^2} = -10x_1 + x_2, \qquad x_2(0) = 2, \ \dot{x}_2(0) = -1.$$

6.11 Figure 6.3 shows a simple spring mass system consisting of three equal masses, each of mass m, connected by springs of stiffness k. Find the normal modes and normal frequencies of the system if it is constrained to move horizontally between the fixed supports shown.

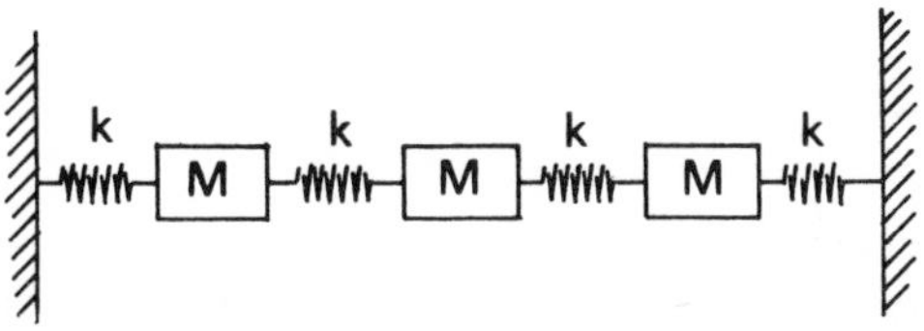

Figure 6.3

6.12 Find the normal modes and normal frequencies of vibrating mechanical system with mass matrix $M = \begin{pmatrix} 2 & 1 \\ 1 & 4 \end{pmatrix}$ and stiffness matrix $K = \begin{pmatrix} 6 & -1 \\ -1 & 2 \end{pmatrix}$.

6.13 Several iterative methods of solving the linear equations $A\mathbf{x} = \mathbf{b}$ exist [Goult, Hoskins, Milner, Pratt 1974]. Such methods rely on an iteration formula of the form $\mathbf{x}^{(r+1)} = M\mathbf{x}^{(r)} + \mathbf{c}$ where $\mathbf{x}^{(r)}$ and $\mathbf{x}^{(r+1)}$ are successive approximations to the solution, M is a constant iteration matrix and $\mathbf{c}$ is a constant vector. Prove that the iterative method is convergent if M is a non-defective matrix with $|\lambda_i| < 1$ for all eigenvalues λ_i.

6.14 $A = L + D + U$ where A is an $n \times n$ matrix, L is a lower triangular matrix, D is a diagonal matrix and U is an upper triangular matrix. The Jacobi iterative scheme for solving $A\mathbf{x} = \mathbf{b}$ is defined by the equations:

$$\mathbf{x}^{(r+1)} = -D^{-1}(L + U)\mathbf{x}^{(r)} + D^{-1}\mathbf{b}.$$

Show that if this method converges it will converge to a solution of the equations. Prove that if $A = \begin{pmatrix} 5 & 2 \\ 1 & 4 \end{pmatrix}$ the method is convergent for any value of $\mathbf{b}$ (see 6.13).

6.15 For a simple linear system:

$$A = \begin{pmatrix} 3 & 1 \\ 2 & 2 \end{pmatrix} \quad B = \begin{pmatrix} 4 \\ 5 \end{pmatrix} \quad C = (-1 \quad 2).$$

Find the value of the transfer function $G(s) = C(sI - A)^{-1}B$:

(a) by direct calculation of $(sI - A)^{-1}$.

(b) by using the algorithm described in 6.2.4.

6.16 $A = \begin{pmatrix} 5 & 4 & -2 \\ -9 & -8 & 5 \\ -6 & -6 & 5 \end{pmatrix} \quad B = \begin{pmatrix} 1 & 2 & 0 \\ 0 & 1 & 2 \\ 0 & 0 & 1 \end{pmatrix} \quad C = \begin{pmatrix} 1 & 0 & -1 \\ 0 & 1 & 0 \end{pmatrix}.$

Express the transfer function matrix $G(s) = C(sI - A)^{-1}B$ as a sum of partial fractions in s.

6.17 Find the centre of the quadric surface:

$$x^2 - 3y^2 + 4z^2 - 6xy + 2x + 4y - 8z = 15.$$

Find the principal axes of this quadric and identify its type.

6.18 Show that the central quadric:

$$11x^2 + 11y^2 + 20z^2 - 10xy - 8xz + 8yz = 6$$

is an ellipsoid, find its principal axes and the lengths of its semi-axes.

6.19 A body consists of a light framework with particles of mass m at the points (1,0,0), (0,1,0), (1,1,0), (0,0,1), (1,0,1), (0,1,1) and (1,1,1). Find its inertia tensor about O. Find its angular momentum when it is rotating about O with angular velocity $\boldsymbol{\omega} = (2,1,1)'$. Find the principal moments of inertia and the corresponding principal axes.

6.20 The stress tensor at a point P in an elastic body is:

$$S = \begin{pmatrix} 5 & -4 & 11 \\ -4 & 20 & -4 \\ 11 & -4 & 5 \end{pmatrix}.$$

Find the three tensor invariants I_1, I_2, and I_3. Find the principal stresses and the directions of the principal axes of stress. Can the invariants be simply expressed in terms of the principal stresses?

Appendix

Matrix Algebra and Determinants

MATRICES – BASIC DEFINITIONS

An $m \times n$ matrix A is a set of $m.n$ elements (usually real numbers) arranged in a rectangular array of m rows and n columns. The element in row i column j of matrix A is identified by the symbol a_{ij}.

Two matrices A and B are **equal** if they are of the same dimensions (that is both $m \times n$) and if all corresponding pairs of elements are equal, or if:

$$a_{ij} = b_{ij} \text{ for } i = 1, \ldots, m \text{ and } j = 1, \ldots, n.$$

If A and B are both $m \times n$ matrices, their **sum** $C = A + B$ is defined by the equations:

$$c_{ij} = a_{ij} + b_{ij} \text{ for } i = 1, \ldots, m;\ j = 1, \ldots, n.$$

The sum is undefined if A and B have different dimensions.

$-A$ is defined as the matrix with element $-a_{ij}$ in row i column j. $A - B$ is then defined as $A + (-B)$.

The $m \times n$ **zero** matrix O is the $m \times n$ matrix with element 0 in every position. Clearly $A + (-A) = 0$.

For any constant λ, $B = \lambda A$ is defined by the equations $b_{ij} = \lambda a_{ij}$.

The **product** $C = AB$ of an $m \times n$ matrix A and an $n \times p$ matrix B is an $m \times p$ matrix defined by the equations:

$$c_{ij} = a_{i1}b_{1j} + a_{i2}b_{2j} + \ldots + a_{in}b_{nj} = \sum_{k=1}^{n} a_{ik}b_{kj}.$$

The element c_{ij} of the product matrix C can be considered as the **scalar product** of the ith row of matrix A and the jth column of matrix B The product AB only exists if the matrices are **conformable** for multiplication, that is if the number of columns in A is equal to the number of rows in B.

The nXn **identity matrix** I is a matrix whose elements δ_{ij} are given by the equations:

$$\delta_{ij} = 0 \text{ if } i \neq j \text{ for } i = 1, \ldots, n;\ j = 1, \ldots, n.$$
$$\delta_{ii} = 1 \text{ for } i = 1, \ldots, n.$$

I has the properties that, for any conformable matrices A and B, $AI = A$ and $IB = B$.

An nXn matrix A is said to be **non-singular** if there is an **inverse** matrix A^{-1} with the properties:

$$AA^{-1} = A^{-1}A = I.$$

The **transpose** of an mXn matrix A is an nXm matrix denoted by A' whose elements α_{ij} are given by the equations:

$$\alpha_{ij} = a_{ji} \text{ for } i = 1, \ldots, n;\ j = 1, \ldots, m.$$

A' can be considered as the matrix obtained by interchanging rows and columns in A.

If, for an nXn matrix A, $A' = A$ then A is said to be **symmetric.**

If, for a square matrix B, $B' = -B$ then B is said to be **skew-symmetric** or **anti-symmetric.**

An nXn matrix P with the properties $P'P = PP' = I$ is called **orthogonal.**

Examples and Algebraic Properties

Let $A = \begin{pmatrix} 1 & 0 & -1 \\ 2 & 1 & 2 \\ 1 & 1 & 3 \end{pmatrix}$ $B = \begin{pmatrix} 2 & 1 & 1 \\ -1 & 2 & 1 \\ 1 & 2 & 0 \end{pmatrix}$ $C = \begin{pmatrix} 1 & 0 \\ -2 & 1 \\ 1 & 3 \end{pmatrix}$ $I = \begin{pmatrix} 1 & 0 & 0 \\ 0 & 1 & 0 \\ 0 & 0 & 1 \end{pmatrix}.$

Then $A + B =$

$$\begin{pmatrix} 1 & 0 & -1 \\ 2 & 1 & 2 \\ 1 & 1 & 3 \end{pmatrix} + \begin{pmatrix} 2 & 1 & 1 \\ -1 & 2 & 1 \\ 1 & 2 & 0 \end{pmatrix} = \begin{pmatrix} 3 & 1 & 0 \\ 1 & 3 & 3 \\ 2 & 3 & 3 \end{pmatrix}. \quad 2C = \begin{pmatrix} 2 & 0 \\ -4 & 2 \\ 2 & 6 \end{pmatrix}.$$

$$AB = \begin{pmatrix} 1 & 0 & -1 \\ 2 & 1 & 2 \\ 1 & 1 & 3 \end{pmatrix} \begin{pmatrix} 2 & 1 & 1 \\ -1 & 2 & 1 \\ 1 & 2 & 0 \end{pmatrix} = \begin{pmatrix} 1 & -1 & 1 \\ 5 & 8 & 3 \\ 4 & 9 & 2 \end{pmatrix}.$$

$$BA = \begin{pmatrix} 2 & 1 & 1 \\ -1 & 2 & 1 \\ 1 & 2 & 0 \end{pmatrix} \begin{pmatrix} 1 & 0 & -1 \\ 2 & 1 & 2 \\ 1 & 1 & 3 \end{pmatrix} = \begin{pmatrix} 5 & 2 & 3 \\ 4 & 3 & 8 \\ 5 & 2 & 3 \end{pmatrix}.$$

$$AC = \begin{pmatrix} 1 & 0 & -1 \\ 2 & 1 & 2 \\ 1 & 1 & 3 \end{pmatrix} \begin{pmatrix} 1 & 0 \\ -2 & 1 \\ 1 & 3 \end{pmatrix} = \begin{pmatrix} 0 & -3 \\ 2 & 7 \\ 2 & 10 \end{pmatrix}.$$

$$IC = \begin{pmatrix} 1 & 0 & 0 \\ 0 & 1 & 0 \\ 0 & 0 & 1 \end{pmatrix} \begin{pmatrix} 1 & 0 \\ -2 & 1 \\ 1 & 3 \end{pmatrix} = \begin{pmatrix} 1 & 0 \\ -2 & 1 \\ 1 & 3 \end{pmatrix}.$$

Summation Properties:

If A, B, C are any $m \times n$ matrices, then

$$A + B = B + A.$$
$$A + (B + C) = (A + B) + C.$$

For any scalar λ, $\lambda(A + B) = \lambda A + \lambda B$, while $A + O = A$, where O is the $m \times n$ zero matrix.

Properties of Matrix Products:

If the matrices below are conformable for multiplication, then:

$$A(BC) = (AB)C,$$
$$A(B + D) = AB + AD \text{ and } (E + F)A = EA + FA,$$
$$AO = O,$$
$$(\lambda A)B = \lambda(AB) = A(\lambda B) \text{ for any scalar } \lambda.$$

If A is a non-singular $n \times n$ matrix, the solution of the matrix equation $AX = B$ is $X = A^{-1}B$ and the solution of $YA = C$ is $Y = CA^{-1}$.

If A and B are both non-singular $n \times n$ matrices, then $(AB)^{-1} = B^{-1}A^{-1}$.

The transpose has the properties:

$$(A + B)' = A' + B'$$

and

$$(AB)' = B'A'.$$

Note that for conformable matrices A and B it is not generally true that $AB = BA$, indeed B and A may not be conformable for multiplication. Even when A and B are both square matrices, the above numerical example shows that AB can differ considerably from BA. If, for any particular matrices A and B, $AB = BA$, then A and B are said to **commute.**

Partitioned Matrices

For some purposes it is convenient to sub-divide a given matrix A into a number of smaller sub-matrices by horizontal and vertical lines or partitions. This is particularly useful for very large sparse matrices with many of the sub-matrices zero.

For reference purposes, the submatrices of a partitional matrix can be indexed in a similar way to the indexings of the elements of a matrix:

For example $A = \begin{pmatrix} \begin{array}{cc|ccc} a_{11} & a_{12} & a_{13} & a_{14} & a_{15} \\ a_{21} & a_{22} & a_{23} & a_{23} & a_{25} \\ \hline a_{31} & a_{32} & a_{33} & a_{34} & a_{35} \\ a_{41} & a_{42} & a_{43} & a_{44} & a_{45} \end{array} \end{pmatrix} = \begin{pmatrix} A_{11} & A_{12} \\ A_{21} & A_{22} \end{pmatrix}$

where, for instance, $A_{12} = \begin{pmatrix} a_{13} & a_{14} & a_{15} \\ a_{23} & a_{24} & a_{25} \end{pmatrix}$.

The sums and products of partitional matrices can be calculated by treating the submatrices of partitional matrices in exactly the same way as the elements of a smaller matrix.

If A and B are $m \times n$ matrices which are both partitioned in the same way, then $A + B =$

$$\begin{pmatrix} A_{11} & A_{12} & \dots & A_{1s} \\ \cdot & & & \cdot \\ \cdot & & & \cdot \\ \cdot & & & \cdot \\ A_{r1} & & & A_{rs} \end{pmatrix} + \begin{pmatrix} B_{11} & \dots & B_{1s} \\ \cdot & & \cdot \\ \cdot & & \cdot \\ \cdot & & \cdot \\ B_{r1} & \dots & B_{rs} \end{pmatrix} = \begin{pmatrix} A_{11}+B_{11} & \dots & A_{1s}+B_{1s} \\ \cdot & & \cdot \\ \cdot & & \cdot \\ \cdot & & \cdot \\ A_{r1}+B_{r1} & \dots & A_{rs}+B_{rs} \end{pmatrix}$$

For the product AB to be calculated in a partitioned form, it is necessary for the partitioning to be conformable for multiplication. If A is an $m \times n$ matrix and B is an $n \times p$ matrix, then the partitioning applied to the columns of A must be identical to the partitioning applied to the rows of B. The resulting product will then be a partitioned matrix whose partitioning matches the row partitioning of A and the column partitioning of B.

For example, if $A = \begin{pmatrix} A_{11} & A_{12} \\ A_{21} & A_{22} \\ A_{31} & A_{32} \end{pmatrix} = \begin{pmatrix} \begin{array}{cc|ccc} a_{11} & a_{12} & a_{13} & a_{14} & a_{15} \\ a_{21} & a_{23} & a_{23} & a_{24} & a_{25} \\ \hline a_{31} & a_{32} & a_{33} & a_{34} & a_{35} \\ \hline a_{41} & a_{42} & a_{43} & a_{44} & a_{45} \end{array} \end{pmatrix}$

and $B = \begin{pmatrix} B_{11} & B_{12} \\ B_{21} & B_{22} \end{pmatrix} = \begin{pmatrix} \begin{array}{cc|cc} b_{11} & b_{12} & b_{13} & b_{14} \\ b_{21} & b_{22} & b_{23} & b_{24} \\ \hline b_{31} & b_{32} & b_{33} & b_{34} \\ b_{41} & b_{42} & b_{43} & b_{44} \\ b_{51} & b_{52} & b_{53} & b_{54} \end{array} \end{pmatrix}$

the product AB can be calculated in partitional form as:

$$AB = \begin{pmatrix} A_{11}B_{11} + A_{12}B_{21} & A_{11}B_{12} + A_{11}B_{22} \\ A_{21}B_{11} + A_{22}B_{21} & A_{21}B_{12} + A_{21}B_{22} \\ A_{31}B_{11} + A_{32}B_{21} & A_{31}B_{12} + A_{31}B_{22} \end{pmatrix} .$$

Determinants

The determinant $|A|$ is a number associated with an $n \times n$ matrix A such that $|A| = 0$ whenever the equations $A\mathbf{x} = 0$ have a non trivial solution. $|A|$ can be defined in several equivalent ways, the simplest definition being an inductive one defining the determinant of an $n \times n$ matrix in terms of determinants of $(n-1)\times(n-1)$ matrices.

$$|a_{11}| = a_{11},$$

$$\begin{vmatrix} a_{11} & a_{12} \\ a_{21} & a_{22} \end{vmatrix} = a_{11}|a_{22}| - a_{12}|a_{21}| = a_{11}a_{22} - a_{12}a_{21},$$

$$\begin{vmatrix} a_{11} & a_{12} & a_{13} \\ a_{21} & a_{22} & a_{23} \\ a_{31} & a_{32} & a_{33} \end{vmatrix} = a_{11}\begin{vmatrix} a_{22} & a_{23} \\ a_{32} & a_{33} \end{vmatrix} - a_{12}\begin{vmatrix} a_{21} & a_{23} \\ a_{31} & a_{32} \end{vmatrix} + a_{13}\begin{vmatrix} a_{21} & a_{22} \\ a_{31} & a_{32} \end{vmatrix}.$$

In general

$$\begin{vmatrix} a_{11} & a_{12} & \cdots & a_{1n} \\ \cdot & & & \\ \cdot & & & \\ \cdot & & & \\ a_{n1} & & & a_{nn} \end{vmatrix} = a_{11}M_{11} - a_{12}M_{12} + a_{13}M_{13} - \ldots + (-1)^n a_{1n}M_{1n},$$

where M_{ij}, the minor of a_{ij}, denotes the $(n-1)\times(n-1)$ determinant obtained by removing row i and column j from A.

Properties of Determinants: (all deducible from the definition).
1. $|A| = |A'|$.
2. If B is obtained from A by interchanging two rows (or columns) then $|B| = -|A|$.
3. If A has two equal rows (or columns) then $|A| = 0$.
4. If B is obtained from A by multiplying any row (or column) by a constant k then $|B| = k\,|A|$.
5. If B is obtained from A by adding to any row (or column) a constant multiple of another row (or column) then $|B| = |A|$.
6. $|AB| = |A|\,|B|$ where AB denotes the matrix product of A and B.
7. $|A| = 0$ if and only if $A\mathbf{x} = 0$ has a solution other than $\mathbf{x} = \mathbf{0}$.

Note that properties 2, 4, 5 above are particularly useful because they provide a facility for simplifying a determinant before expanding in accordance with the definition.

The **cofactor** of a_{ij} in A is the coefficient of a_{ij} when the determinant is exapnded fully. The cofactor of a_{ij} is usually denoted A_{ij}. From the determinant definition the following properties of the cofactors can be deduced:

$C1$; $A_{ij} = (-1)^{i+j} M_{ij}$, where M_{ij} is the minor of a_{ij}.

$C2$; For all $i = 1, \ldots, n$ $\sum_{k=1}^{n} a_{ik} A_{ik} = |A|$,

and $\sum_{k=1}^{n} a_{ik} A_{jk} = 0$ if $j \neq i$.

$C3$; For all $j = 1, \ldots, n$ $\sum_{i=1}^{n} a_{ij} A_{ij} = |A|$

and $\sum_{i=1}^{n} a_{ij} A_{ik} = 0$ if $j \neq k$.

The **Adjoint** of an $n \times n$ matrix A, denoted Adj A, is an $n \times n$ matrix with element α_{ij} in row i, column j, defined by the equations:

$$\alpha_{ij} = A_{ji} \text{ for } i = 1, \ldots, n,\ j = 1, \ldots, n.$$

[Adj A can be considered as the transpose of the matrix of cofactors of A.]

From properties $C2$ and $C3$ we can deduce that:

$$\mathrm{A(Adj\ A) = (Adj\ A)A = |A|I}$$

where I is the $n \times n$ identity matrix.

From this it follows that if $|A| \neq 0$ then A^{-1} can be obtained from the equation:

$$A^{-1} = \frac{1}{|A|} \text{Adj } a.$$

In practice this gives a very inconvenient method of computing the inverse of a large matrix.

REFERENCES

Archbold, J. W., *Algebra,* Pitman and Sons, 1964.

Bachman, G., Narici, L., *Functional Analysis,* Academic Press, 1968.

Burghes, D. N., Downs, A. M., *Classical Mechanics and Control,* Ellis Horwood, 1975.

Copson,, E. T., *Metric Spaces,* Cambridge University Press, 1966.

Dixon, L. C. W., *Nonlinear Optimisation,* English Universities Press, 1972.

Faux, I. D., Pratt, M. J., *Applied Geometry for Computer Aided Design and Manufacture,* Ellis Horwood.

Fletcher, R., Reeves, C. M., *Function Minimisation by Conjugate Gradients,* Computer Journal 7, 149-154, 1964.

Goult, Hoskins, Milner, Pratt, *Applicable Mathematics,* Macmillan, 1973.

Goult, Hoskins, Milner, Pratt, *Computational Methods in Linear Algebra,* Stanley Thornes, 1974.

Goult, R. J., Lipscombe, J. M., 'An Algorithm to Obtain the Transfer Function Matrix', I.M.A. Bulletin, 1975.

Gray, J. R., *Probability,* Oliver and Boyd, 1967.

Hunter, S. C., *Mechanics of Continuous Media,* Ellis Horwood, 1976.

McCallion, H., *Vibration of Linear Mechanical Systems,* Longman, 1973.

Nering, E. V.., *Linear Algebra and Matrix Theory,* Wiley-Interscience, 1970.

Rosenbrock, H. H., 'An Automatic Method of Finding the Greatest or the Least Value of a Function', Computer Journal, 1960.

Rosenbrock, H. H., *State-Space and Multivariable Theory,* Nelson, 1970.

Semple, J. G., Kneebone, G. T., *Algebraic Projective Geometry,* Oxford University Press, 1952.

Stewart, G. W., *Introduction to Matrix Computations,* Academic Press, 1973.

White, A. J., *Real Analysis, an Introduction,* Addison-Wesley, 1968.

Whittaker, E. J., Watson, G. N., *A Course of Modern Analysis,* Cambridge University Press, 1927.

Wilkinson, J. H., *The Algebraic Eigenvalue Problem,* Oxford University Press, 1964.

Problem Solutions and Hints

CHAPTER 1

1.1 (a) not a vector space, V_1, V_4 violated; (b) vector space; (c) vector space; (d) V_1, V_4, V_6 violated.

1.2 One possible basis of subspace is $[x-2, x^2-2x, x^3-2x^2]$ adding 1 gives a basis of P^3. (Many other answers).

1.4 (b) and (c) are subspaces.

1.5 (a) and (c) are subspaces but (b) is not closed under addition unless $S \subset T$ or $T \subset S$.

1.6 Hint: find suitable bases of S and T and show that they can be combined to give a basis of V.

1.7 (a) and (c) are linearly dependent sets of vectors.

1.8 (a) dimension = 3; (b) not a subspace, not closed under additiion; (c) dimension = 6; (d) dimension = 8.

1.9 Space must be of infinite dimension since $[1, \sin x, \cos x, \sin 2x, \cos 2x, \ldots]$ are linearly independent vectors in this space.

1.10 Basis of S is $[(1,1,0), (2,3,1)]$ basis of T is $[(2,1,0), (2,0,1)]$ basis of $S \cap T$ is $[(4,3,-1)]$.

1.11 $P = \begin{pmatrix} 1 & 1 & 1 & 1 \\ 0 & -1 & -1 & -1 \\ 0 & 0 & -1 & -1 \\ 0 & 0 & 0 & -1 \end{pmatrix}$ $\mathbf{a} = 10\mathbf{w}_1 - 6\mathbf{w}_2 - 3\mathbf{w}_3 - \mathbf{w}_4$, $\mathbf{b} = 4\mathbf{w}_1 - 3\mathbf{w}_2 - 2\mathbf{w}_3 - \mathbf{w}_4$

1.13 rank $A = 2$, rank $B = 3$, rank $C = 3$.

1.14 Rank is 2 if $\theta^2 - 4\theta = 0$, hence $\theta = 0$ or 4.

1.15 Hint: assume if possible $\mathbf{v} = \sum_{i=1}^{n} \alpha_i \mathbf{v}_i = \sum_{i=1}^{n} \beta_i \mathbf{v}_i$; proves that $\alpha_i = \beta_i$ for all i.

1.16 Hint: show that if dimension $V > m+1$ then any $m+1$ basis vectors of V will generate a proper subspace of dimension $m+1$.

1.17 $\begin{pmatrix} \frac{1}{2} & \frac{1}{2} & \frac{1}{2} \\ \frac{1}{2} & -\frac{1}{2} & \frac{1}{2} \\ 0 & 0 & 1 \end{pmatrix}$, $3 + 2x + x^2 = 3(1) + 2(x) + 1(x^2) = 3(1 + x) + 1(1 - x) + 1(x^2 - 1)$.

1.18 Hint: use row operations to determine the row ranks of the matrices whose rows are the given vectors. (a) 3, (b) 4, (c) 4.

1.19 $A^{-1} = \begin{pmatrix} 1 & 0 & -\frac{3}{2} \\ 0 & 1 & 0 \\ 0 & 0 & 1 \end{pmatrix}\begin{pmatrix} 1 & 0 & 0 \\ 0 & 1 & \frac{1}{2} \\ 0 & 0 & 1 \end{pmatrix}\begin{pmatrix} 1 & -1 & 0 \\ 0 & 1 & 0 \\ 0 & 0 & 1 \end{pmatrix}\begin{pmatrix} 1 & 0 & 0 \\ 0 & -\frac{1}{2} & 0 \\ 0 & 0 & 1 \end{pmatrix}\begin{pmatrix} 1 & 0 & 0 \\ -1 & 1 & 0 \\ 0 & 0 & 1 \end{pmatrix}$

$A = \begin{pmatrix} 1 & 0 & 0 \\ 1 & 1 & 0 \\ 0 & 0 & 1 \end{pmatrix}\begin{pmatrix} 1 & 0 & 0 \\ 0 & -2 & 0 \\ 0 & 0 & 1 \end{pmatrix}\begin{pmatrix} 1 & 1 & 0 \\ 0 & 1 & 0 \\ 0 & 0 & 1 \end{pmatrix}\begin{pmatrix} 1 & 0 & 0 \\ 0 & 1 & -\frac{1}{2} \\ 0 & 0 & 1 \end{pmatrix}\begin{pmatrix} 1 & 0 & \frac{3}{2} \\ 0 & 0 & 0 \\ 0 & 0 & 1 \end{pmatrix}.$

1.20 Hint: let s be the least integer such that $[\mathbf{v}_1,\mathbf{v}_2,\ldots,\mathbf{v}_s]$ is a linearly dependent set, prove that $\mathbf{v}_s$ depends upon $[\mathbf{v}_1,\mathbf{v}_2,\ldots,\mathbf{v}_{s-1}]$.

CHAPTER 2

2.1 Equations are only soluble if $\mathbf{b}$ is linearly dependent upon the column vectors of A. Solution must be unique otherwise the column vectors are linearly dependent and rank $<n$. One value of $\mathbf{b}$ is $(0\ 0\ 0\ 1)'$.

2.2 $\mathbf{x} = (1\ 0\ 1)'$.

2.3 A basis of this space is $[(1,0,1)', (2,1,-1)']$.

2.4 General solution is $\mathbf{x} = (2+\alpha, 1+3\alpha, \alpha, 0)'$ condition $x_1^2 = x_2^2$ gives $\alpha = \frac{1}{2}$ or $-\frac{3}{4}$.

2.5 $4c_1 + 25c_2 - 15c_3 + c_4 = 0$. Hint: reduce the augmented matrix to echelon form.

2.6 (a) $\mathbf{x}' = (13.84, -4.418, 2.715)$; (b) $\mathbf{x}' = (13.85, -4.420, 2.720)$.

2.7 (a) $(2n^2 + 6n - 2)n/6$. (b) $(n^2 + 2n - 1)n$ (assuming no pivoting in the elimination process).

2.8 $A^{-1} = \begin{pmatrix} 4 & -3 \\ -1 & 1 \end{pmatrix}$ $B^{-1} = \frac{1}{7}\begin{pmatrix} -14 & 11 & 5 \\ 7 & -3 & -2 \\ 0 & -2 & 1 \end{pmatrix}$ $C^{-1} = \begin{pmatrix} 1 & 0 & -2 & -2 \\ 0 & 0 & 1 & 1 \\ -2 & 1 & 3 & 3 \\ -2 & 1 & 3 & 4 \end{pmatrix}.$

2.9 $\mathbf{x}' = (1.684, 0.4918, 0.06504)$.

2.10 Coefficient matrix is non-singular if $t \neq 7$. If $t = 7$ equations are soluble if $\theta = -1$.

2.11 Hint: $a_{ij} > 0$, $b_{ij} > 0 \Rightarrow \theta a_{ij} + (1-\theta)b_{ij} > 0$ for all θ in $0 \leqslant \theta \leqslant 1$. Not a subspace since $A \in S \Rightarrow -A \in S$.

2.12 (a) False, a counter example is obtained by choosing $\mathbf{x} \in S$, $\mathbf{y} \in T$ such that $\frac{1}{2}\mathbf{x} + \frac{1}{2}\mathbf{y} \notin S \cup T$.

(b) False, as a simple counter example consider S and T as the interiors of concentric circles in R^2.

(c) True.

2.13 Not every convex subset of V is a subspace. For example let $V = R^2$, let S be the set of all $\mathbf{x} \in V$ with $x_1 = 1$.

2.14 Maximum value of f occurs at point (2_36) which is a vertex of the set of feasible points.

Maximum value of g is at point (3.2,3.6) which is along one edge of the set of feasible points. (Edge is tangential to the circle $g =$ constant).

2.15 Maximum value of $3x_1 + 2x_2 = 18$ occurs at $x_1 = 2, x_2 = 6$.

2.16 $x_1 = 0, x_2 = 60, x_3 = 0, x_4 = 40, x_5 = 0, x_6 = 60$ gives optimum value of $f = 2300$. Constraints will always be linearly dependent since total output = total requirement.

2.17 Maximum is $f = 122/3$ at $x_1 = 14/3, x_2 = 16/3, x_3 = 0$.

2.18 Maximum $f = 170$ at $x_2 = 0, x_3 = 5$ $(x_1 = 15)$.

2.19 Optimum daily output 0 of A, 684.2 of B, 52.64 of C.

2.20 Optimum distribution:

	1	2	3	4
A	0	0	70	130
B	90	80	30	0

CHAPTER 3

3.2 Hint: jth column vector $\mathbf{c}_j$ is $\mathbf{c}_j = (\mathbf{v}_1 \cdot \mathbf{v}_j, \ldots, \mathbf{v}_m \cdot \mathbf{v}_j)'$. Show that $\sum_{j=1}^{m} \alpha_j \mathbf{c}_j = 0 \Rightarrow \mathbf{v}_i \cdot \sum_{j=1}^{m} \alpha_j \mathbf{v}_j = 0$ for $i = 1, \ldots, m$; $\sum_{j=1}^{m} \alpha_j \mathbf{v}_j \cdot \sum_{j=1}^{m} \alpha_j \mathbf{v}_j = 0$ $\Rightarrow \mathbf{v}_1, \ldots, \mathbf{v}_m$ linearly dependent.

3.3 Hint: [(1,0,0)′,(2,0,0)′] is a simple example of a linearly dependent orthogonal set since (1,0,0)′ is self orthogonal.

3.5 Hint: the vectors added to the basis of S to form an orthogonal basis of R^4 form a basis of T. [(1,1,0,0)′, (−½,½,1,0)] and [(1,−1,1,0)′, (0,0,0,1,)].

3.6 Hint: use Gram-Schmidt algorithm. Orthogonal basis is $[\sin x, \cos x, \sin^2 x, \cos^2 x - \frac{1}{3}\sin^2 x]$.

3.7 Hint: show that any extension of an orthonormal basis of S to an orthonormal basis of V provides a basis of T. $\mathbf{t} = \mathbf{v} - \sum_{i=1}^{m} (\mathbf{v}.\mathbf{s}_i)\mathbf{s}_i$.

3.8 $[\frac{1}{\sqrt{2}}(1,0,1,0)', \frac{1}{\sqrt{2}}(0,1,0,1)']$.

3.9 The row vectors have the same property since P' is also orthogonal.

3.10 Hint: proof is similar to Theorem 3.2 [(1,0,0)′, (−1,1,0)′, ½(−1,1,1)′].

3.11 $\frac{1}{\sqrt{3}}(1,i,0,1)', \frac{1}{\sqrt{(33)}}(3+i,2-3i,3,i)', \frac{1}{\sqrt{(176)}}(-2-4i,6+i,-3-3i,1+10i)'$.

3.13 A will be diagonal with positive elements if basis is orthogonal.

3.14 $A = \begin{pmatrix} 2 & 0 & 2/3 \\ 0 & 2/3 & 0 \\ 2/3 & 6 & 2/5 \end{pmatrix}$ Hint: $x^3 - 1 = (x - 1)(x^2 + x + 1)$.

3.15 $h(x) = x^2 - 1/3$. Orthonormal basis is $[1/\sqrt{2}, (\sqrt{3}/\sqrt{2})x, (3\sqrt{5}/2\sqrt{2})(x^2 - 1/3)]$.

3.17 Hint: see Section 4.3.2.

3.18 7, 3.873, 3.332, 3.

3.19 $P = \begin{pmatrix} 1 & 4 & 2 \\ 0 & -1 & 0 \\ 0 & 1 & 1 \end{pmatrix}$ is one solution. Hint: the coefficients of x_i obtained when completing the square are the elements of P^{-1}.

3.20 Hint: if $\mathbf{y} = A'\mathbf{x}$ then $\mathbf{x}'AA'\mathbf{x} = \mathbf{y}.\mathbf{y}$.

3.21 A and C are positive definite.

CHAPTER 4

4.1 (a) $0.99806x - 0.1575x^3$; (b) $0.90351p_1(x) - 0.063035p_3(x)$ which simplifies to solution (a).

4.2
$$\begin{aligned} 5a_0 + 5a_1 + 15a_2 &= 24 \\ 5a_0 + 15a_1 + 35a_2 &= 45 \\ 15a_0 + 35a_1 + 99a_2 &= 116 \end{aligned}$$
Solution: $a_0 = 2.5571$, $a_1 = 1.8143$, $a_2 = 0.1429$

4.3 Coefficient matrix is $\begin{pmatrix} 2 & 2 & 8/3 \\ 2 & 8/3 & 4 \\ 8/3 & 4 & 32/5 \end{pmatrix}$ Condition number 578.2.

4.4 $\frac{1}{2}p_0(x) - \frac{5}{8}p_2(x)$, $0.3634T_0(x) - 0.4244T_2(x)$, at $x = 0$ series give 0.8125, 0.7878; at $x = 0.9$ results are 0.0531, 0.1003.

4.5 Coefficients are in ratio 0:–3:0:5.

4.6 $\frac{3}{4} + \sum_{m=0}^{\infty} \frac{2}{\pi(2m+1)^2} \cos(2m+1)x + \sum_{n=1}^{\infty} \frac{(-1)^n}{\pi n} \sin nx.$

4.8 $\frac{4}{\pi}\left(1 - \sum_{m=1}^{\infty} \frac{1}{4m^2 - 1} \cos 2mx\right)$. Half rectified sine wave given by $\frac{1}{2}(f(x) + \sin x)$.

4.9 $1 - \frac{\pi}{2} + \sum_{m=0}^{\infty} \frac{4}{\pi(2m+1)^2} \cos 2(m+1)x$. At $x = \frac{\pi}{4}$ sum of first three terms is 0.3295, Chebysev sum is 0.2642.

4.10 $\frac{1}{2}a_0 + \sum_{n=1}^{\infty} (a_n \cos nx - b_n \sin nx)$, $\frac{1}{2}a_0 + \sum_{n=1}^{\infty} a_n \cos nx$,

$\frac{1}{2}a_0 + \sum_{n=1}^{\infty} (a_n \cos 2nx + b_n \sin 2nx)$,

$\frac{1}{2}a_0 + \sum_{n=1}^{\infty} (-b_n \cos nx + a_n \sin nx)$ $\sum_{n=1}^{\infty} (nb_n \cos nx - na_n \sin nx)$.

4.11 cond(A) = 44.1. Hint: worst errors will occur when $\|\delta\mathbf{x}\| = \|A^{-1}\|\,\|\delta\mathbf{b}\|$ and $\|\mathbf{b}\| = \|A\|\,\|\mathbf{x}\|$. One solution is $\mathbf{b} = \begin{pmatrix} 2.1 \\ -2.0 \end{pmatrix}$, $\delta\mathbf{b} = \begin{pmatrix} 0.01 \\ 0.01 \end{pmatrix}$.

4.12 $\mathbf{x} = (0.315, 0.459, -0.391)'$. $M = \begin{pmatrix} 0 & -0.1 & 0.1 \\ 0 & 0.02 & 0.18 \\ 0 & -0.018 & 0.038 \end{pmatrix}$ $\|M\|_\infty = 0.2$.

4.14 $\|A\|_\infty = 7$. One solution is $\mathbf{x} = (1,-1,1)'$.

4.15 Using ℓ_∞ norms $\chi(H_2) = 27$ $\chi(H_3) = 748$ $\chi(H_4) = 28375$.

4.16 (0.9576, 2.728).

4.17 Sufficient conditions are $g = 0$ and H negative definite. Maximum is at (0.78,0.84,−1.0).

4.18 Approximate location of maximum is (0.80,0.784,−0.98).

4.19 (0.619, −0.198).

4.20 (25/24,−2/24,7/24) gives location of minimum.

CHAPTER 5

5.1 Ker ϕ has basis $[x^2y,y^3]$, $\phi(V)$ has basis $|x,x^3|$.

5.2 (ii) and (iii) are linear transformations.

5.5 $A = \begin{pmatrix} 0 & -1 & 0 & 0 \\ 6 & 0 & -2 & 0 \\ 0 & 2 & 0 & -3 \end{pmatrix}$ Ker ϕ has basis $[(x_3 + 3x)]$ $f(x) = -3x + k(x^3 + 3x)$.

5.6 Hint: equivalent matrices have same rank. $A \sim D$ and $B \sim C$.

5.7 Hint: find bases of ker ϕ and $\phi(V)$ and extend these. One solution is $[v_1,v_2,v_1-v_3]$, $[w_1+2w_2,2w_1+3w_2]$.

5.8 Dimension of S is 6 since each transformation is represented by a 2 X 3 matrix.

5.9 Solution is not unique, one solution is:

$$P = \begin{pmatrix} 1 & 0 & 0 \\ -4 & 1 & 0 \\ 2 & -1 & 1 \end{pmatrix} \quad Q = \begin{pmatrix} 1 & 2/5 & 1 & 1 \\ 0 & -1/5 & -1 & -2 \\ 0 & 0 & 1 & 0 \\ 0 & 0 & 0 & 1 \end{pmatrix}$$

Hint: P corresponds to row operations used to reduce A to echelon form, Q corresponds to the column operations used in the further reduction to cononical form.

5.10 $\left[\begin{pmatrix} 0 & 0 \\ 1 & 0 \end{pmatrix}, \begin{pmatrix} 0 & 1 \\ 0 & 0 \end{pmatrix}, \begin{pmatrix} 1 & 0 \\ 0 & -1 \end{pmatrix}\right]$.

5.11 Hint: columns of Q give the old basis vectors in terms of new basis.

$$Q = \begin{pmatrix} ½ & ½ & -½ \\ ½ & -½ & -½ \\ 0 & 0 & 1 \end{pmatrix}, \ A = \begin{pmatrix} 2 & -1 & 0 \\ 0 & 2 & -2 \\ 0 & 0 & 2 \end{pmatrix}, \ B = \begin{pmatrix} 3/2 & ½ & -1 \\ -½ & 5/2 & 1 \\ 0 & 0 & 2 \end{pmatrix}$$

$(= QAQ^{-1})$.

5.12 $[\sin x, \cos x]$.

5.13 $A = \begin{pmatrix} 1 & 0 & 0 \\ 0 & 1 & 1 \\ 1 & -1 & 1 \end{pmatrix}$ Hint: $A = PDP^{-1}$ where D is diagonal and P is modal matrix.

5.14 $\lambda_1 = 1$ $\mathbf{v}_1 = (3,2,1)'$, $\lambda_2 = 2$ $\mathbf{v}_2 = (1,3,1)'$, $\lambda_3 = -1$ $\mathbf{v}_3 = (1,0,1)'$.

$$A^5 = \begin{pmatrix} -9 & 11 & 8 \\ -31 & 32 & 31 \\ -10 & 11 & 9 \end{pmatrix} \quad A^{-1} = \tfrac{1}{2}\begin{pmatrix} 3 & 1 & -5 \\ 1 & 1 & -1 \\ 1 & 1 & -3 \end{pmatrix}$$ Hint: $A^n = PD^nP^{-1}$.

5.15 $A^5 = 306A^2 - 103A + 230I$. Hint: use identity $A^3 = 7A^2 - 3A + 5I$ to eliminate A^3 and higher order terms.

5.16 Hint: since $f(A)\mathbf{v}_i = \mathbf{0}$ the product of $f(A)$ with any vector linearly dependent upon $[\mathbf{v}_1, \mathbf{v}_2, \ldots, \mathbf{v}_n]$ is zero.

5.17 B and D are similar but A is defective.

5.18 $\lambda = 10.076$ to 3 decimal places. (After 6 iterations).

5.19 Hint: the coordinates of points on the axis of rotation are unaltered hence axis is eigenvector for $\lambda = 1$. Axis has direction cosines (–0.565,0.786, –0.250).

5.20 Hint: If A and B commute, show that $B\mathbf{v}_i$ is an eigenvector of A for λ_i. Note that if A and B have the same eigenvevtors they have the same modal matrix. Eigenvalues are 1,2;–2,1;–2,2;3,1. All matrices have $\mathbf{v}_1 = (5,3)'$, $\mathbf{v}_2 = (2,1)'$.

5.22 S has dimension 6. R has dimension 1. Basis for ker ϕ is $[xy, xz, yz, x^2-y^2, y^2-z^2]$.

5.23 Hint: the matrices must have the same modal matrix and diagonal canonical form.

5.24 Hint: $Q = RP^{-1}$ where P, R are modal matrices. One solution is

$$Q = \begin{pmatrix} -5 & 5 & -3 \\ 5 & -4 & 3 \\ 4 & -5 & 3 \end{pmatrix}.$$

5.25 Hint: if $P = (\mathbf{u}_1, \mathbf{u}_2, \ldots, \mathbf{u}_n)$ then P^{-1} has rows $\mathbf{u}_i'$.

$$A = \frac{1}{6}\begin{pmatrix} 13 & -2 & -5 \\ -2 & 10 & -2 \\ -5 & -2 & 13 \end{pmatrix}.$$

5.26 Hint: if Q is any orthogonal matrix $\|AQ\mathbf{x}\|_2 = \|A\mathbf{x}\|_2$, choose Q so that $Q'A'AQ$ is diagonal.

CHAPTER 6

6.1 Ker ϕ contains all functions of form $g(y)$ where g is an arbitrary function.

Solution is $\frac{1}{y} e^{xy} + g(y)$.

6.2 $(9e^{4x} - 5e^{2x} - 4e^{-x})/30$.

6.3 $5/36 - x/6 + (41/60)e^{-2x} + (53/45)e^{3x}$.

6.4 Rank $A = 2$. $\mathbf{x} = (0,1,0,0)' + \alpha(-5,1,3,0)' + \beta(-2,1,0,3)'$, α,β arbitrary.

6.5 **x.y** is generally altered by a translation.

6.6 $\mathbf{p}_0 = \frac{1}{23}(6,7,4,6)'$.

6.7 Hint: to prove A^n is stochastic let $B = A^{n-1}$ and use induction on n.

6.8 $\mathbf{p}_0 = (¼,½,¼)'$. Unless $\mathbf{p} = \mathbf{p}_0$ the behaviour is oscillatory. (Note: $\lambda = -1$ is also an eigenvalue.)

6.9 $x_1 = e^{2t} - e^{-3t}, x_2 = 2e^{2t} - e^{-3t}, x_3 = 2e^{2t} - 3e^{-3t}$.

6.10 Hint:the uncoupled equations are $\ddot{y}_i = -\omega_i^2 y_i$ where $\omega_i^2 = -\lambda_i$. Solution

$$x_1 = \cos 2t - ½ \sin 2t + \frac{1}{3}\sin 3t, x_2 = 2\cos 2t - \sin 2t + \frac{1}{3}\sin 3t.$$

6.11 Normal modes are $(1,0,-1)'$, $(1,\pm\sqrt{2},1)'$ with associated frequencies of $\sqrt{(2k/M)}, \sqrt{((2 \pm \sqrt{2})k/M)}$.

6.12 $\omega_1 = 1.970$, $\mathbf{v}_1' = (1, -0.361)$; $\omega_2 = 0.636$, $\mathbf{v}_2' = (0.271,1)$.

6.13 Hint: let $\mathbf{d}_r = \mathbf{x}_r - \mathbf{x}_E$ where $\mathbf{x}_E$ is the exact solution satisfying $\mathbf{x}_E = M\mathbf{x}_E + \mathbf{c}$. Show that $\mathbf{d}_{r+1} = M\mathbf{d}_r$ and deduce that $\lim_{r\to\infty} \mathbf{d}_r = 0$.

6.14 Hint: eigenvalues of Jacobi iteration matrix have modulus $1/\sqrt{(10)}$.

6.15 $5/(3(s-1)) + 13/(3(s-4))$.

6.16 $$\frac{1}{s-1}\begin{pmatrix} 3 & 8 & 3 \\ -3 & -8 & -3 \end{pmatrix} + \frac{1}{s-2}\begin{pmatrix} 2 & 6 & 2 \\ -1 & -3 & -1 \end{pmatrix} + \frac{1}{s+1}\begin{pmatrix} -4 & -12 & -6 \\ 4 & 12 & 6 \end{pmatrix}.$$

6.17 Centre is at $(-¼,-5/12,1)$. Principal axes have direction cosines $(0.8817,-0.4719,0)$, $(0.4719,0.8817)$, $(0,0,1)$. Hyperbloid of one sheet.

6.18 Principal axes are in direction $(1,1,0)'$, $(1,-1,1)'$, $(1,-1,-2)'$, semi-axes have lengths $1, 1/\sqrt{2}, 1/2$.

6.19 Angular momentum $= m(12,2,2)'$. Principal moments of inertia are 4m, 10m,10m. Principal axes are in direction of $(1,1,1)'$ and two orthogonal directions such as $(1,0,-1)'$ and $(1,-2,1)'$.

6.20 $s_1 = -6$, $s_2 = 12$, $s_3 = 24$. Direction cosines of principal axes are $1/\sqrt{2}(1,0,-1)$, $1/\sqrt{3}(1,1,1)$, $1/\sqrt{6}(-1,2,-1)$. $I_1 = s_1 + s_2 + s_3$, $I_2 = s_1 s_2 + s_2 s_3 + s_3 s_1, I_3 = s_1 s_2 s_3$.

Index

R

S

T

U

V

W